LIVING ENERGIES

An Exposition of Concepts
Related to the Theories of
VIKTOR SCHAUBERGER

by
CALLUM COATS AA Dipl, ARAIA, ARIBA.

GATEWAY BOOKS, BATH, UK

First published in 1996
by GATEWAY BOOKS
The Hollies, Wellòw,
Bath, BA2 8QJ, UK

Reprinted 1996

Distributed in the USA by
NATIONAL BOOK NETWORK
4720 Boston Way, Lanham, MD 20706

Set in 9.4 on 11 Palatino, by
Character Graphics (Taunton) Ltd,
Printed and bound in Great Britain by
Biddles Ltd, Guildford and King's Lynn

Cover design by Synergie, Bristol

British Library Cataloguing in Publication Data
A catalogue record for this book is
available from the British Library

ISBN 0 946551 97 9

TABLE OF CONTENTS

This book is dedicated to my sons

ANGUS and OLIVER

*and to all those of their generation,
who will require enormous courage and perseverance to tackle the
Herculean task of cleaning up the awesome legacy of
environmental destruction, that we and previous generations have
ignobly bequeathed them. It is my earnest hope that the
information contained in this book will contribute to the changes
that are now so urgently necessary and will provide present and
future generations with some of the wherewithal with which to
restore the Earth and the health, wealth and well-being of its
human family.*

ACKNOWLEDGMENTS

I would like to express my sincerest and heartfelt thanks to my family and to all my close friends and others, who have helped and fortified me over these many years in countless ways. Without their timely assistance, encouragement and generosity, freely given, all would doubtless have come to nothing. In retrospect I have come to realise that those who have supported me in this long endeavour have in the main been women. Why this should be so is not entirely clear to me, but perhaps it is a reflection of the movement of the times and the innately natural concern amongst women for the urgent rehabilitation of our Mother-Earth, the Great Provider, upon whose grace and bounteousness all our existences depend. While I would like to name each and every individual in gratitude and recognition for his or her contribution towards the success of this venture, they are too numerous to be able to do justice to each. To two such, however, I make exception. My warm appreciation goes to Christopher Bird for his valuable and timely critique of the typescript and for helping to unravel what happened in America. Finally, I would like to express my special thanks to my publisher, Alick Bartholomew, who has had the endless patience and endurance to wait 15 years for the eventual arrival of my manuscripts.

Callum Coats, 1995.

FOREWORD

It is very difficult to observe the extraordinary creativity and fruitfulness of Nature without a sense of *wonder*. But wonder is at odds with reason. It has been said that humanity's schism with Nature was contrived so that we could develop our sense of reason to the extent that we now experience. One of the outcomes of this, because they are preoccupied with physical form, is that our contemporary biological sciences seem to believe that this munificent fecundity of Nature 'just happens'. Viktor Schauberger's vision was that this 'happening' is the result of a complex interaction of subtle energies, a process that is initiated and sustained from what he called the 4th and 5th dimensions of Being.

Viktor Schauberger was a man who was undoubtedly inspired by more exalted levels of reality and meaning than most of us experience. His great gift was to be able to show how it is the finer and 'higher' energies that are responsible for creating form and structure, not the other way round as contemporary science would suggest. The story of his life is tragic at a personal level, for he was constantly ridiculed, because of the vested interests of science for whom he was a threat. He died a broken man when he saw that the gift he wanted to make was corrupted by the powerful for material gain. His prophetic vision was that humanity was bound for self-annihilation if steps were not immediately taken to change course. In a real sense we have had to see many of his specific prophecies come true before we were ready to take him seriously.

Schauberger died in 1958. Why has it taken so long before a book could be published that is so vital to the salvation of humanity? Part of the answer lies in history. When Austria was absorbed by Nazi Germany in 1938 there was a cultural melding. Viktor Schauberger was an Austrian, as was Hitler, who saw that this remarkable inventor could be valuable to his cause. Although Viktor was coerced to work for the Third Reich, he has inevitably been associated with it. Postwar German consciousness, being anxious to distance itself from the Hitler period, could not then easily embrace Schauberger's vision.

It took a Swedish engineer inspired by the vision of Rudolf Steiner to rescue Viktor Schauberger from oblivion in 1976. Steiner and Schauberger were contemporaries, and it is tempting to believe that they were both inspired by a similar source of profound wisdom of universal meaning. They had some lengthy discussions, and one wonders how much common ground they found!

This Swedish engineer's book was published by a small publisher better known for its music publishing. I heard of Olof Alexandersson's *Det Levande Vattnet* in 1979 from some Swedish-speaking British friends. I do not read Swedish, and so could not make a 'rational' assessment of the book. But as sometimes happens in publishing, I had a 'hunch' this book was important, and that it must be translated into English and published widely.

My previous company, Turnstone Press, in 1982 published *Living Water* which is a popular introduction to Viktor Schauberger, the man and his mission. This lovely little book has since gone through five reprints and has caused a strong demand for an authoritative book on Viktor Schauberger's practical ideas for working with Nature, rather than against her, as we currently do. Clearly Schauberger's time has come, as millions of people all over the world realise that we are dangerously off-course.

It was when I was preparing *Living Water* for press that Callum Coats came into my life. Through his mother Callum met Viktor's physicist son, Walter Schauberger in 1977 and, sensing that his future work lay here, began an intensive study of Schauberger theory. In 1981 Callum helped edit the translation of *Living Water*, during which he confided with me his ambition to write a definitive work on Viktor Schauberger.

This was to prove a much more ambitious task than he anticipated, and he has devoted all his resources and energy for over 15 years to this end. It is a remarkable body of research, and Callum undertook to replicate some of the experiments. A crucial part of the process was to spend three years with Walter's Pythagoras-Kepler-System Institute at Lauffen in the Salzkammergut near Salzburg. Walter has now passed on, but the Schauberger family has cooperated with Callum in helping this book be born, as with its companion work *Eco-technology,* Viktor Schauberger's own writings in three volumes, which Callum has compiled and translated.

Some thoughts on how to approach this book. Callum and I talked about how to arrange the text of *Living Energies.* As the publisher, I did not want readers to be put off early in the book by a discussion of energy and motion. Callum, persuaded me that the more popular material – about **water** as the life-blood of the Earth, and how we need to cherish it, and about the magic of **trees** and the biomass of the Earth – can really only be appreciated with some understanding of what is energy. However, if you do find the discussion of energy and motion (for energy *is* motion) daunting, my suggestion is that you skip to a later chapter to get the sense of our lost inheritance. You can always return to put in the theory later. I suspect, in any case, that this is not a book that most will read

through in one swoop. Rather it is an inspired fountain of wisdom to be dipped into, here and there, for many a season. Another hint, I was finding the chapter on energy hard going until I read it on an Orkney beach. Surrounding yourself with nature makes the ideas come alive!

Schauberger, in common with other pioneers of radical thinking, realised that words carry associations. Therefore, in order to wean people away from a conventional word which is often inadequate for the task, it is sometimes appropriate to coin a new word, to allow their imaginations to grasp a more inclusive or specific concept or idea. This is especially relevant for the subtle energies which are responsible for the interaction of all creation and the incredible abundance and fecundity of Nature. We have tried to cross-reference these in the text, and there is a glossary in the back of the book.

Viktor Schauberger, besides being an impeccable observer of Nature, was also an inventor who saw how the practical application of his ideas could transform our society. Just as other visionaries have heard the harmony of the Universe as 'The Music of the Spheres', so Viktor Schauberger saw the symmetry of all creation in terms of sacred geometry. Inevitably this requires a modicum of mathematics in the text. But to show that it is not necessary for an appreciation of Schauberger's ecological understanding, we have, where possible, extracted the more theoretical material into boxes. So, if you are daunted by mathematical symbols, don't be dismayed, for you will still find most of the text inspiring and enthralling.

Living Energies may become the catalyst for re-writing all the textbooks of science and the manuals of politics and planning. It shows how humanity can take its place as the responsible guardians of a very precious centre of life in the Universe. We see this as required reading for anyone planning to participate in the next century. It is a guide to the new millennium!

Alick Bartholomew,
Wellow, September 1995.

Viktor Schauberger

Born: 30th June 1885
Holzschlag 2,
Pfarramt Ulrichsberg,
Upper Austria.

Died: 25th September 1958
Linz,
Upper Austria.

1
WHO WAS VIKTOR SCHAUBERGER?

1.1 Viktor Schauberger – The Man

Throughout recorded history humanity has been periodically uplifted by the contributions of a few gifted and enlightened individuals, whose teachings and philosophy have gradually raised the level of human awareness; the Buddha, Jesus Christ and the Prophet Mohammed being the most familiar examples of how a single individual can produce far-reaching changes in the consciousness of humanity. Lesser mortals have also played a vital role in this process and the seeding of human consciousness with higher truths always seems to come at a time when humankind as a whole is ready to receive them.

It is sometimes said that these great teachers, themselves ardent students of Nature and the Divine, lived ahead of their time. At first view this would appear to be true, but on further reflection it becomes apparent that they lived precisely when they should have, for otherwise they could not have provided the vision or the direction necessary for humanity's upward evolution and progress. In most instances a signpost is long forgotten and unheeded if it lies behind, and to be of any use it must of necessity stand out ahead in order to indicate the new way. Many such human signposts have punctuated the passage of humanity's progress, but have received recognition for their great contribution only long after their own passing.

These exceptional individuals are indeed visionaries in the truest sense of the word, for they are endowed with a far higher sense of perception than their contemporaries. For their work an enormous dedication and courage is necessary. Historically, and Viktor Schauberger was no exception, the lives such individuals have led have been dogged with confrontation, difficulty, doubt and the great loneliness of the path-finder, or the individual who stands alone far out in front on evolution's upward way. As pioneers, apart from breaking new ground, they also suffer great adversity in their encounters with the powerful opposition of those whose interests and beliefs are rigidly immured in the current status quo.

Such great leading lights as Copernicus, Johannes Kepler and Galileo Galilei, come to mind who devoted their whole lives to the understanding of the universe and the raising of human consciousness. In the main they were only permitted a view into their Promised Land, a vista over the unfolding of their life's work, but almost without exception had to forgo the passage into the new and the reaping of the fruits of their travails. Denied any recognition for their contribution, their end was often clothed in misery and penury, as though the gods would exact from them the very last ounce of personal surrender. Many of these enlightened individuals died alone, unloved, unwanted and unsung.

Kepler was reduced to total insolvency and, although owed a considerable sum for his services by the Duke of Regensburg, he died a pauper and was buried in a common grave outside hallowed ground, for he, like his contemporary Galileo, had dared to question the authority of the Church. To this day no-one knows where Kepler's body lies. He too had had a vision and, through his meticulous study of the movement of the planets, produced his great work, *Harmonices Mundi*, "The Harmonies of the World". Having finally completed it in 1618, he dedicated it to James I of England, declaring that now that he had discovered the harmonious qualities and proportions of all things, there would no longer be the need for human conflict. Kepler's opus had barely been published when the Thirty Years' War broke out, thoroughly obscuring and interring all his endeavours. This happened as a result of the so-called 'Defenestration of Prague' in which on May 21st, 1618 the envoys of the Austrian Kaiser were hurled from the windows of the Great Hall.

Mozart, who took music, its resonances and harmonies to new heights, also suffered a similar fate – oblivion at the age of 35 and burial in a common grave. Max Planck, the great physicist who brought an end to the purely materialistic world view of the late 19th century with his quantum theory in December 1900, was another who, bereft of adequate clothing, food or other means of support, died alone in extreme poverty and cold.

Viktor Schauberger's life followed a path similar to those of his illumined predecessors, for in his life too he was met with derision, slander and deceit in a long confrontation with the Establishment in its various forms. He was a man of enormous strength of purpose; he was warm and encouraging, particularly to young people in whom he took a great interest, for he saw in them the possibility for the restoration of a secure and bountiful future. But to those whose view of life he considered irretrievably perverted spiritually and intellectually, he was absolutely uncompromising, seeing them as obstacles on the path of human evolution and in the rehabilitation of the environment.

Naturally he made many enemies in the process, but on the other hand a certain balance was achieved by a very few encouraging and loyal friends such as Prof. Philipp Forchheimer, a hydrologist of world repute. Another was Prof. Werner Zimmermann, a Swiss, who published articles by Viktor in his ecologically oriented magazine *Tau* between 1935 and 1937. Werner Zimmermann frequently entered the lists in Viktor's defence against the narrow-minded, self-interested attacks of academia and entrenched bureaucracy, which on occasion were very intense. More often than not Viktor's discoveries totally contradicted established theory and in their flawless functioning and practical implementation seriously threatened the credibility and reputation of scientist and bureaucrat alike.

There are many more such individuals who have given themselves wholly to the betterment of their fellow human beings. Without exception they were endowed with extraordinary perceptive and intuitive abilities, which afforded them fresh insights into the way in which the world functioned, enabling them to understand phenomena hitherto inexplicable to their contemporaries. They were aware of another dimension of reality, that 'Dimension of Comprehension' which makes sense of the whole – just as the 3rd dimension makes a two-dimensional world understandable.

Some of these great teachers were born with this ability, while others fought long and hard external and personal battles to acquire it, their struggles fraught with hardship and ridden with disappointment. Often assailed by doubt, they nevertheless courageously persevered, urged ever onward to finish the task they had set themselves to complete. If ever there was a true exponent of the person described in Rudyard Kipling's poem *If*[1], it was Viktor Schauberger.

He was one of those rare human beings, those explorers in human thought and endeavour, whose chosen path was to throw light on the future. It is therefore inevitable that he too will eventually take his place amongst the ranks of these exalted, self-sacrificing beings. In the years to come he will be acknowledged as one of the principal guiding spirits of the 21st century and beyond, who brought about a fundamental shift of Copernican proportions in humankind's appreciation of Nature and natural energies.

There can be very few of his contemporaries whose comprehension of the sublime energetic interdependencies, upon which life at all its levels is founded, was so profound. Nor, apparently, has any other person had Viktor's deep understanding of that living substance so vital to all life processes – water, which he viewed as the blood of Mother-Earth, for like Sir James Lovelock, the originator of the Gaia hypothesis[2], Viktor too saw the whole Earth as an organism and expressed this view in his early writings of the 1930s.

Viktor Schauberger was born on June 30th, 1885 in the parish of Ulrichsberg, in Upper Austria. He was descended from a long line of foresters, who had devoted their whole lives to the natural management and administration of the forest, a dedication mirrored in their family motto, *'Fidus in silvis silentibus'* or 'Faith in the silent forests'. With this as his background and much against his father's will, but with the support of his mother, at the age of 18 he flatly refused to follow in the footsteps of his two elder brothers and attend university, having seen how it had affected his brothers' thinking. Apart from his earnest desire to become a forester, the main reason for his refusal was that he did not wish to have his natural way of thinking corrupted by people he considered totally alienated to Nature. He did not want to be forced to see things through other jaundiced eyes, but through his own. For, as he later wrote:

The only possible outcome of the purely categorizing compart-mentality, thrust upon us at school, is the loss of our creativity. People are losing their individuality, their ability to see things as they really are and thereby their connection with Nature. They are fast approaching a state of equilibrium impossible in Nature, which must force them into a total economic collapse, for no stable system of equilibrium exists. Therefore the principles upon which our actions are founded

are invalid, because they operate within parameters that do not exist.

Our work is the embodiment of our will. The spiritual manifestation of this work is its effect. When such work is done properly, it brings happiness, but when carried out incorrectly, it assuredly brings misery.[3]

Taking his mother's advice and following his natural instincts, Viktor became a junior forest warden, spending the next few years often in areas of remote forest. There he was able to perceive movements of energy and natural phenomena in Nature's own laboratory, because in Austria in the early part of this century, circa 1900–1915, there were large tracts of forest still untouched by human hand. After the 1914–1918 war in which he was wounded, Viktor returned to forestry, eventually entering the employ of Prince Adolph zu Schaumburg-Lippe, the owner of a large hunting and forestry reserve in Steyrling.

In these districts there had been no interference in the balance of Nature and Viktor was thus able to observe events that are today inconceivable, and which no longer take place because of the enormous deterioration of the environment. It was here that he acquired the insights into the natural movement of water that resulted in the building of his first log flume, which will be described in detail in chapter 12. Here too he first became aware of other levitational energies inherent in water, for one day in the middle of a very cold winter, as he was about to cross over a fast-flowing mountain stream, he flushed a stationary trout from its lair as he sought a firm hold for his staff on the stream bed. Its lightning flash upstream immediately caused a number of questions to race through his mind:

How did the trout actually manage to get to this spot – and later I saw dozens of them in the same stream – which was cut off by a 60 metre high waterfall about a kilometre downstream, where the water was atomised into a veil of mist?

How was it able to flee upstream like a streak of greased lightning in mockery of all the laws of gravity?

How was it possible for this fish to stand so motionlessly, only steering itself with slight movements of its tail-fins, in this wildly torrential flow, which made my staff shake so much that I could hardly hang onto it?

What forces enabled the trout to overcome its own body-weight so effortlessly and quickly and at the same time overcome the specific weight of the heavy water flowing against it?

Why didn't the water freeze even during periods of severe frost with temperatures below –30°C?[4]

While Viktor undoubtedly had an especial talent for observation, a penetrating power of perception undimmed by preconceptions, he also developed what might be called an active consciousness, an ability to go beyond the merely visual in search of what lay behind a given phenomenon. This taught him a great deal and how this ability gradually evolved, he explained as follows:

The Schaubergers' principal preoccupation was directed towards the conservation of the forest and wild game, and even in earliest youth my fondest desire was to understand Nature, and through such understanding to come closer to the truth; a truth that I was unable to discover either at school or in church.

In this quest I was thus drawn time and time again up into the forest. I could sit for hours on end and watch the water flowing by without ever becoming tired or bored. At the time I was still unaware that in water the greatest secret lay hidden. Nor did I know that water was the carrier of life or the ur-source[5] of what we call consciousness. Without any preconceptions, I simply let my gaze fall on the water as it flowed past. It was only years later that I came to realise that running water attracts our consciousnesses like a magnet and draws a small part of it along in its wake. It is a force that can act so powerfully that one temporarily loses one's consciousness and involuntarily falls asleep.

As time passed I began to play a game with water's secret powers; I surrendered my so-called free consciousness and allowed the water to take possession of it for a while. Little by little this game turned into a profoundly earnest endeavour, because I realised that one could detach one's
own consciousness from the body and attach it to that of the water.

When my own consciousness was eventually returned to me, then the water's most deeply concealed psyche often revealed the most extraordinary things to me. As a result of this investigation, a researcher was born who could dispatch his consciousness on a voyage of discovery, as it were. In this way I was able to experience things that had escaped other people's notice, because they were unaware that a human being is able to send forth his free consciousness into those places the eyes cannot see.

By practising this blindfolded vision, I eventually developed a bond with mysterious Nature, whose essential being I then slowly learnt to perceive and understand.[6]

It is very interesting to compare this with a statement taken from *The Urga Manuscript*[7], which is the record of a letter by Do-Ring, a scholar and scribe to the Panchen Lama, written in the early 1920s to his friend, Wing On concerning the inner life and describing the functions and phases of spiritual evolution.

It [the 6th function] is the one in which the initiate is given the power of sending his intellect or conscious mind right away from his body, directing it to any part of the material earth he desires it to visit, and then recalling it still conscious of all that it has seen.[8]

Truly the intellect, or that part of life that sees and records its observations, can and does leave the body and travel great distances, observe detail at those distances and return, giving to the mind as a whole an accurate picture of where it has been and what it has seen. This function occurs at the immeasurable will and is preceded by a short, deep meditation.[9]

These perceptions of truth presented Viktor with considerable problems in translating them into everyday language, for when it comes to transferring spiritual imagery into mundane word-pictures – regrettably still the only means of human communication – enormous difficulties are encountered due to the limitation of language. While all languages are in a constant state of evolution or devolution, the words and terminology at any given moment are a reflection of the current state of conceptual awareness. Thus for someone who is 'ahead' of his time, generally speaking the conceptual framework of language does not necessarily extend to the clear and unequivocal explanation of new concepts for which new acceptable words may have to be coined.

In many instances therefore, when he came to describe these phenomena, Viktor uses not the conventional terminology of physics, chemistry or biology, etc., but his own words. In this he was greatly assisted by the structure of the German language, which facilitates the formation of new concepts through additive nouns. Despite this and for lack of suitable technical vocabulary, their interpretation and comprehension is still sometimes extremely difficult, which in his writings he freely admitted, *"Few will understand the meaning of the above! Some individuals, however, will obtain an indefinable inkling."*[10]

In an attempt at clearer explanation he did eventually study these subjects on his own in order to acquaint himself with their respective terminologies. However, in his writings they are often used merely as indicators of the theme under discussion and therefore cannot always be taken literally.

Water, forests, natural energies and their generation were ever his passionate concern. In our present way of looking at things he would probably be considered one of the world's first 'greenies'; Dr. Richard St. Barbe Baker, founder of 'The Men of the Trees' in 1922, and Viktor's friend, being another.

Viktor had tremendous foresight and an enormous capacity for writing, reputedly having composed many, many thousands of pages. At times, apparently in a trance-like state, he wrote for hours on his typewriter with no idea of what he had written until finally reading it at the end. Amongst other things, he set down all that he saw would inevitably happen, if we did not mend our ways and change our whole approach to the environment, both technologically and conceptually. All the various crises that are today engulfing humanity, he foresaw as long ago as 1930. When questioned on the accuracy of his predictions, he answered

very simply, saying that, *"For a person who lives 100 years in the future, the present is no surprise."*[11]

In the late 1920s as a result of the successful operation of Viktor's Steyrling log-flume, Prof.Philipp Forchheimer was asked by the Austrian Government to investigate Viktor's unusual theories. Through their collaboration, Forchheimer gradually became aware of the truth of Viktor's ideas, eventually insisting that Viktor put all his discoveries down on paper, saying that he thought Viktor's theories were not only valid, but extremely valuable. Forchheimer later confided that he was delighted to have retired, because he would now be relieved of the humiliating task of telling his students that he had been teaching them rubbish for the previous forty-five years.

With the cooperation of Prof. Wilhelm Exner, President of the Austrian Academy of Science and inventor of the Exner electroscope, a treatise of Viktor Schauberger's entitled "Turbulence", which described the braking function of vortices and their relation to water temperature, was placed under seal and on deposit at the Austrian Academy of Science on January 1st, 1930. This was done, not only to ensure the precedence of Viktor Schauberger's theories on water movement, but also to safeguard them for some time in the future. While stressing its value, Forchheimer considered there to be no point in publishing it at the time, because the hydrological world was not ready. The science of hydraulics would first have to change its values and way of thinking before these trail-breaking concepts could be taken seriously. It wasn't until 1974 that this document was released to Viktor's son, Walter Schauberger.

Forchheimer did change his views later, however, and saw to it that Viktor's pioneering theories on temperature and its effect on the movement of water were published in 1930–31 in a series of articles in *Die Wasserwirtschaft,* the Austrian Journal of Hydrology. This showed Forchheimer to be all that a true scientist should be, and rarely is. It demonstrated the honesty and humility of a sincere academic who was prepared to accept that his former ideas had been wrong and that current thinking could be changed; that there was another way of looking at things.

Viktor's aim was always to try to perceive the dynamic reality behind what he saw as physical illusion. He claimed, and rightly so, that by and large we human beings are extremely superficial, looking for and only seeing direct relations between cause and effect, whereas Nature always moves indirectly. But worse than this, in our ignorance of the unseen dynamic behind the seen manifestation, we mistake the effect for the cause, greatly compounding this error by failing to see that an effect becomes the cause for a further effect in an endless chain of causes and effects. In this regard Viktor comments:

Our thinking is inconsistent with what we actually see. The eye is a perfect, natural organ. The seen image is a reaction phenomenon. Using an artificial optical apparatus the same effect, for example, can only be obtained by a roundabout way, by means of a negative. The eye, on the other hand, immediately presents us with the diapositive, namely the true image.

Our sight constitutes an unconscious, automatic transformation process, whereby the negative image – like a photographic negative – i.e. the effect, is transformed into a positive one, like a diapositive colour slide. Our thinking, however, is really a purely individual, conscious process and therefore learnable. If our thinking is to attain the same perfection as our seeing, then we must change our way of thinking and learn to see reality, not as an action, but as a reaction. Perfect thought lies in the apprehension of the correct reaction, for before the eye can show us the positive, it must first transform the negative and in a certain manner must break up what it records. What we see, therefore, is the turning inside out of what we receive. What our mind grasps in this way must be re-formed and re-thought if we wish to attain that for which we strive.[12]

Our direct mental approach towards the understanding and investigation of natural phenomena; our present materialistic and scientifically ingrained view that only the physically palpable and measurable represents the true reality, has lead to greater and

greater confusion and the necessity to elaborate more and more complex theories to explain the various functions of the physical world. Our great omission has been our total disregard and our failure to come to grips in depth with the more ephemeral, unseen, yet fundamental energetic causalities. Like the negative mentioned in the quotation above, these energies manifest themselves only indirectly, the physical constructs of the outer physical world being a positive reflection of their respective functions. What we perceive as the foundation of physical reality – a reality to which we have ascribed laws – is therefore only half of the truth, for in their dynamic these formative magnitudes conform to a sublime inner law of energetic reciprocities which will be discussed more fully in chapters 3 and 4, and about whose mutual interaction Viktor commented:

Nature is not served by rigid laws, but by rhythmical, reciprocal processes. Nature uses none of the preconditions of the chemist or the physicist for the purposes of evolution. Nature excludes all fire on principle for purposes of growth; therefore all contemporary machines are unnatural and constructed according to false premises. Nature avails herself of the biodynamic form of motion through which the biological prerequisite for the emergence of life is provided. Its purpose is to ur-procreate 'higher' conditions of matter out of the originally inferior raw materials, which afford the evolutionally older, or the numerically greater rising generation, the possibility of a constant capacity to evolve, for without any growing and increasing reserves of energy there would be no evolution or development. This results first and foremost in the collapse of the so-called Law of the Conservation of Energy, and in further consequence the Law of Gravity, and all other dogmatics lose any rational or practical basis.[13]

In Viktor's view Western science and education generally left much to be desired. Our civilisation suffered from a myopic compartmentalisation of the mind, which prevented a detached overview, a synthesis of what was observed:

Today's science thinks too primitively; indeed it could be said that its thinking is an octave too low. It has still not ventured far enough into the realm of energy, and its attitude has remained purely materialistic. For this reason it is principally to blame for the state of affairs we are experiencing today. In all probability, this development was necessary, for how else should a misguided humanity perceive the true interdependencies?[14]

Without doubt, therefore, there is a definite intention to teach young people upside-down methods of working with which they have to misearn their daily bread. That is to say, instead of moving forwards, they go backwards all the more rapidly in step with the improvements in the contrary methods of motion. For only thus can today's teaching principles flourish.[15]

In contrast to contemporary science, Viktor saw *will* and *spirit* as the principal causative forces of physical existence. They deploy themselves through the agency of various lower orders and magnitudes of energy belonging to the 4th and 5th dimensions, i.e. through those more subtle, non-spacial dimensions of being that are inherent, but are not perceived in the three dimensional world to which we are accustomed. Of ethereal nature and endowed with very high frequencies and formative potencies, they could also be termed 'potentialities', which in their extremely sensitive and unstable state of energetic equilibrium await the right stimulus and occasion to manifest themselves. In being able to speak of these higher and therefore more powerfully and profoundly structuring dimensions of reality, Viktor's own comprehension of them must have been at the level of the 6th dimension, a level where the encapsulation and understanding of a given concept or phenomenon is both simultaneous and total. Perhaps this might be termed the dimension of 'throughth' or pure truth, a crystal-clear transparency, a complete comprehension of the wholeness devoid of all uncertainty and unclarity.

From 1930–1933 Viktor Schauberger worked with systems for water regeneration and the production of high-quality drinking water for which patents were applied in 1934 (see fig. 15.2). This rather cumbersome prototype was later followed by an egg-shaped device which was much smaller and far more efficient. When tested to its extreme power, however, it developed such powerful internal suction that even mercury seals (of extremely densely packed molecular structure) were unable to withstand the enormous suction generated and leaked into the water undergoing treatment. Despite the fact that this leakage occurred only when extremely high vacuum effects were present, which were absent under normal conditions of operation, the Government argued through its consultant Professor Diering that the public could not be exposed to the hazard of mercury poisoning. Laying heavy emphasis on this, all further use of the machine for the regeneration and production of spring-quality water and super-distilled water was forbidden. Indeed Viktor Schauberger's machine had evidently offended somebody in high places, for it was confiscated and destroyed by the Austrian police.

Always a thorn in the side of scientific and government institutions, Viktor's long battle to save both the Rhine and the Danube from total ruin was ultimately lost through their rejection of his practical suggestions. In early 1932 he wrote a paper about the rehabilitation of the Danube detailing the measures that needed to be taken in order to reinstate it as the magnificent river it had been in days of yore. This paper was included as a separate chapter in "The Danube", a study undertaken by the International Danube Commission and consisting of submissions from the Danube's various contiguous countries.

When officialdom discovered with horror that Viktor's contribution had been incorporated into this major work, the whole edition was recalled, destroyed and republished in October 1932 omitting the offending article, disregarding the publishing costs of the original edition which amounted to over 100,000 schillings – a very large sum at the time. All this happened largely due to the actions of Viktor Schauberger's implacable antagonist Dr.Ehrenberger, who hounded him wherever he went. This eventually provoked a sharp response from Viktor Schauberger largely in the form of a letter containing twenty-nine questions of which the following are representative:

Are you aware that, before a large assembly of university professors in the lecture rooms of the Technical University for Agricultural Science, Prof. Dr. Forchheimer was able to demonstrate on the blackboard that water temperature plays not only an important, but actually the principal role in the movement of water?

Are you aware that Prof. Dr. Forscheimer urged me to publish these observations in the Wasserwirtschaft and that the Professor himself saw to it that my articles were accepted for publication?

Are you aware that the river engineering departments of Vienna, Linz, Prägarten and Bregenz, the Chairs for Hydraulic Engineering in Danzig and other places demanded the immediate withdrawal of these articles otherwise they would officially cancel their subscriptions to this scientific journal?

Are you aware that over 100 academics jointly resolved not to permit my presence in government service and to enforce my dismissal?

Are you aware that with the encouragement of Assistant Secretary, Engineer Kober I stated my preparedness to explain the principles of my system of river regulation publicly at the Technical University for Agricultural Science?

Are you aware that this lecture was cancelled at the last minute by the Rector, Dr. Olbrich?

Are you aware this professor publicly declared before witnesses, that this event was the darkest episode of his whole period as rector?

Are you aware the Federal Austrian Forestry Department had to pay A. Sch. 5,000 per 1,000 logs after I was able to prove that I could transport this timber over a distance of 30km in a wild, unruly watercourse simply with the aid of temperatures and that the competent authorities were unable to raft one log even 50 metres?

Are you aware that your articles created great difficulties for me in the German Patent Office, because there I was apparently held to be a liar and a swindler?

Are you aware that I have entered into negotiations with the widest variety of Foreign Ministers and that on each occasion the negotiations were always broken off at the last minute due to the receipt of untrue information?

Are you aware that I was invited by His Majesty the King of Bulgaria and that there too similar slanderous material was sent from Vienna?

Are you aware that Mr. Werner Zimmermann has also been warned repeatedly never to have anything more to do with me?[16]

Whatever might have been thought of Viktor Schauberger in Austria, word of his abilities and the statements contained in his then recent book, *Our Senseless Toil – the Source of the World Crisis*[17], evidently reached others ears including those of Adolf Hitler. At a time when the relations between Austria and Germany were at an all-time low, Viktor Schauberger was summoned to an audience with the Reichschancellor in Berlin. Special papers were arranged and all the documentation carried out within one day. Suddenly Viktor Schauberger left for Berlin and a meeting with Hitler, who greeted him warmly as a fellow countryman, telling him that he had studied all the reports about Viktor's work thoroughly and was very impressed with what he had learned.

Thirty minutes had been allocated for the discussions, which Prof. Max Planck had been requested to attend as scientific adviser shortly before he was rudely deposed from his position as Privy Councillor. This exchange of views eventually lasted 1½ hours, during which Schauberger explained the destructive action of contemporary technology and its inevitable consequences. He contrasted this with all the processes of natural motion and temperature, of the vital relation between trees, water and soil productivity, indeed all the things he considered had to be thoroughly understood and practised in order to create a sustainable and viable society.

When Viktor had finished his explanations, Max Planck, who had remained silent, was asked his opinion about Viktor's natural theories. His response was the remarkable and revealing statement that *"Science has nothing to do with Nature"*.[18] Pausing for a moment to take in this astonishing admission, Viktor then referred to the proposed four-year plan, the so-called Goering Plan, stating that not only was the time frame was far too short, but if instituted it would gradually undermine and ultimately destroy Germany's biological foundations. As a result, the Third Reich would last only ten instead of the boasted 1,000 years. (Viktor was not far out in his estimate!)

During the earlier part of the discussion, Hitler had been enthusiastic, but he became greatly perturbed at what he had just heard and ordered his technical and economic advisers, Messrs. Keppler and Wiluhn, to discuss with Schauberger what could be done. Once outside the door these two men demanded to know how Viktor had got in there in the first place. Angered at their truculently condescending air, he replied "Through the same door I've just come out of!" Seeing that his ideas had no hope of acceptance, and leaving them gaping, he returned to his hotel and left for Austria the following morning. Keppler and Wiluhn, however, were to get their revenge later after the Anschluss on March 13th, 1938.

In Vienna later that year, at one moment while taking tea with Mrs Mäda Primavesi, a well-known figure in the upper echelons of society, Viktor excused himself saying that he would be away for about twenty minutes for a routine medical examination of his First World War wounds at the nearby Vienna University clinic, to assess his eligibility for a continuing war pension. When he did not return, and furious at being so rudely deserted, Mrs Primavesi set out to find him. Fuming, she went to where he lived, and being told by his wife that he had not returned and that it was quite unlike him to behave in such a way, she then went to the clinic. Collaring the director, Professor Pölzl, whom she knew well, she refused to leave until Viktor had been found and eventually found where he was – in the section reserved for lunatics. He was lying quietly on a bed trussed in a straitjacket waiting for the lethal injection, which was then the standard procedure in the Third Reich for the removal of the mentally insane and other 'undesirables'. Viktor's guardian angels must have been very alert, for despite his status as *persona non grata* in the Third Reich, he somehow always managed to survive.

Despite the new order after the Anschluss and the Sword of Damocles now hanging over his head, by now hardened to setbacks and with indomitable courage and a mind never still for a moment, Viktor quietly continued his research. His main drive was to investigate phenomena and correlations that interested him. Once he had discovered that something worked, he noted the fact, and then got on with the next project. He was never very interested in commercialising his discoveries.

As ever he pursued ways of generating energy with water through the interaction of complementary, but opposite, forms of energy, i.e. heat and cold, electricity and magnetism, and centrifugence and centripetence, both aspects of which combine to create a unity, a wholeness through their synthesising, reciprocal interaction. Viktor also saw that suction and pressure could be used in similar fashion on the same axis to produce a powerful propulsive effect. In 1936 he successfully applied for patents for an air-turbine, which made use of a centripetal 'compressor' and rifled central exhaust pipe (Austrian patent no. 145141). This was followed by further patent applications in which this concept was improved. Although all trace of them has since been lost, the device described in these later patents was not only able to convert sea water into fresh water, but could also be exploited to power aircraft and submarines. Yet once again Viktor was the victim of deceit and his ideas were usurped. In documents dated 1941, he describes how Professor Ernst Heinkel, the designer of the first successful jet-plane (first flight 27 Aug.

Fig. 1.1   **First Jet Aircraft (Heinkel)**

1939 – fig. 1.1), had illegally obtained sight of Viktor's preliminary applications at the Patent Office in Berlin through his patent attorneys, Lehmann-Harlens. Having studied them carefully, Heinkel then expressed his disinterest in them, but immediately inaugurated a covert research programme using this information in modified form to improve the performance of his 1,000 kph fighter, most probably the He 280. This was an indictable infringement of Viktor's still confidential application. Wishing to avoid discovery and in order to continue to make use of the unlawfully obtained data, Heinkel fraudulently attempted to have Viktor's patent restricted to the conversion of sea water into fresh water only, by having its application to aircraft and submarine propulsion disallowed. Continuing his undercover experiments all the while, but without success due to lack of proper understanding, Heinkel, with a certain absence of ethical principle, then sought Viktor's collaboration in the project. Although some initial discussion eventually took place, Viktor did not cooperate, having become aware of the facts of the matter, and further contact between the two men ceased. Using his ill-gotten gains and keeping all the kudos for himself, however, Heinkel persevered with his research, which, as a direct result of the application of Viktor's theories, finally culminated in a much improved turbine. In the light of this Viktor Schauberger, in company with others, such as Sir Frank Whittle, inventor of the English jet engine, could also be viewed as an early contributor to the present jet-age. Indeed, in terms of aircraft design, he even went as far as to state that in order to develop and build fast-flying, supersonic aircraft successfully, the bodily forms of deep-sea fish should be copied. Today's 'stealth bombers' very much emulate these forms (fig. 1.2).

In 1939 Viktor's personal research virtually came to an end, all the materials he needed being appropriated for war production. In 1941, however, he was summoned by Air Marshal Ernst Udet to discuss the growing crisis of energy production and means of solving it. Premises were subse-

Fig. 1.2   **Stealth bomber and flat fish.**

quently set up near Augsburg for research and development, all of which came to nothing partly due to the death of Udet and partly because it was bombed by the Allies in 1942.

In 1943, despite his incapacitating war wounds and 58 years of age, Viktor was declared fit for active duty and was inducted into the Waffen-SS, very much under duress. He came under the control of Heinrich Himmler, who forced him into research to develop a new secret weapon. Provided with suitable accommodation at Schloss Schönbrunn, the nearby Mauthausen Concentration Camp to supply the workforce of prisoner engineers, Viktor was threatened with his life if he did not comply with orders and carry out this research.

In spite of these threats, however, Viktor put his foot down and demanded from the SS Command the absolute right to select the various engineers he needed. He further demanded that any technicians he chose were to be removed entirely from the camp, fed properly, dressed in normal civilian clothes and billeted in civilian accommodation, otherwise they would be unproductive. As he explained, people who live in fear of their lives and under great emotional stress could work neither consistently nor creatively. Surprisingly the SS agreed and so Viktor selected somewhere between twenty and thirty engineers, craftsmen and tradesman from Mauthausen, to be accommodated in various houses near the plant.

When they were all assembled. Viktor exhorted them to work as hard as they could, but under no circumstances were they to attempt to escape, otherwise his own life would be forfeit. They set to work with a will and, while not understanding what Viktor was trying to achieve, they nevertheless carried out his instructions faithfully. Two machines were eventually built, one called a 'Repulsator' and the other a 'Repulsine', reflecting the forces of recoil active in them. Both machines operated with the densifying forces of implosion, which are far more powerful than those of explosion.

Although these will be examined in more detail in chapter 21, accurate information about them is difficult to obtain, because after the end of the War all top secret information was confiscated and sequestered by the Allies – the Russians, French, English and Americans – and is therefore no longer available to the general public. Nor is there any trace of Viktor's wartime patents, for which according to his usual custom he is certain to have applied.

From a certain point of view, Viktor Schauberger could have been considered lucky at the end of the war, because together with his team of engineers, he had been moved by the SS to Leonstein in Upper Austria due to the bombing of Vienna and therefore in May 1945 came under the jurisdiction of the American forces of occupation. In Leonstein Viktor was placed in protective custody for nine months by the Americans and quartered inside a doubly-fenced and guarded perimeter. This was done partly to glean information about his involuntary, though to him useful, wartime research into 'higher' atomic energies at Mauthausen and Leonstein and partly to prevent his abduction by the Russians. Confirmation of this can be found in a letter Viktor wrote to the German Minister of Defence, Franz Josef Strauss, on the 28th of February 1956. Here he relates how the last device upon which he had been working had been seized only a few days after its successful flight by American intelligence investigators, who appeared to be very well informed about it. Its most important component on the other hand, which was forgotten in the haste to move to Leonstein, had been removed by the Russians from his Vienna apartment and the apartment subsequently blown up. Once Viktor had been thoroughly 'de-briefed', he was apparently threatened with further internment should he be foolish enough to continue his research in this field. Apart from time spent on interrogation during this period of confinement, however, for Viktor – now almost entirely penniless – this was a time of reflection and reassessment of his future.

During this immediately postwar period food was still extremely scarce and many people were suffering from malnutrition. When he was ultimately released, eventually moving to Salzburg in late 1946, he then set about applying his wide knowledge to agriculture and the systems of cultivation then in use. In collaboration with Franz Rosenberger (and as discussed later in chapter 19), he was able to demonstrate that significant increases in productivity could be achieved using the knowledge he had acquired in Bulgaria before the war. All progress in this area subsequently being blocked by corrupt politicians in 1949, Viktor then returned to his study of implosion, energy generation and water movement, trying with his limited funds to pick up the threads of his earlier research, culminating in a scientific investigation and vindication of his theories on the natural flow of water at Stuttgart Technical University in 1952 under the direction of Prof. Franz

Pöpel, which will be addressed in more detail in chapter 14.

With enquiring mind and tenacity of purpose, Viktor continued to work on his various devices. Aloys Kokaly, the publisher of *Implosion*, a magazine devoted to Viktor Schauberger's theories, and a former corporal in the Waffen-SS who had managed by devious means to procure materials for Viktor's research at Schloss Schönbrunn, asked him why he was still working so hard, to which Viktor replied:

I must furnish those who would protect or save life, with an energy source, which produces energy so cheaply that nuclear fission will not only be uneconomical, but ridiculous. This is the task I have set myself in what little life I have left.[19]

The product of this last personal effort is the home-power generator shown in figs. 1.3 a&b, which due to Viktor's very limited pensioner's funds and its resulting crude, unso-

Fig. 1.3a **The Home Power Generator.**

Fig. 1.3b

phisticated construction, did not function as well as he had hoped, for as it transpired, this machine was an unfortunate compromise between the geometry of mechanics and that of organics. It was a miserable culmination to the life's work of this quite remarkable man.

Being the enlightened individual he was, Viktor Schauberger had a remarkable standard of personal integrity, honesty and responsibility. His word in any undertaking was always his bond, even if he was ultimately the loser. He would brook no deceit or underhand activity in any of those with whom he worked either as employers or employees. This often created enormous difficulties for him and he suffered considerable personal losses as a result. He was not a businessman, nor had he any interest in the commercial exploitation of his inventions for personal gain.

His overriding desire was to provide present and future generations with the ability in terms of knowledge and machines with which to usher in and sustain a golden age of prosperity, peace and harmony. His chief problem was always to find honest and unselfish people to help in the development and production of the various apparatuses needed to bring this about. In many instances his trust was sadly misplaced, as illustrated in extracts from a letter of the 4th February 1958 to a friend, a certain Mr. 'R', about 7½ months before Viktor died.

I was always challenged to provide proof. Whenever I did this, I was robbed to such an extent that no other course was open to me, other than to remain silent once more. In the February issue of Weltgewissen you will be able to read that these apparatuses which the Austrian State Police took from me, are now being manufactured in Germany with enormous success. This has happened to me twelve times. Every time I had something produced, all I was given were the leftovers, while the best part was retained and exploited commercially by others. Or the apparatus was never made public, although I had paid all the agreed development costs myself. Subsequently large sums were demanded of me,

which lay far beyond my capacity to pay, and the machines I was struggling to build were withheld as security against payment.

I then began to work covertly and in this way succeeded in producing workable machines. I then first became aware of what I had discovered, namely higher-grade atomic energies. At this stage 'Demonstrate it!', 'Prove it!', 'Let it be examined!' was and is always demanded. If I concur, then all is lost. If I do not, however, then I am a fraud.

Then along came a major German industrialist with his scientific advisors. He investigated the process and found it in order. Statements were made expressing readiness to proceed with fabrication and cost evaluation and then, yes, then one will just have to wait and see. All they are, are empty promises, never kept.

Now representatives of the U.S. government have announced themselves. They too want to see and evaluate everything first, and then, only then will it be considered what might be done.

I requested a provisional agreement, which would only come into force once I proved that I could achieve significantly increased output. This was rejected. First see, then negotiate and the outcome was always the same.

Professors also want first to see, evaluate and then, aye, and then take over.

My dear Mr. R, I have now reached the point where they can all kiss the place where my spinal column terminates. I am old and seriously ill. My only concern now is for all the poor children who are faced with a grisly future.

If I reveal everything it will only be hushed up, because it not only involves the whole scientific establishment, but also the doctrines of the Church. All power politics will collapse once the truth emerges that science is the actual causative agent of cancer.

I intend to return to the forest once more, there to die in peace. The whole of science and all its hangers-on are nothing but a band of thieves, who are suspended like marionettes and must dance to whatever tune their well-camouflaged slave-masters deem necessary.[20]

This letter, most probably written to Alois Renner in the light of what follows, heralded the final disastrous chapter of Viktor Schauberger's life, a chapter that started

Questions for Science

ENERGY

- What is it that keeps the Earth floating in space?
- Why does a top stand upright when it is spun from the side?
- What is temperature? What is heat? What is cold?
- What is energy?
- What is evaporation?
- What is vaporisation?
- What is dissolution?
- What is combination?
- What is absorption?
- On what effects are these processes founded?

MAGNETISM

- Why do the magnetic lines of force run from south to north?
- Why does the Earth rotate from west to east?

THE SUN

- What serves the sun as a carrier of light and heat, if, in the view of our learned scientists, space is a vacuum?
- Why do gases condense with a decrease in temperature?
- Why don't the fiery gases of the Sun, with supposed temperatures of over 6000°C, stream out into space?
- Why is the light and heat in the tropics more diffuse and at the poles the Sun's light more intense and its radiant heat less?

ATMOSPHERE

- Why doesn't the Earth's warm air rise?
- Why is it so cold at the top of a mountain, i.e. nearer the Sun?
- Why in our houses is it warmer nearer the ceiling and colder at the floor, when an artificial source of heat is used?
- Why does marble expand with heat and why doesn't it contract again with cold?

EVAPORATION

- Why is the desert so dead despite all the heat?
- Why do damp tiled roofs dry out from the eaves towards the ridge?

WATER

- Why does the groundwater in walls rise far above the surface of the ground?
- Why don't wooden posts rot under water, but above it always?
- Why can rising cold water pierce through the hardest rock?
- Why does water pulsate and breathe?
- Why does groundwater manage to remain on the sides of mountains?
- Why, growing colder and heavier, does it rise upwards?
- Why does it frequently spring from high peaks?

RIVERS

- Why do west-to-east flowing watercourses fertilise their banks?
- Why are the banks of east-to-west flowing rivers so barren?
- Why are the banks of south-to-north flowing watercourses fertile on one side only?
- Why do rivers flowing into cold seas migrate laterally to the north?
- Why do deltas and estuaries develop?
- Why does a trout stand still in a raging torrent, as if by magic?

THE SEA

- Why is the water at the poles warmer at the bottom?
- Why is the sunlit surface at the poles so icily cold?
- Why doesn't the warmer, lighter bottom-water of the sea rise upwards?
- Why are the water temperatures at the equator so warm?
- Why is it that it gets colder with increasing depth?
- Why does it get warmer again below the boundary layer of +4°C?
- Why does life below this boundary layer begin anew?
- Why does the salt content of the seas vary?
- Why do herrings migrate northwards in winter?
- Why do deep-sea fish glow?
- Why can the warm Gulf Stream push the cold seawater aside and wend its way for thousands of kilometres over mountains and valleys in a reversed temperature gradient without the assistance of a mechanical gradient?

BLOOD

- Why do cold-blooded animals carry fever-inducing poison?
- Why does a cold fever occur in the tropics?
- Why does a warm fever arise from a chill?
- What is fever anyway?
- Why is our body temperature subnormal when climbing a mountain and above normal as we descend?
- Why does the heart beat in our breast?
- Who gives this muscle its impulse to move?
- Where is the motor for this pump?
- Why does blood circulate in our blood vessels?
- Why do the fluids in a chicken's egg circulate without a heart?
- Why do we breathe day and night, when asleep and even when totally unconscious?
- Does the heart beat because we breathe, or do we breathe because the heart beats?

TREES

- Why have light-demanding timbers a thick bark and shade-demanders only a thin one?
- Where is the heart of a plant?

[from *Our Senseless Toil*]

with much hope for the final realisation of all that he had striven for in his life. Having had no appreciation or support from the government or anyone else in Austria, when he was eventually approached by the Americans, who expressed an enthusiastic interest in developing his theories on implosion, Viktor felt that at last something positive would happen as America was such a powerful country with tremendous entrepreneurial energy. He was by this time quite exasperated at the behaviour of Europeans and what he had suffered at their hands, and in a conversation with Aloys Kokaly, Viktor somewhat embittered declared:

"An American aircraft consortium offered me 3.5 million dollars, a similar offer was made by Canadian interests."[21]

"You didn't want it in Europe, so now you'll have to get it back from America expensively !"[22]

This all came to pass, but as we shall see, nothing ever came back to Europe, nor to the rest of the world for that matter, which for humanity at large has been the greatest loss and misfortune for humanity at large. But before proceeding to this final tragic episode and to obtain some insight into the scope of Viktor's thinking, let us examine and present it by directly quoting a passage taken from his book *Our Senseless Toil* (see p. 14). Here he poses a number of questions relating to phenomena that apparently had not been satisfactorily investigated at the time. Since its publication in 1933, many of these may well have been answered, but not perhaps in the way that he would have himself, because of his different view of life processes. While presented here under their original heading, they are not in the same sequence as first written, but have been arranged according to subject and more or less in the order in which some of them will be discussed in this book.

1.2 What Happened in America

Before embarking on this last and lamentable chapter in Viktor Schauberger's life, I would like to state at the outset that signifi-

cant and verifiable detail about it is extremely difficult to ascertain, mainly because all those involved, with the exception of Karl Gerchsheimer with whom I spent two days, have passed away in the interim. In whatever information is available concerning this tragedy, there is a profusion of conflicting statements, interpretations and timetables which, 37 years after the event, makes the unravelling what precisely took place in this, for all concerned, abortive endeavour rather problematic. That nothing eventually came of this unfortunate affair in my view is due largely to cumulative misunderstandings, misapprehensions and inadequate clarification on both sides, which finally culminated in a complete breakdown, not only in communication, but in mutual trust. The three principle factors that brought this about were firstly, the difficulty Viktor Schauberger had in describing accurately in language that others could understand exactly what forces, motion and energies were involved in the processes of implosion. His demonstration of their most elementary form, the centripetal inwinding vortex that forms over a waste pipe, was deemed far too simple and too familiar a phenomenon to be of any consequence. This provoked a rising scepticism and dwindling belief in the validity of Viktor's theories. The second factor relates to Viktor's and Walter's nervousness about possible theft and exploitation of the implosion idea, the result of the many misfortunes experienced by Viktor, as told to Mr `R' in the above letter. The third factor was the absence of a working prototype.

While earlier accounts of this 1958 venture infer the involvement of the United States government, the initiative actually came from Karl Gerchsheimer. Born in 1903 to a well-connected family in Würzburg, Bavaria, in his youth Gerchsheimer spent a great deal of time in the surrounding forests and had developed an understanding of Nature, of the importance and function of trees and water very similar to that of Viktor Schauberger. In this particular area both Gerchsheimer and Viktor seem to have had a great deal in common. Leaving Germany in

1922, Gerchsheimer's life followed an eventful path. Under contract to the Mexican Government from 1926 to 1935 he reformed Mexican agriculture and introduced the pineapple and banana. He also installed the potable water supply system for the whole of Mexico City and set up the Mexican Highway Police, which under his stewardship became renown for its incorruptibility. Moving to Texas in 1937, where he married his present wife, it would appear that he later became involved in US counter-espionage activities during World War II, the most likely agency being the C.I.C. (Counter Intelligence Corps). From war's end in 1945 to 1950 he was the U.S civilian property administrator-in-chief in charge of all civil administration, logistics, transport and accommodation under the American Army of Occupation, and in this role was the most powerful non-military individual in the American zone. Returning to the United States in 1950, he set up his own metal fabrication business, which manufactured a large number components under contract to NASA and from which he retired at age 81.

In the years immediately following his return to America in 1950, Gerchsheimer gradually developed a close friendship with Robert Donner, who was the former owner of the Donner Steelworks of Philadelphia, a large and prosperous company. Very much a patriot who waged constant war against subversive activity in the United States, Donner eventually retired to Colorado Springs, Colorado, an extremely wealthy man (Gerchsheimer placed his personal fortune in 1958 at about US$400 million). He was also the chief executive of the Donner Foundation, a philanthropic organisation set up by his father in Philadelphia in the mid-1940s to fund cancer research which in the 1950s and 1960s awarded grants for educational and other charitable ventures.

Over the years Gerchsheimer had become increasingly disenchanted with technology's use of explosive forces to generate power and motion. Viewing with disdain Werner von Braun's efforts to conquer space with rockets powered by explosion, a matter he discussed with von Braun himself at NASA, Gerchsheimer gradually became convinced that some other antithetical system of propulsion would solve the problems of powered flight and open the way towards a safe and effective exploration of space. During the course of their rising friendship, Gerchsheimer had often expressed these views to Robert Donner, engaging the latter's interest in the potential of these other forces, if they could be harnessed. In late 1957 these convictions of Gerchsheimer's became more concretised upon reading about Viktor Schauberger and implosion in a German publication – most probably Leopold Brandstätter's booklet "Implosion statt Explosion" published in 1956, although Gerchsheimer does not confirm this, in which Viktor's theories were elaborated.

With this more definite information to hand, Gerchsheimer then enthused Donner with the idea of visiting Viktor Schauberger himself, because if valid, his theories were worthy of closer examination. Moreover to maintain American supremacy as a world power, it was important that an invention of such promise should be developed in the United States rather than in any other country. Agreeing to this, Donner then told Gerchsheimer to make arrangements for immediate travel to Austria. In addition, however, and much to Gerchsheimer's annoyance, Donner also insisted that he be accompanied by his financial adviser, Norman Dodd, who was to be in overall charge of the expedition. A man in his early 60s, Norman Dodd moved in financial and investment circles in New York and was Donner's trusted financial consultant, a position he had held for the preceding 10 years or so, which had resulted in a firm friendship between the two men. Dodd was also the author of an investigative study carried out on behalf of Congress into the financial structures, administrative procedures, taxation, etc., both legal and fraudulent, of various American foundations and like organisations. According to Gerchsheimer, this study, though completed and backed by Congress, was never published, because too many people in high places would have been implicated.

Donner's decision having been made, Gerchsheimer then contacted his business acquaintance, Harald W. Totten (some reports claim that Gerchsheimer actually worked for Totten), the proprietor of the Washington Iron Works Inc., in Sherman, Texas. He suggested that Totten's foundry, pipe-making and precision engineering works would be the ideal venue for developing and replicating Viktor's devices. Totten's interest was immediately aroused and he agreed to make his premises available. All this having been arranged, Gerchsheimer and Dodd informed Viktor of their impending visit. Flying to Frankfurt in mid-April 1958, they proceeded from there by chauffeur-driven car to Linz on the Danube, where Viktor lived.

After the initial introductions were over, at which Walter Schauberger was also present, Gerchsheimer began to explain the purpose of their visit. Speaking in fluent German with a Bavarian accent, Gerchsheimer told Viktor, or the "Old Man" as he came to be called, that they had come as representatives of Robert Donner, an American financier interested in the rapid development and practical implementation of Viktor's theories on implosion, for which almost unlimited funds could eventually be made available. Gerchsheimer relates that at the time both Schaubergers seemed to be in a state of high anxiety about espionage and surveillance, even to the point of expressing concern over the identity and presence of the German chauffeur and guide who had been left outside. Mindful of his 9-month surveillance by American intelligence in 1945/46, a period when Walter Schauberger had also been interrogated, Viktor was certain that they were once more being watched and expressed his deep-seated unease to Gerchsheimer. At this Gerchsheimer laughed, but at the same time offered to find out. In front of the Schaubergers he rang up the Criminal Investigation Department of the Austrian police. Though this produced assurances that neither Viktor nor Walter were under surveillance, Viktor was still not happy. Well acquainted with U.S. intelligence agencies as former U.S. property administrator, Gerchsheimer then contacted the F.B.I.'s offices in Germany, thus demonstrating an intimate familiarity with intelligence agencies. Gerchsheimer himself admits that in hindsight this well-intentioned action probably did more to confirm the Schaubergers' suspicions than to allay them.

All this took place at a time when Viktor was involved in a legal wrangle at the Salzburg District Court to recover a number of machines that he had commissioned Sebastian Thurner, a mechanical engineering professor at the Salzburg Polytechnic School, to build for him. These devices were a further development of the home-power generator shown in figs. 1.3a and 1.3b, which apparently had ruptured when first switched on. Due to obstructions or constrictions in the spiral core-pipes, strong pressures had been created within them instead of the anticipated suction, resulting in an explosion. Three redesigned models were apparently built incorporating a pressure-relief valve, one of which Viktor had obtained, the other two being withheld against payment of Thurner's costs.

As discussions with the Schaubergers progressed it became apparent to Gerchsheimer and Dodd that they were not the only parties interested in the development of Viktor's theories on implosion. A number of other organisations including certain Swiss interests were also in the process of negotiating for Viktor's devices. Wishing to put paid to any competition, Gerchsheimer regaled Viktor with assurances as to how much easier it would be to obtain large sums of research money in the United States than in Europe, where so much still had to be directed towards reconstruction. Taking Gerchsheimer's lead, Dodd then urged Viktor to come over to America to complete his life's work, pointing out that historically America had often shown that it was prepared to undertake ventures considered Utopian in Europe. Moreover Viktor's and Walter's work had the potential to solve a problem, whose solution despite much research had long remained unsolved, namely the generation of virtually free energy.

Financing such research and development would present few problems in the United States, however, for once a small operational prototype had been successfully built, then a research foundation would be set up into which millions of tax-free dollars could be invested. Gerchsheimer then revealed that there was an engineering facility in Texas well able, ready and willing to develop and build Viktor's machines.

His interest awakened, Viktor asked for time to consider their proposal. After Viktor and Walter had discussed the offer between themselves and with Viktor's still reluctant agreement, because he did not really want to leave Austria, Viktor then gave his provisional assent. Under psychological pressure from the rumoured competitors and fearing a successful outcome to their already advanced negotiations with the Schaubergers, the following day Dodd offered Viktor US$15,000 in down payment on his various data and models, a sum that Viktor had previously requested in order to pay Thurner. In taking this step, however, Dodd apparently exceeded his authority for he had insufficient funds to back the offer up. Promising Viktor that they had every intention of developing implosion in America and asking him to sign nothing until they returned, Gerchsheimer and Dodd hastened back to the United States to confer with Robert Donner and finalise arrangements. Just before they left, however, Viktor warned them stating that:

"I am neither a technologist nor an engineer, all I understand is the principle. I could only agree to come provided certain conditions are met as I don't feel very well physically and I don't think I am really up to the rigours of the journey."[23]

Viktor's concern in this respect was well-founded, for his physical condition at the time was not good. Apart from suffering from emphysema and an ailing heart – the result of his wartime experiences, the preceding winter had taken an enormous toll of him, to the point where he felt that he had

little time left to live. In response it was immediately proposed that Viktor should be accompanied by an Austrian doctor in whom he had confidence and who would look after him, all expenses being paid by the Americans. At this Viktor brightened and was eventually accompanied by his son-in-law, Dr Walter Luib.

A few days later at Donner's house in Colorado Springs, Gerchsheimer and Dodd delivered a full report on events in Austria. While agreeing to authorise payment of Dodd's offer in full, Donner also wanted to secure his investment and asked his lawyer to draw up a contract for eventual signa-ture by Viktor. The substance of this contract required Viktor to acknowledge the receipt of the US$15,000, to be paid in cash as an initial payment towards the acquisition by the Donner, Dodd, Gerchsheimer consortium of all relevant data, designs, drawing and models related to Viktor's implosive theories. Walter Schauberger was also to receive an advance of US$5,000 at the same time.

Returning to Europe in early May, Gerchsheimer and Dodd drove to Linz in a white Mercedes two-seater sports-car that Gerchsheimer had bought on arrival in Germany. Finding Viktor unwell when they arrived, they picked him up or arranged for his transfer to Bad Ischl. Here Viktor was accommodated in a villa just outside the town, where they could keep an eye on him while his health improved and also ward off any further contact with possible competitors. First on the agenda was the contract. This stated that Viktor's sojourn in the United States would be for 3 months only, and that Walter Schauberger, a physicist and mathematician, was to accompany his father and would be expected to stay for a year in order to assist in the scientific interpretation of Viktor's ideas for which there was often no recognised scientific terminology. One further condition required that Viktor grant permission for all pertinent data and devices necessary for the success of 'Project Implosion' to be transferred to the United States. Before agreeing to sign the contract, however, Viktor stipulated that Alois Renner, his trusted friend and exceptionally gifted machinist who had manufactured some of Viktor's devices, would have to be brought over to the United States to collaborate with Viktor in building the models. Renner's salary in this regard was to be paid by Donner or the Washington Iron Works. Concurring with Viktor's demands, this first agreement, whereunder Viktor and Walter were required henceforth to maintain total secrecy, was signed on the 9th of May.

While waiting for Viktor's health to recover sufficiently for the journey and the better to acquaint themselves with his ideas, Gerchsheimer and Dodd continued their discussions with Viktor and Walter on a daily basis, talking first with Viktor in the morning and Walter in the afternoon. While it has been contended that seeing Viktor and Walter separately was intentional, it was far more probably due to the fact that Viktor's health was better in the morning and that there was insufficient space in the Mercedes for more than two people comfortably.

In their morning talks over and after breakfast, Viktor tried to explain everything about his theories of implosion and how they could be implemented practically. Gerchsheimer admits that he was very impressed with Viktor's wide knowledge of forestry and water, though not comprehending his detailed explanation of implosion. In the afternoon the attention of the two Americans turned to Walter, who, while alluding to a good knowledge of physics, mainly elaborated on his activities in connection with the "Grüne Front" (Green Front), a movement started by Viktor in the early 1950s to inaugurate large scale reafforestation. In this way Gerchsheimer and Dodd gradually obtained a more concrete idea of what the Schaubergers had to offer. In my discussions with Gerchsheimer, he revealed that in his opinion Walter neither knew nor understood much about his father's theories.

While Gerchsheimer was relatively well versed in the overall concept of implosion and also had a greater understanding of Nature's processes, Dodd's life had been devoted to finance and investment. Dodd was therefore something of a layman during these discussions and unable to take any really effective part, having to rely on Gerchsheimer's opinion as to the substance and validity of Viktor's ideas. In this way their roles gradually reversed with Gerchsheimer gaining the more commanding position. In some ways, however, Dodd was more instrumental in bringing the Schaubergers to America than Gerchsheimer. His quiet, forthright and sincere nature inspired the Schaubergers with confidence and it was essentially because of him that they eventually agreed to the Americans' overtures. After about three weeks of talks and feeling in better health, Viktor finally agreed to go, but reiterated categorically that:

"One thing is to be thoroughly understood. This whole affair is not to take longer than three months; three months only and not a single day longer !"[24]

Early in June Viktor and Walter were requested to fill out a comprehensive questionnaire for the purposes of obtaining visas to the United States. Shortly thereafter on the 17th of June, 10 days before their departure, they were taken to the American consulate in Salzburg to have the necessary visas stamped into their passports. 10 minutes after their arrival, their passports were returned to them. Shaking their hands after the formalities had been completed, the consul then congratulated them on the four-year duration of their visas. Both Viktor and Walter found this remark rather unsettling, for contrary to the original agreement, whereby Walter would be in the United States for only one year and Viktor for only three months, it now appeared that their presence was required for four years. At this early stage of the affair, however, this mooted extension of their sojourn may in no way have reflected what was actually planned at the time, because visas are often issued with a currency of four years. The Schaubergers' trepidations, while well-founded from their point of view owing to their limited experience of post-war travel, would therefore have had no basis in fact.

From the 18th of June onwards at Gerchsheimer's request and expense, Walter set about gathering together all the proto-types, working models, documents, designs, drawings, patents, of whatever kind, which he thought would be material to the research and development of implosion. These were eventually packed into cartons and crates and forwarded by sea to the Washington Iron Works Inc. in Texas, where Viktor devices were to be fabricated. Prior to leaving for Frankfurt to arrange the necessary air-tickets, Gerchsheimer advised the Schaubergers to leave all traditional Austrian clothing, `trachten', `lederhosen', etc., behind as they would be unsuited to the climate in Texas. More normal apparel would also permit their discrete and in-conspicuous integration into American life.

On the 25th of June Viktor, Walter and Dr. Luib left Linz for Frankfurt by train. There

Fig. 1.4   **Viktor Schauberger embarks for Dallas**

they were met by Gerchsheimer and Dodd, who had arrived two days earlier, and were taken to an American-owned hotel for the night. At 10 pm the following day all five boarded a Pan American Airways flight and were flown non-stop to New York, a rela-tively low-altitude, bumpy flight of 11 to 13 hours according to headwind, which for Viktor in his low state of health would have been a gruelling experience. Here Dodd had arranged for the Schaubergers and Dr. Luib to be put up for two or three days at the University Club at 1 West 54th Street, of which Dodd was a member, so as to allow Viktor to recover from the long flight. The following day, while Viktor remained in his room, Walter went sight-seeing and was taken to the top of the Empire State building. On the 30th June a small celebration was held for Viktor's 73rd birthday. While earlier reports have stated that a large banquet was held in their honour by the U.S. Chamber of Commerce, Gerchsheimer denies this on the grounds that Donner would have shunned any such publicity.

When the time came for departure for Texas on the 1st of July, Dodd, who hitherto had been their constant companion, was apparently no longer to accompany them. In an unguarded remark by Gerchsheimer, Walter learned that Dodd was about to be dismissed by Donner. Dodd himself was only informed of this about three weeks after the Schaubergers had arrived in Texas. The reasons for Dodd's dismissal are not recorded, but a newspaper article of the 21 August 1959 in the *Gazette Telegraph* of Colorado Springs reports on a law suit against Donner in which Dodd sought US$100,000 in damages for wrongful dis-missal. Unaware of his impending dismissal, however, Dodd set about arranging for the immigration of Renner and his wife to the United States as stipulated in the contract signed in Linz. In this endeavour he appar-ently pulled a number of strings in high places in order to expedite matters, as no fur-ther progress could be made on the project until Renner had arrived. This took consider-ably longer than anticipated owing to the emergence of certain unstated irregularities,

Fig. 1.5   **On the ranch outside Sherman**

which delayed the Renners arrival in Texas until September 3rd.

Boarding the American Airlines plane (fig. 1.4), Viktor, Walter, Dr. Luib and Gerchsheimer then flew non-stop to Dallas. As they flew over the mid-western States, Viktor looked down despondently at the near treeless landscape passing by underneath, which was dotted here and there by bores and high water towers, all of which provoked the remark:

"What's the point? From a biological point of view what's down there is a dying land. The water's had it. The soil's had it and the earth is as dry as a hot plate! You haven't the vaguest idea what water is! Water belongs inside the earth and not above it. What's in these water towers is no longer water, but firewater !"[25]

Arriving in Dallas they were greeted by Gerchsheimer's family and Harald W. Totten and taken to a restaurant to have something to eat and relax from the journey. Pending decisions as to their final accommodation,

the Schaubergers and Dr Luib spent two or three days in motel in Sherman before being comfortably installed in Harald Totten's large, air-conditioned ranch-house complete with swimming pool about 3 miles from town. Encouraged to rest and acclimatise themselves while waiting for Renner to arrive, here they were provided with all they needed, which included a telephone, a cook and a car and chauffeur to take them into town when necessary (fig. 1.5).

For the first three weeks while waiting for Renner's arrival, Gerchsheimer continued to try to gain greater insight into Viktor's ideas. As has been mentioned earlier, however, the language and terminology Viktor used to describe the dynamics of implosion and the functioning of his machines was very difficult to understand in any concrete way. Moreover, Viktor continually reiterated that to understand it all properly it was imperative that an actual machine should be examined. This never happened. Walter was apparently of no use whatsoever in any of these explanations either, because at the time he too was insufficiently acquainted with his father's theories and their implementation. As a result Gerchsheimer found Viktor's description of the processes of implosion and his higher form of atomic energy increasingly incomprehensible – gobbledygook was how Gerchsheimer described it to me. Becoming more and more exasperated and frustrated with the whole affair, he eventually came to the conclusion that the Schaubergers had nothing to offer. Viktor also had problems, but of a different nature. Coupled with the difficulties of communicating his ideas to Gerchsheimer, isolation in the oppressive heat and vastness of Texas, and inactivity due to Renner's non-arrival, Viktor's psychological and physical condition declined. On Gerchsheimer's advice and with Dr Luib's agreement, Viktor was removed to a clinic near Sherman for observation. Eventually staying some four weeks, he apparently responded satisfactorily to treatment. The end-effect of Viktor's physical lapse, however, was to increase his longing to return to his natural habitat in Austria. One full moonlit night in August, while standing in the evening cool, Viktor said to Walter:

"You have no idea how wonderful it will be, when I can tread European soil once more ! I felt myself obliged to come to America despite my health and age. Whatever it was that I could do, I do believe I have now done."[26]

Seriously concerned for Viktor's physical condition, Walter proposed a plan of work which he submitted to Gerchsheimer on the 9th of August. In this Walter suggested that once Viktor was well enough to travel, both he and Walter should then return to Austria, where Viktor would continue to act as consultant. Having safely installed his father, Walter would then return to America with his family for a year with visitor status only to oversee the development of the implosion devices. This proposal was evidently rejected by Gerchsheimer, who, unable to evaluate Schauberger's data himself, but being financially committed to the project, had meanwhile voiced his rising disquiet and disbelief to Donner.

Upset at hearing this and anxious for the success of the venture Donner then flew to New York and on to the National Atomic Research Laboratories at Brookhaven, Long Island, to seeking expert scientific opinion on Viktor's theories and his new form of atomic energy. In discussions held over the next three days from the 15th – 17th August culminating in a written agreement, the services of Eric A. Boerner, a native German speaker and the head of a team of design engineers working on the Cosmotron Project, were retained to act as go-between. (Used for the investigation of atomic structures and nuclear particles, the Cosmotron was a proton (ionised hydrogen atom) accelerator or synchrotron, which made use of a large toroidal electromagnet to generate high electric and magnetic fields. These were required to guide and accelerate the particles to an energy of 3,000,000,000 electron volts (3 GeV) in preparation for subsequent collision with atomic nuclei through which the behaviour of the scattered nuclear particles could be evaluated.) While no nuclear physicist himself, Boerner was sufficiently conversant with the terminology and fundamentals of nuclear physics to be able to translate and transmit any information to the scientific evaluators that the Schaubergers might provide. At one point during these negotiations, Boerner apparently suggested that a multi-million dollar implosion research centre be set up in Arizona, perhaps with an idea of leading it himself. Boerner evidently mentioned this proposal to the Schaubergers, who seem to have misinterpreted it as fact, although it had already been rejected by both Gerchsheimer and Donner. Having finalised the agreement, Donner returned to Colorado Springs the next day. From this point matters began to accelerate, reaching their zenith in early to mid-September.

On the 20th of August, some seven weeks after their arrival in Texas, Gerchsheimer instructed the Schaubergers to write up their own separate reports about implosion, at the same time announcing that a decisive conference was to take place in three weeks' time. Viktor was told that he should write his reports in his own words, regardless of whether the concepts or terms he used might or might not be correct, because any pearls of wisdom they contained would still be extracted. Headed *P.O. Box 28, Sherman, Texas*, Viktor Schauberger's reports were addressed to *Mr Eric. A. Boerner, National Atomic Research Laboratory, Brookhaven, Upton, New York State*. As a subheading it was further indicated that their submission was *at the behest of Mr Robert Donner or his representative, Mr Karl Gerchsheimer, in accordance with the agreement drawn up on the 15th, 16th & 17th August 1958 at Brookhaven*. The writing of these reports took about 10 days from the 20th to the 31st August, Walter's mainly addressing and reinterpreting the known facts of physics, one 12 page report discussing various aspects of bio-magnetic axes. When finished these were collected on a daily basis by Gerchsheimer, who forwarded them post-haste to Boerner for translation and transmission to the scientific evaluators.

On all accounts it seems that much of the communication between the Schaubergers and Gerchsheimer were fairly perfunctory, with few chances of real clarification about the personalities, project and programme. Being thus kept largely in the dark, patience and tolerance between both sides began to be very strained with Gerchsheimer's communication becoming increasingly terse and he himself more distant. It would therefore seem quite likely that the Schauberger's were not wholly informed as to who Boerner actually was and came to believe that he was the director of the Cosmotron Project. Thus erroneously invested with high office at the National Atomic Research Laboratories, Boerner inevitably became bracketted with the cutting edge of nuclear research and in consequence fallaciously accredited with government backing and top secret clearances. As a result the Schaubergers came to believe that Boerner was an expert on all questions concerning energy. On occasion during discussions at which I was present, Walter Schauberger admitted that in the process of producing their reports, it dawned on them that a bomb could possibly be produced through implosion that was magnitudes more powerful than the hydrogen bomb. Assuming Boerner to be more influential than he was, Viktor and Walter became convinced that all the information they were supplying to him was being passed directly to the U.S. government and the military. Since the Schaubergers' principal preoccupation concerned the enhancement of Life and no doubt anxious not to enable or participate in any way in the development of such a lethal device, this may well have contributed to the communication difficulties that peaked towards the end of the project. These problems were indubitably exacerbated by Viktor's later vow of silence, which in the light of the above realisation could well have been more than accidental and would also go a long way towards explaining Walter's behaviour at the third and most important meeting in Colorado Springs, described later.

The cartons and crates despatched from Europe having meanwhile arrived in Sherman, on the appointed day in early September the conference was convened. It was attended by Viktor, Walter, Donner,

Boerner and possibly Renner. This first of three meetings then took place at Totten's ranch outside Sherman. Although chaired by Donner, it was addressed principally by Boerner, who declared that Project Implosion was now a viable proposition, because Viktor's ideas and basic premises had been found to be in agreement with newly established facts of physics, namely the functional dynamics of implosion. An energy concept in accord with Nature's processes could therefore be realised. In Boerner's view the solution of the problem of energy lay in the proper interpretation of Max Planck's equation $E = hv$, formulated in 1900, and the Friedrich Hasenöhrl-Albert Einstein equation $E = mc^2$.[27] Walter's unveiling of the true interpretation of c^2 had clarified the way in which Nature's energies were accumulated and therefore there was now a sound mathematical and physical basis upon which Project Implosion could proceed (see boxed data entitled "The Consonances between $E = hv$, $E = mc^2$ and Kepler's 3rd Law of Planetary Motion", p.24). This having been established a start could now be made. Viktor and Walter were then told that a four-year period of development would be required before fruition. Energy was problem No. 1 for the United States and its solution required an all-out effort, particularly from Viktor and Walter, which would necessitate their presence in America for eight years. With this statement no doubt all Viktor's and Walter's earlier suspicions about the four-year currency of their visas were thoroughly confirmed. To be fair, however, the possibility exists that a stay of such length had not originally been envisaged, but evolved into a necessity, the result of the far more comprehensive information the Schaubergers had supplied. Viktor was deeply shocked at this announcement, partly at the prospect of an 8-year sojourn in a foreign land isolated by language, but more importantly at the enormous deceit, if deceit it was, that had been perpetrated on them. When Viktor interjected animatedly that in the initial agreement he was only required to stay for three months, he was told that he would have two days to accustom himself to

The Consonances between $E = h\nu$, $E = mc^2$ and Kepler's 3rd law of Planetary Motion

In clarification of the above, Planck's equation $E = h\nu$ or hf relates to his law of radiation which states that: *"Energy only exists in multiples of whole numbers. The total action of energy is always a whole-numbered multiple of h."* (postulate of quantum theory). In this equation the energy of electromagnetic radiation E is the product of a universal and fundamental physical constant h (= 6.62 x 10^{-34} joules/second – Planck's constant) times a frequency f or ν, which can only be emitted or absorbed in discrete packets or quanta. This leads to the concept of energetic periodicities, which can be variously interpreted as longitudinally pulsative, cyclical, rotational, helical or wave-like forms of motion, Nature expressing herself physically and exclusively through the properties of the whole number or the creation of discrete individualities, atoms, trees, humans, etc. The analogous Hasenöhrl- Einstein equation $E = mc^2$ on the other hand states that energy E is the product of mass m times the speed of light c squared. However, since electromagnetic radiation can only be manifested in discrete quanta, as above, then the speed of light squared as a factor in electromagnetic radiation, which according to relativity is assumed to be an invariable constant, should also be interpretable in terms of periodicities – whole numbers and their reciprocals, the latter being inversely proportional to and therefore true harmonics of the former. In consequence of this, if as Walter Schauberger claimed at the time, radiation is propagated through space not in linear fashion, but spirally, then the absolute speed of light, i.e. the combined spiral and translatory (radial) velocities at which light travels along a given trajectory through space, must vary according to frequency, its speed being a product of angular acceleration and spiral radius of action.

Evidence substantiating this spiral movement was produced by Prof. Felix Ehrenhaft at the Physics Department of Vienna University in 1949 through a process known as photophoresis. Reported in the *Acta Physica Austriaca* (Vol. 4, 1950 and Vol. 5, 1951), the behaviour of barely perceptible particles of matter and gas particles enclosed in glass tubes were observed when illuminated by concentrated light-rays of various frequencies. Observations of this phenomenon were made under conditions varying from high pressure to high vacuum (30 atm to 1 x 10^{-6} mm Hg [Hg = mercury]) and it was concluded that since the spiral movement of the observed particles was caused by light-rays, the particles had to be propelled along the same spiral path as the light itself (fig.1.6). It was also determined that light magnetises matter and noted that while some particles spiralled away from the light source, others such as chlorophyll, gyrated towards it. Measurements also determined that the observed particles orbited up to 650 times per second while rotating at 4,000 cps about their own axes, an effect only possible because the calculated energies involved, apparently endowed with antigravitational properties, were 70 times more powerful than gravity.

According to Walter Schauberger's formulation derived from standard physics, where energy E in the form of work W is the product of mass m x acceleration a x displacement s, e.g. W or $E = mas$, the speed of light squared c^2 can be equated with as, or more specifically as angular acceleration $r\omega^2$ x radius r. For each rotation through 360°, long wavelength, low frequency radiation would therefore describe a wider (greater radius) and thus longer (slower angular acceleration) spiral path than short-wave, high frequency radiation. In view of this the absolute speed of light as it travels forwards along a given axial path over this same distance is NOT CONSTANT, but as stated above is the varying product of the reciprocities of spiral radius r x angular acceleration $r\omega^2$. Wavelength thus becomes either the spiral or axial distance between 360° nodes and frequency the number of 360° rotations within a given period of time. Long-wave and short-wave frequencies would therefore arrive at fractionally different times over a given distance. This may well account for the equally fractional differences in the measured speed of light to be found in various textbooks, different because the frequencies of the light measured were marginally different. By extension the mass m of a given elementary particle, atom, etc., or its momentum could therefore be deemed to be dependent upon its characteristic rate of rotation, which in turn is the product of the energy-packet's or quantum's radius of action and angular acceleration; the tighter the radius, the faster the angular acceleration and periodicity (frequency), the more powerful the energetic effect and the greater the mass, and vice versa. This reciprocity would also explain why the measured intensities and energies of cosmic radiation, for example, are higher than those of x-rays, the radius of the cosmic ray spiral being significantly smaller and therefore its kinetic

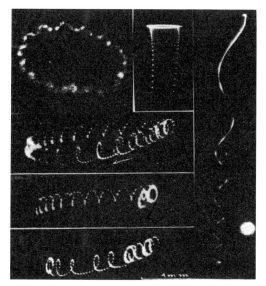

Fig. 1.6 Spiralling particles of fine matter under the influence of light – a process called 'photophoresis'.

the idea, because Viktor too would have to make some sacrifices. Donner then closed the conference and all present left for their cars except for Viktor and Walter, who remained behind.

The second conference, which was scheduled not long after the first, took place in the main workshop of the Washington Iron Works in which the crates despatched from Austria had meanwhile been placed. Some employees were ordered to dismantle the most important prototype, namely the one built by Thurner, whose central core element was a single casting consisting of a number of whorl-pipes (figs. 1.3a & b). As an eye-witness, Walter relates how this was brutally cut open with metal-cutting power-saws, leaving Viktor totally speechless. While some continued their examination unmoved by this event, Viktor and Walter were asked to accompany the

---

energy and translatory velocity commensurately higher. With implosive vortical motion, where the radius of action constantly reduces, the increase in angular acceleration and therefore the magnification of the energetic effect would be automatic.

A second factor here may relate to Walter Schauberger's re-interpretation of Sir Isaac Newton's reformulation of Kepler's 3rd law of planetary motion. In Johannes Kepler's original formulation this states that the square of the orbital period T is proportional to the cube of the orbital radius a. in the form:

$$\left(\frac{T_1}{T_2}\right)^2 = \left(\frac{a_1}{a_2}\right)^3$$

Taking the periods and radii of all the planets into account, the average value for T^2/a^3 amounts to 2.987 773 813, which seems to have a connection with the values of 29 elaborated in fig. 3.4 (p. 45). In Newton's equation for gravitational attraction between two celestial bodies

$$(1)\ \frac{mv^2}{r} = \frac{GMm}{r^2}$$

where $G = 6.67 \times 10^{-11}$ N.m^2/kg^2 = Gravitational constant; M = the mass of the Sun; m = a given planet's mass; r = the radial distance from the Sun; v = the planet's mean orbital velocity.

According to Walter Schauberger's re-interpretation, M can have the value of 1 and since G is a constant, it is merely a multiplier and therefore can be removed from the equation without negating the equation's validity. Thus equation (1) above becomes

$$(2)\ \frac{mv^2}{r} = \frac{m}{r^2} : (3)\ \frac{r^2}{r} = \frac{m}{mv^2} : = (4)\ \frac{r^2v^2}{r} = \frac{m}{m} :$$
$$= (5)\ \frac{r^2v^2}{r} = \frac{m}{m} : = (6)\ rv^2 = 1 = \text{constant}$$

If r is equal in length to 1 astronomical unit (1 AU = the distance between Sun and Earth), and the Earth's mean orbital velocity = 29.799 328 85 km/sec, then $rv^2 = 888$. Using 888 as the hyperbolic constant, the orbital velocities and radii of any planet can be calculated and plotted on a rectangular hyperbola. The combined concept that light travelled or orbited spirally about its axis of propagation and the simplification of Kepler's 3rd Law, may therefore provide the basis for determining the actual speed and radius of action of any given electromagnetic radiation, for once the radius of action of a particular frequency can be determined, then the radii and actual spiral velocities should be determinable for all other forms of electromagnetic radiation. It is these congruencies that may have provided the *"sound... basis on which... to proceed"*.

others to a nearby office for further detailed discussion of the project. Both Viktor and Walter had many questions arising from the previous meeting and urgently asked for more information and clarification. Their questions were brushed aside, however, and they were told that these would be answered at the next conference. On the way back to their quarters, Viktor confided to Walter that he was going to insist that he be returned to Austria after the agreed three months had passed, otherwise he would henceforth remain silent. When Gerchsheimer appeared the next day Viktor at once informed him that, since they had broken their agreement with him, he would remain silent and would not cooperate in the project.

About three days after this 2nd meeting, Viktor having returned to hospital, Walter accompanied Gerchsheimer on a trip to Colorado Springs for a decisive 3rd meeting with Donner and executives of the Eastern Oil Company and Trunk Line Company. Attended by their scientific advisers, they had flown specially from New Mexico for the meeting to be held on the following day. While Gerchsheimer stayed with Donner, Walter was put up at a nearby hotel, Gerchsheimer having lent him his imported white Mercedes to drive to the meeting at the Broadmoor Hotel in the morning. The meeting took place as scheduled, but without Walter's attendance. Instead he had apparently driven up to the top of the famous Pike's Peak (about 14,000 ft), returning from there only in the late afternoon. When he eventually arrived at the Broadmoor Hotel Gerchsheimer was almost speechless with fury, because Walter's attendance had been crucial to the success of the conference, which in his absence had been a total fiasco. Demanding an explanation, Walter apparently answered that he had simply forgotten. This only added fuel to Gerchsheimer's fire, because Walter was an intelligent man and his non-attendance could therefore not have been an accident. Why Walter did this will never be known. Perhaps he was motivated by his and Viktor's desire to withhold any further information on implosive nuclear

energies. Whatever the reason, it effectively scuttled the whole project. Donner was equally furious and after ordering Gerchsheimer to send the Schaubergers home at once, instructed his lawyer, Mr Ross, to draw up a final contract for the Schauberger's immediate signature.

Two days later on the 13th of September at about 5 pm, Viktor and Walter were collected by Gerchsheimer for the fourth and final meeting, which took place in Totten's office. While Totten looked on grimly from behind his desk, Donner sat at a small table in the middle of the room. When Viktor entered he was shown to a seat opposite Donner, the remaining company, Gerchsheimer, Donner's lawyer and Walter standing at the back of the room. Donner then signed a document in front of Viktor and passed his golden pen over for Viktor's signature. Picking up the document Gerchsheimer handed it to Viktor and announced that it had been decided to permit his return to Austria, the only stipulation being that he should countersign the document. At first Viktor demurred, because it was written in English, a language he could neither read nor understand. Looking to Walter for help, an argument then broke out between Walter and Gerchsheimer, Walter insisting that the document be translated into German so that Viktor would know what he was supposed to sign. Gerchsheimer became extremely irritated at this and asked Walter to keep silent. He then turned to Viktor and assured him that he could safely sign the document unread, for with its signing all his wishes would be fulfilled.

At this point Gerchsheimer reminded Donner that they had to be at the airport in ten minutes, whereupon Walter demanded that the contents of the 'contract' should at least be translated to Viktor orally. By this time in a state of semi mental paralysis born of his desperation to return home and to get the whole matter over quickly, Viktor told Walter that he wanted to sign the agreement whatever it contained. Walter then asked Gerchsheimer for a copy of the document, so that he could check as far as he was able, the accuracy of the salient points of the oral translation.

It is not known how fluent Walter's English actually was. In London in 1951, however, he was invited by Richard St. Barbe Baker to give lectures and conduct experiments at the Dorchester Hotel to which the full diplomatic corps had been invited, an event that St.Barbe Baker described as highly successful. While in England Walter gave lectures in Cambridge, Birmingham and Oxford, and also took the opportunity to visit Sir William Lawrence Bragg (Nobel prize for physics 1915 for his x-ray study of crystal structures) and Sir James Chadwick (Nobel prize for physics 1935 for his 1932 discovery of the neutron). Apparently there had been few communication difficulties during their exchanges of view, although both Bragg and Chadwick may well have spoken German. All this having happened some seven years previously, however fluent Walter may have been at the time, his English had no doubt become extremely rusty in the interim.

This demand to sight the document, however, provoked even further argument. When it was finally explained to him in German, Viktor quickly signed it. It was only later that the soul-destroying realisation dawned on him that he had signed away his whole mind, his whole life and everything for which he had striven. I have studied this document myself and it does state in quite unequivocal terms, that not only were all Viktor's models, sketches, prototypes, reports and other data to become the sole property of the Donner-Gerchsheimer consortium, but that Viktor was to commit himself to total silence on anything connected with implosion thereafter. Moreover, any further concepts or ideas he might develop in the future were also to belong to Donner and Gerchsheimer, and under no circumstances whatever could he discuss these or anything else with anyone else.. While on the face of it this coercive action by the Americans might appear reprehensible, it could equally well be argued that, having expended considerable sums on this venture, they at least wanted to recuperate some of

their losses by legally acquiring possession of Viktor's apparatuses as collateral. This would no doubt have been done with a view to exploiting them commercially in some way in the future. The manner in which this was achieved notwithstanding, to legitimise such acquisition, the signing of the above document by Viktor personally would have been a legal necessity.

The deplorable upshot of all this, however, is that all Viktor's models, prototypes, drawings, detailed data, including Professor Pöpel's original report implying that what might be termed "Negative Friction" was an actuality, have remained the possession of the Donner-Gerchsheimer consortium. That this report was actually part and parcel of this project is confirmed by Viktor's reference to it in one of his reports to Boerner dated 23/24 August 1958.

On the evening of the 17th of September Viktor and Walter were told to prepare for an early start the following morning at 5.45 am. Ready and waiting, nobody appeared until 8.30 am. Gerchsheimer had overslept. In great haste they left for the airport, Viktor being transferred to Totten's car in Sherman. Walter continued the journey with Gerchsheimer, who reminded him once more of the conditions stipulated in the last agreement signed with Donner, namely that all further discussion of implosion and implosive devices in the future was restricted to U.S. personnel. In other words, that once in Europe, both father and son were constrained to total silence on the subject and the associated project.

Due to this late start, Viktor and Walter arrived at the airport only eight minutes before take-off for New York. Arriving there several hours later, they changed planes and flew to Frankfurt by way of London, where they had to make an emergency landing. Always a man to stand by his word or signature whatever the ultimate outcome to himself, on the way back in the plane Viktor turned to Walter and expressed the deep sadness of his innermost being, saying with utter resignation words to the effect that;

"I no longer own my own mind. I don't even own my thoughts. After all I've done, finally there is nothing left. I am a man with no future."

Leaving Frankfurt by train a few hours later, they arrived in Linz on the 20th of September at about midnight. On the afternoon of the 25th of September 1958, five days after arriving home in Linz, Viktor Schauberger, who throughout his whole life had fought so hard to heal the environment and improve the lot of humanity, died a broken man.

"They call me deranged. The hope is that they are right. It is of no greater or lesser import for yet another fool to wander this earth. But if I am right and Science is wrong, then may the Lord God have mercy on mankind!!"[28]

Viktor Schauberger – 30 June 1885 – 25 Sept. 1958.

Notes

1. 'IF'

   ___*___

   If you can keep your head when all about you
   Are losing theirs and blaming it on you,
   If you can trust yourself when all men doubt you,
   But make allowance for their doubting, too;
   If you can wait and not be tired by waiting,
   Or being lied about, don't deal in lies,
   Or being hated, don't give way to hating,
   And yet don't look too good, nor talk too wise;
   If you can dream and not make dreams your master,
   If you can think, and not make thoughts your aim,
   If you can meet with triumph and disaster,
   And treat those two impostors just the same;
   If you can bear to hear the truth you've spoken
   Twisted by knaves to make a trap for fools,
   Or watch the things you gave your life to broken,
   And stoop to build them up with worn-out tools;
   If you can make one heap of all your winnings,
   And risk it on one turn of pitch-and-toss,
   And lose, and start again at your beginnings,
   And never breathe a word about your loss;
   If you can force your heart and nerve and sinew
   To serve your turn long after they are gone,
   And so hold on when there is nothing in you
   Except the will which says to them: 'Hold on!'
   If you can talk with crowds and keep your virtue,
   Or walk with kings, nor lose the common touch,
   If neither foes nor loving friends can hurt you,
   If all men count with you, but none too much;
   If you can fill the unforgiving minute
   With sixty seconds' worth of distance run,
   Yours is the Earth and everything that's in it,
   And – which is more – you'll be a Man, my Son!
                  Rudyard Kipling (1865–1936)

2. *The Ages of Gaia*, by James Lovelock: W.W. Norton, New York

3. *Our Senseless Toil*, Pt.I, pp.28–29 (see ftnt. 16).

4. *Implosion*, No.27, p.29 "The Winding Way to Wisdom" ("Der gewundene Erkenntnisweg")
   Implosion, No.48, p.27, "Nature's Secrets Unveiled" ("Entschleierte Naturgeheimnisse")

5. In Viktor Schauberger's writings in German, the prefix **'UR'** is often separated from the rest of the word by a hyphen, e.g. 'Ur-sache' in lieu of 'Ursache', when normally it would be joined. By this he intends to place a particular emphasis on the prefix, thus endowing it with a more profound meaning than the merely superficial.

   This prefix belongs not only to the German language, but in former times also to the English, a usage which has now lapsed. According to the Oxford English Dictionary, 'ur' denotes 'primitive', 'original', 'earliest', giving such examples as 'ur-Shakespeare' or 'ur-origin'.

   This begins to get to the root of Viktor's use of it and the deeper significance he placed upon it. If one expands upon the interpretation given in the OED, then the concepts of 'primordial', 'primeval', 'primal', 'fundamental', 'elementary', 'of first principle', come to mind, which further encompass such meanings as:
   - pertaining to the first age of the world, or of anything ancient;
   - pertaining to or existing from the earliest beginnings;
   - constituting the earliest beginning or starting point;
   - from which something else is derived, developed or depends;
   - applying to parts or structures in their earliest or rudimentary stage;
   - the first or earliest formed in the course of growth.

   To this can be added the concept of an 'ur-condition' or 'ur-state' of extremely high potential or potency, a latent evolutionary ripeness, which given the correct impulse can unloose all of Nature's innate creative forces.

6. *Implosion* No.7, p.1, "The Ist Biotechnical Practice" ("Die erste biotechnische Praxis").
   Implosion, No.67, p.1, "Let the Upheaval Begin!" ("Den Umbruch beginnen!").

7. Published 1: Pearson Foundation of Canada, 1949. Transl. by Maj.Gregory Pearson in Outer Mongolia 1921 with the Panchen Lama's permission. Pub.2: Colin Smythe, Gerrards Cross, U.K.

8. *ibid.*, p.23, para.73.

Schauberger Junior forest warden in remote areas of forest in Austria 1900 - 1915. Wounded in 14-18 war — returned to forest-work after war — whilst crossing a fast flowing stream, disturbed a stationary trout which immediately ~~this~~ flashed ~~this trout~~ upstream. without apparent effort.

Late '20s. log-flume successfully operated ~~&~~ Austrian Govt asked Prof Forchheimer to investigate the unusual theories. — became convinced it they were true & is reported to have said it he was delighted to have retired from teaching otherwise he would have to be telling his students it what he had been teaching them had been rubbish. Full details were documented & placed under seal in Austrian Academy, to ensure Victor Schauberger's precedence. These papers were released to Victor's son, Walter in 1974 but Forchheimer published the theories in 1930/31 in the Austrian Journal of Hydrology.

Events in America pp 15 et seq

Victor had difficulty in describing accurately, in a language it others could understand, exactly what forces, motion & energies were involved in the process of implosion hence scepticism & ~~note~~ disbelief in the validity of Victor's theories. Most of the negotiations with ~~America~~ America businesses was conducted by Karl ~~Gerchheimer~~ Gerchsheimer who was born & brought up in Bavaria & its forests. Hence had similar background to Victor.

(Offered 3½ million dollars by an American aircraft consortium. A similar offer also made by Canadian interests ✗. No details as to when or if this taken up)

Gerchsheimer enthusiastic abt Victor's theories & persuaded ~~Donner~~ Robert Donner, a retired owner of the large & prosperous Donner steelworks in Philadelphia, to explore the situation; In 1958 Gerchsheimer & Dodd (a financial advisor to Donner)

THE SOUTH EAST ESSEX
HOMOEOPATHY GROUP

INVITE YOU TO JOIN THEM AT THEIR MONTHLY MEETINGS AND LEARN HOW TO LOOK AFTER YOUR SELF AND YOUR FAMILY WITHOUT USING DRUGS.

THE FOLLOWING PROGRAMME HAS BEEN PLANNED FOR 1997.

EACH MEETING WILL OPEN WITH THE DESCRIPTION OF A REMEDY SUITABLE FOR YOUR *FIRST AID* BOX. AFTERWARDS, ONE OF THE FOLLOWING TOPICS WILL BE DISCUSSED IN MORE DETAIL IN ORDER TO SHOW YOU HOW YOU CAN AVOID UNNECESSARY USE OF DRUGS.

REMEDIES FOR PREGNANCY, LABOUR & POST PARTUM; HOMOEOPATHY & IMMUNIZATION; COPING WITH POLLUTION; NUTRITION; BACKGROUND TO THE DEVELOPMENT OF HOMOEOPATHY; AN INTRODUCTION TO KINESIOLOGY; AN INTRODUCTION TO REFLEXOLOGY; CAUSES & TREATMENT OF ASTHMA; HEART & ASSOCIATED PROBLEMS.

ALL MEETINGS TAKE PLACE ON THE 2ND TUESDAY OF EACH MONTH, (EXCEPT AUGUST & DECEMBER), IN SWANS GREEN HALL, HART ROAD, THUNDERSLEY. DOORS OPEN AT 7.30 FOR AN 8PM START. ADMISSION IS FREE TO MEMBERS. VISITORS £1.50 (£1 CONCESSIONS)

ALL SPEAKERS ARE QUALIFIED PRACTITIONERS.

IF NECESSARY, A SHORT INTRODUCTION TO HOMOEOPATHY WILL BE GIVEN AT THE BEGINNING OF EACH MEETING

FOR FURTHER INFORMATION, - tel. 01268 753544

7/lflet97

9. *ibid.*, p.24, para.74.
10. Sec.7.4 spec.ed. *Mensch und Technik*, Year 24, Vol.2, 1993, wholly devoted to recently discovered information on Viktor Schauberger contained in the Swiss, Arnold Hohls' notebook.
11. A handwritten note, dated July 1936, on the back of a photograph of Viktor Schauberger.
12. "Return to Culture" ("Zuruck zur Kultur"), by Viktor Schauberger, p.1.
13. *Implosion*, No.81, p.6, extract from letter to Mr. Kroger.
14. *Implosion*, No.10, p.30. "Natural Farm Husbandry" ("Naturnahe Landwirtschaft").
15. Letter from Viktor Schauberger to Josef Brunnader, 20.10.1956.
16. *TAU*, No.144, p.31: Letter (12.Mar.1936) to Dr.Ehrenberger, M.Eng., Research Inst. for Hydraulic Engineering, Ast.Sec'y to the Minister, Federal Ministry for Agriculture and Forestry, Vienna, Austria.
17. *Our Senseless Toil – The Source of the World Crisis* ("Unsere Sinnlose Arbeit – die Quelle der Weltkrise"), Pts.I & II, 1933–34: Krystall Verlag, Vienna. Defunct in 1938.
18. *Implosion*, No.51, p.23, "What happens next?" ("Wie geht esweiter?") by Leopold Brandstätter.
19. *Implosion*, No.29, p.22, "Home Power Generator – an Illusion ?" ("Das Heimkraftwerk – eine Illusion?") by Aloys Kokaly.
20. *Implosion*, No.17.
21. *Implosion*, No.83, p.20, "Harmony as a Question of Existence" ("Harmonie als Existenzfrage") by Ing.Wilhelm Reisch.
22. *Implosion*, No.49, p.17, "The Legacy of Viktor Schauberger" ("Die Erbe Viktor Schaubergers") by Aloys Kokaly.
23. *Implosion*, No.93, p.3, "The Death of Viktor Schauberger" ("Der Tod des Viktor Schauberger") by Raimund Lackenbucher.
24. *ibid*, No.93, page 3.
25. *ibid*, No.93, page 5.
26. From "The Death of Viktor Schauberger" ("Der Tod des Viktor Schauberger") by Raimund Lackenbucher, 'Neue Illustrierte Wochenschau', No. 8, Sunday 22nd February 1959.
27. While Einstein is generally credited with its formulation – and it may well have been an almost simultaneous, but independently arrived at discovery – chronologically it was first postulated in 1903 by Prof. Friedrich Hasenöhrl (30.Nov.1874–7.Oct.1915), Head of Physics at the Univ. of Innsbruck and later Vienna, Austria, in the form

$$m = \frac{E}{c^2}$$

Since Hasenöhrl died in the First World War, he was never able to establish his priority in the formulation of this equation.
28. *Implosion*, No.99, p.13. Quotation.

2
ENERGY

2.1 Energy Today

As we observe the world around us today, signs of deterioration and symptoms of degeneration are everywhere evident. We are engulfed by a concatenation of interrelated crises; crises in energy, crises in the global water-balance, crises in agriculture and, worst of all, crises in Nature herself. Wherever we look, things are not going nearly as well as we have been led to believe. The downward spiral of disintegration seems to be accelerating at an alarming rate, with few if any really concrete proposals or action being implemented to arrest it. All of which provokes the question: Has science, the leading light in all our much-vaunted technological progress, somewhere grossly erred?

Had science been in tune with Nature, if scientists had truly understood Nature's inner workings, if science itself operated according to Nature's laws, we ought to have an abundance of everything we need, energy, food, water; but we have not! In actual fact, science has been far less successful than it claims. It has failed to take note of Nature's innumerable hints and indicators as to how things should be done and instead has taken the opposite path. This is not to deprecate the sincere and untiring efforts of many individuals to improve conditions generally.

The recent activity of an international group of concerned scientists from all continents of the globe is proof enough of this. Under the auspices of the World Commission on Environment and Development and the stewardship of Mrs. Gro Harlem Brundtland, the former Prime Minister of Norway, these scientists contributed their time and combined expertise to a thorough evaluation of the present state of the world, which culminated in the production of a detailed report entitled "Our Common Future"[1].

The thinking of many other scientists, however, has been coloured by the increasingly mechanistic approach towards life – *Deus ex machina* – which is not to imply that all the established facts of science and the painstaking, dedicated research that has been carried out are invalid, but to suggest that their interpretation could perhaps be different. To date there has been far too much emphasis placed on analysis, the pursuit of minutiae, the development of specialist terminology incomprehensible to other scientific disciplines, let alone the rest of a humanity ever subservient to the dictates of a science that has become the infallible new God.

According to Viktor Schauberger, science thinks an octave too low and, due to its purely materialistic approach, neglecting the underlying energetic basis for all physical manifestation, has lost sight of the integrated whole. Prof. David Susuki, the eminent biologist, once stated that there were at least twenty branches of biology, each of which had it own jargon, unable to communicate coherently with the others. The individual feels insignificant in the face of all this vast array of scientific expertise, a condition one has noticed among acquaintances, when confronted by the towering edifice of the apparently all-knowing, 'Scientific Establishment'.

Overwhelmed by this indecipherable complexity and in the belief that any understanding was impossible, the public at large has relinquished control over its health and future to the high-priests of science. Viktor Schauberger, however, had other ideas:

The majority believes that everything hard to comprehend must be very profound. This is incorrect. What is hard to understand is what is immature, unclear and often false. The highest wisdom is simple and passes through the brain directly into the heart.[2]

What use, therefore, is all this analysis if ultimately no synthesis results through which all the research can be effectively implemented? There is doubtless an ample sufficiency, nay an oversupply of detail, but what is now of crucial importance to our survival on this planet is that all this vast fund of knowledge should be coordinated and applied practically.

Science, however, is by no means solely to blame for this unhappy state of affairs. Politics and power have also played a major, controlling role. The pursuit of profit and power for its own sake, coupled with the necessary systems of control, have relegated the mass of humanity to a state of almost total dependency for everything it needs in the way of food, energy, health and all other necessities of life. The artificial procurement, sometimes aided by climatic fickleness, of shortages in commodities, ensures the continuance of this dependency. According to Viktor Schauberger, *"Capital interest only thrives on a defective economy"* and there can be little doubt that the economic system resulting from this manipulation is totally unnatural. What there is no shortage of today, however, is misery and privation, two developments which are on the increase worldwide. People despair of improvement and a pall of gloom for the future descends. Not only are parents desperately concerned for the survival of their children, but their children also view their future with enormous despondency.

While millions of our fellow human beings are dying from acute starvation, we are daily aware of the gross, at times incomprehensible, inequities in food distribution; of the 'butter mountains', 'grain mountains', all of which are the result of market forces open to all manner of manipulation. People are saddled with enormous debt, mortgages, loans, interest payments and so on; to a large extent due to the withholding of all systems that would grant them independence. Indeed there are many cases where significant improvements in energy generation, health treatment and agricultural productivity, to name a few, have been suppressed for the sake of the vested interests of those whose natural humanitarian sensibilities have been corrupted by the lust for power and material gain.

Independence, however, is the last thing these dubious individuals and megabusinesses wish to bestow on humanity, because their ultimate dominance would thereby be lost. Independent people are free people and not answerable to control. The observation of the famous Russian novelist and philosopher, Count Leo Nikolayevich Tolstoy (1828–1910), is here very much to the point:

Thoughts that have important consequences are always simple. All my thinking could be summed up with these words: 'Since corrupt people unite amongst themselves to constitute a force, then honest people must do the same.' It is as simple as that.

At the forefront of this battle is the control over the systems of energy. The present lamentable condition of the planet, our only home in this vast universe, has now reached such a parlous state that for our own survival we simply cannot afford to allow present methods of energy exploitation to continue. Unless we can arrive at a different way of looking at things, unless science is prepared to adopt a more open and universal approach towards the concept of energy itself and realise that there are more powers unseen than seen, then we shall continue down the sombre road to oblivion.

All his life Viktor Schauberger strove to improve the lot of his fellow human beings and fought an often acrimonious, running battle with academia. Despite their continual, uninformed deprecation by science, his trail-breaking ideas have vital relevance for the present state of the world, and their validity becomes all the more apparent when one gradually comes to understand the processes of his thinking and the energy processes he describes. This book will elaborate Viktor Schauberger's ideas and practical demonstrations for generating energy, improving the quality of water and increasing agricultural productivity for the benefit of humanity.

2.2 Relative Energies

Before addressing the question of energy and our concepts of it, however, let us make a few comparisons to get things in perspective. The following examples are intended to show how much the energy consumption of our technical civilisa-

---

The amount of energy a human being requires for survival over one year is averagely 1,000 kilowatt-hours (kWh). According to Walter Schauberger's calculations a human being operates at the relatively insignificant energy level of an electric light bulb, namely 100 watts. 1,000kWh is also the average amount of energy received from the Sun annually per square metre of ground surface. Theoretically, therefore, all a human being needs to do is to stand on its square metre and obtain its energy from the Sun. Were it able to transmute this energy directly, then its annual energy requirement would be satisfied. This amount of energy, however, is associated with the consumption of 260kg of molecular oxygen (O_2) per year, which is equal to 29.659gr of oxygen per hour. These are the amounts of energy and oxygen required by a human being for the maintenance of bodily functions, reproduction, creativity and intelligent thought for a whole year.

The average petrol consumption of a car with a 1.6lit. engine, however, amounts to between 10–11lit per 100km. Walter Schauberger has calculated that to travel a distance of 1,000km requires an energy expenditure of 1,000kW. Therefore to highlight the ludicrous mechanical efficiency we have so far managed to achieve and of which we are apparently so proud, a car travelling 1,000km destructively consumes the same amount of energy in a few hours that a human being uses far more economically and productively in a whole year. The car, however, does not think, it does not reproduce, nor is it creative. It has none of these abilities. Equating 1,000km travelled with the annual activity of one human being produces a very poor energy relationship.

Once again, the amount of oxygen used per human being per year is 260kg. To drive a car at 50km an hour requires 22.25kg of oxygen per hour, which is roughly 750 times the amount needed by a human being. Therefore as we drive happily along in our cars, we unknowingly take 750 oxygen-breathing slaves along with us. These slaves, however, do not breathe out nice, healthy carbon-dioxide and water as we do, but they spew out a noxious concoction of poisonous gases.

In a journey lasting eleven hours, all the oxygen required by one human being for one year has been consumed. According to the scientific television program "Quantum" (11.Oct.89), it has been estimated that there are presently 450 million vehicles in use worldwide. If we multiply this figure by 750, we arrive at an oxygen consumption equal to that of 337,500,000,000 people, about 67.5 x the present world population. We are forced to admit, therefore, that the relationship between our technology and its use of energy is diametrically opposed to that of Nature.

In Australia, for example, the amount of oxygen consumed annually through fossil fuel combustion for the purposes of industry and power generation equals 214,465,670 tonnes of molecular oxygen (O_2) [1977 figures]. At a consumption rate of 0.26 tonnes O_2 per annum per person, this is sufficient to keep 824,868,073 people alive for 1 year. In contrast, the amount of oxygen consumed by the Australian population over the same period amounts to 4,290,000 tonnes O_2, which is 1/50th of the first figure above.

But where does our oxygen originate? Based on Canadian figures for conifer forests, the number of hectares required to produce sufficient oxygen to satisfy the above combined demand at a production rate of 10.0619 tonnes of O_2 per hectare = 21,740,990ha or 217,410km². This area is marginally less than that of the whole of Great Britain = 229,523km². Australia has a population of about 17 million, whereas Great Britain's population amounts to some 60 million odd. Extrapolated world-wide in relation to total world consumption of oxygen and the rapid eradication of the world's forests, the picture becomes quite horrendous.

Fig. 2.1   **Energy, Oxygen Consumption and Production**

tion is totally out of harmony with that of Nature (see fig. 2.1).

To obtain some inkling of the possible magnitude of global oxygen consumption, for example, and to provoke some interest in the question, I have used the figures in Fig. 2.1 as a basis for calculation[3]. I do not claim any high degree of accuracy, however, because there are so many variables and data involved, which are unknown to me. Be that as it may, according to my calculations the annual demand for oxygen world-wide could be as much as 38,496,255,232 tonnes, which may be an underestimate. To satisfy this demand would require an area of healthy, productive forest amounting to 38,259,432km^2. This represents 28.3% of the world's total land area of 135,000,000km^2, whereas we know the forests are being decimated at a precipitous pace. A higher annual rate of O$_2$ consumption would naturally require a commensurately larger area of forest for replenishment. On the other hand, it is also possible that the point may have already been reached where existing areas of forest and vegetation are insufficient to compensate for what is presently being consumed, thus creating a nett oxygen deficit.

While it is normally assumed that the available oxygen pool is so large as to be almost inexhaustible (it comprises 20–21% of the atmospheric gases by volume), it could be mooted that, although the relative proportions of these gases remain the same, their actual atmospheric depth may be diminishing. In other words, when initially measured, the abundance of molecular oxygen may have

reached a height of, say, 100km, but due to its rapid and unnatural overconsumption, its overall depth may now have been considerably reduced in a manner similar to the draining of a bucket. For those who live in the water at the bottom of the bucket, however, there would appear to be no change to the quantity of available water (the oxygen), until such time as the bucket is empty! Remaining at all times thoroughly immersed until this catastrophic event, they are oblivious to the slow death that inexorably approaches. It would therefore be of great interest to know whether an accurate audit of the residual oxygen pool has recently been undertaken. If not, then perhaps it should be put in hand as a matter of some urgency.

If we now consider the famous Hasenöhrl-Einstein equation for energy *(E=mc^2)*, in which the amount of energy E in a given system is the product of mass *m* times the speed of light *c* squared, then in 1 gram of undifferentiated matter 25 million kWh of energy are stored (fig. 2.2). It matters not what the gram of substance is. It could be of human flesh, of carpet, of wood, of whatever we choose, but in this minuscule gram this seemingly huge and disproportionate amount of energy is concentrated. This means that the relatively minute volume of 1cm^3 of water contains 25 million kWh of energy. As Viktor Schauberger once said:

More energy is encapsulated in every drop of good spring water than an average-sized power station is presently able to produce.[4]

We do not seem to know how to unlock it in a creative way, however, because we have failed

---

Fig. 2.2   The energy content of 1 gram of matter

Hasenöhrl-Einstein energy equation:	E	$= mc^2$
		= mass(kg) x speed(metres/sec) of light^2
therefore	E gram	$= m \times c^2$
		= 0.001kg x (2.997 924 58 x 10^8)^2
		= 0.001 x 8.987 551 787 x 10^{16}
		= 8.987 551 787 x 10^{13}
Mass-energy equivalence of grams vs joules		= 8.987 551 787 x 10^{13} J
Conversion of joules to electron-volts	(eV)	= 8.987 551 787x10^{13}J x 6.24 x 10^{18}eV
therefore	E gram	= 5.608 232 315x10^{32}eV
Converted to Kilowatt Hours *(kWh)*:	E gram	= 5.608 232 315x10^{32}eV x 4.45x10^{-26}kWh
therefore	E gram	= 24,956,633.8kWh

In round figures therefore **The energy content of 1gram of matter = 25,000,000kWh**

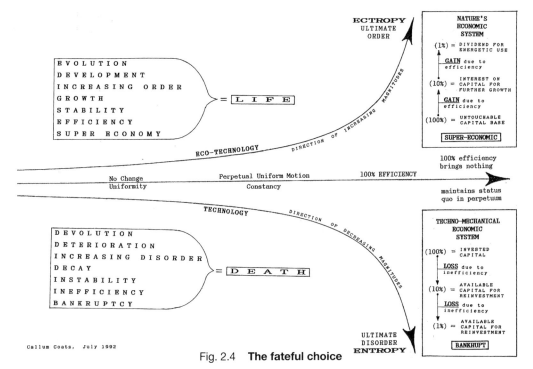

Callum Coats, July 1992

Fig. 2.4   **The fateful choice**

to make a thorough investigation of natural energetic processes. Our attempts to release this huge potential of energy through atomic fission, through the destruction of natural, resonant systems (atoms), have only created a lethal legacy for future generations, not only for humanity, but also for countless other living things, upon whose existence our own depends.

2.3 *The Fateful Choice*

Two systems are therefore available to us. We are presented today with an extremely fateful choice. We can choose for Life or for our ultimate oblivion. Viewed as evolutionary paths over a long period of time (fig. 2.4), there have been two simultaneous developments, which initially followed almost parallel paths, because humanity's activities were largely in tune with Nature. As the population grew and a scientifically-based technology gradually developed, these two paths began to diverge. In the last 150 years or so, the advance and application of technology has accelerated enormously, with the result that the divergence has become quite dramatic, and the far more subtle energy systems of Nature have been overwhelmed by the ceaseless onslaught of a merciless, mechanistic technology, with the direst consequences for us all.

The upper, rising path is that of the course of natural evolution from the simple to the increasingly complex, building higher, more evolved systems and species, on the foundation of earlier ones. It denotes a path of increasing diversity. It follows the curve of an increase in natural capital, the interest based on the sound economy of the evolution and development of new life-forms suited to the improved conditions, the latter providing the ecological niches for these new life-forms, so that no opportunity is lost for further creative expression. In Nature's super-economical system, in which nothing is wasted, the surplus on her own interest is represented by the various fruits, seeds, cereals, nuts, etc., freely given for the sustenance of the life-forms currently in existence at any given moment. This is the way Nature operates and also the way we should operate, for as Viktor has stated:

The most natural is always the most technically perfect and the only system economically viable long-term.[5]

Nature's 100% base capital – the mineral and other resources of the Earth – should be inviolable. For evolution to proceed, Nature increases her capital by, say 10%, in terms of growth, movement, evolution of new life-forms. We should therefore learn to live off the surplus on Nature's interest on her own capital, which is probably quite ample for our needs. With such a system, stability would increase, because increasing diversity means more legs to stand on, so to speak, and if one leg is accidentally removed, the whole system does not collapse. The natural system is, and has ever been, demonstrably sustainable.

The middle line in fig. 2.4 on the other hand, represents 100% efficiency. However apparently ideal this may be, it is still no solution, because it is like going round in a circle. As a uniform condition it never gets more, it never gets less. It just stays the same. Nature, however, has no use for uniformity; her overriding purpose being constant change and upward transformation.

The path we have so far chosen, the lower curve, is one that not only uses energy in an extraordinarily profligate and unsustainable way, but has also placed the whole of the ecosphere under the hard, insensitive heel of economics. Where high forest, rich in a wide variety of interdependent species of tree and animal alike, once flourished, there are now only monocultures, ecological deserts of uniformity. Where hedgerows, burgeoning with wild life, once surrounded highly productive, largely organically managed fields, there are now vast, wind-swept acres in which only one species of crop is grown without rotation, propped up with artificial fertilisers which ultimately ruin the soil. Almost daily we hear that one species or another is in danger of becoming extinct or has already become so, thereby reducing the diversity so vital to the health and existence of everything on this planet.

This is a downwardly accelerating curve, the steepness of descent increasing in step with the broadening application of our unnatural systems of energy. Quite apart from their manifest inefficiency, the systems we exploit pollute the very air we breathe. A conversation in the 1970s between Walter Schauberger and Dr. Fritz Kortegast, the head of research and development for Mercedes-Benz, revealed that the greatest efficiency hitherto achieved with their most sophisticated engines amounted to only 13% of the total energy input. In other words, if 100 energy-units are initially input into such a car, the useful energy that produces forward propulsion amounts to only 13%, the remainder being lost through the dissipation of heat. If such a car were a business, it would very quickly go bankrupt.

But such is the business we have created, namely a form of technology bolstered and fostered by vested interests that consumes energy through the massive exploitation of unrenewable resources. The continuing use of such a technology must therefore inevitably lead us into a state of instability, bankruptcy, disorder, devolution, deterioration, decay and ultimately death. If we observe all that is taking place around us, all these things are happening, and all because we are actually imprisoned in an energy system which is self-annihilating. In our present mechanistic system, an investment of $100 is reduced to 13 productive dollars. Reinvested in the same system at 13% efficiency, these $13 return only 1.69 usable dollars.

But we humans, presumed arrogantly to be the highest level of life on this planet, do everything to destroy the very basis of our existence. If the myriads of different species or qualities, representing every element of life, are viewed as a heap of dry sand, the highest quality in the form of humankind sits right at the top of the heap. However, when lesser qualities are removed from the lower parts, oil extracted here, coal there, deforestation here, overfishing there, then it is inevitable that the relatively few grains of 'human' sand, these extremely soft and vulnerable creatures astride the top, must start to sink down, because the lower grains of sand, the various supportive qualities, are gradually and inexorably being removed. It is a known fact that poor quality water will only support poor quality fish. The same applies to us. If we allow the natural capital of the environment to depreciate, our own human capital depreciates commensurately.

The use here of the word *qualities* rather than the apparently more appropriate *quantities* is important and of great significance. Indeed in the view of Gallilei and Johannes Kepler, Nature could only be conceived of in terms of mathematics and qualities. In Nature no two things are identical. As noted earlier, Nature's supreme condition is that of constant change and transformation and her greatest law states that *Repetition of the identical is forbidden*. 1 + 1 does therefore not make 2, because no two natural systems are wholly identical and thus cannot be summated.

Repetition would mean the repeat of an energetic or experiential process that has already happened, in which no new development, no advance, however slight, is possible. Identical repetition is therefore wasteful of energy, and Nature wastes nothing! In an evolutionary sense, there is quite obviously nothing to be gained from mere repetition. Something can only be gained and progress made in the development of a new process or system, even only marginally different.

Having now discussed some of the more technical aspects, let us look at the question of energy from a different point of view. Viktor Schauberger frequently stated that we humans are blind, that we are extraordinarily superficial creatures who look, but never see. Most of our seeing is concentrated to the point of recognition only, but not on deep examination. Relying on outward appearance alone, everything we observe we deem to be the totality. We mistake effect for cause. Whatever we perceive, however, all movement, all the external garb of manifestation, are secondary effects. The primary cause we never see. The primary cause is energy.

2.4 But What is Energy?

What is the essential nature of energy? Where do we begin to search for the answer to this age-old question? Surprisingly, despite all scientific investigation, nobody seems to have come up with a definitive answer! All we know of are the ways in which energy manifests itself. We can see that energy is involved in flowing water. We can see that energy is associated with creating clouds. Energy is active in an engine combusting petrol or gasoline. But what is it? What is its essence? What is this sublime process that always seems intimately connected with motion?

An honest physicist would answer, We don't know. We might also ask a bishop or a priest, *What is spirit or the substance of spirit?* While many propositions may be put forward, in the final analysis they may also be forced to admit their ultimate ignorance. It could be argued, however, that what is called energy by the scientist and spirit by the priest are essentially the same. Its origin, however, remains problematic.

Since we cannot actually see energy, but only its outward manifestation, its origins may well lie in a reality beyond our senses. Perhaps energy is the culmination of a desire to create, to afford every possibility for the gaining of new experience. While there are many extremely high energies of which science is aware and has actually measured, there are also forms of energy of which we are aware, but which defy all scientific quantification and measurement. These are too subtle and cannot be detected by even the most sophisticated scientific instruments.

Although it must recognise their existence, for scientists are also human beings, science cannot accurately measure various human energies such as thought, desire, love, enthusiasm, hatred, anger, etc., all of which are emanations from the human psyche and motivators for action. While science may be able to detect brain activity related to these phenomena, it cannot actually measure their intrinsic power, size, frequency or vibrational state, nor their true point of origin. As immaterial forms of energy emanating from other-placeness – the physical void – which Viktor Schauberger claims operate according to the law of anti-conservation of energy, they are therefore conveniently ignored. This is because they do not conform to, nor are calculable by the famous Hasenöhrl-Einstein equation (fig. 2.1) and its derivation, the law of conservation of energy. As H.H. Price, Wyckham Professor of Logic at Oxford (*Hibbert Journal*, 1949) comments:

We must conclude, I think, that there is no room for telepathy in a materialistic universe. Telepathy is something which ought not to happen at all, if the materialist theory were true. But it does happen. So there must be something seriously wrong with the materialist theory, however numerous and imposing the normal facts which support it may be.

Goethe too says of scientists: "*Whatever you cannot calculate you do not think is real.*"

To place the matter in its proper perspective, Sir William Grove (1811–1896), Professor of Experimental Philosophy at the London Institution, states: "*Science should have neither desires nor prejudices. Truth should be her sole aim.*" He goes on to predict that "*...that day is fast approaching when it will be confessed that the 'forces' we know of are but the phenomenal manifestations of realities we know nothing about, but which were known to the ancients and – by them worshipped.*"[6]

This neglect of immaterial energies, or life-energies, whose tremendous power has long been recognised by earlier cultures and individuals variously as Ch'i, Ka, Prana, Mana, Archeus, Vis Vitalis, may also be because, as Viktor Schauberger often said, scientific thinking should take more account of higher metaphysical realms and is unaware of what he called the 4th and 5th dimensions. Ch'i, for example, is the life-force that moves along the energetic meridians of the body and which was pinpointed several thousand years ago by the Chinese and used for healing. Acupuncture, a treatment using fine needles to correct bio-energetic imbalances of Ch'i in the body, is still not recognised by orthodox medicine, although widely used in China and in many Western countries by accredited practitioners and more open-minded doctors.

Taking this as our cue in the search for these other dimensions, we might begin with the highest and most powerful form of natural energy experienced by human beings – love. If this is raised several octaves, dimensions and magnitudes higher, we may begin to perceive the outlines of what energy actually may be, namely the outpouring of unconditional love for the purposes of manifold experiential fulfilment.

Notes

1. *Our Common Future:* Oxford Univ.Press, Oxford.
2. From list of Viktor Schauberger quotations in the Schauberger archives.
3. ROUGH CALCULATION FOR WORLD ANNUAL CONSUMPTION OF OXYGEN (O_2)

    Let us assume that the Australian industrial O_2 consumption of 214,465,670 tonnes is typical for all industrialised countries. Using Australia's population as a basis for the extrapolation of industrial O_2 consumption world-wide, therefore:

Australia's population = 17,000,000
World population = 5,000,000,000.

$\dfrac{5,000,000,000}{17,000,000}$ = 294.117 (extrapolation coefficient)

If all the countries of the world were equally industrialised, then by multiplying the Australian figure by the above extrapolation coefficient the amount of world industrial O_2 consumption (100% industrialisation) would be

214,465,670 tonnes O_2 x 294.117 = 63,078,137,856 tonnes O_2 annually.

The world is not 100% industrialised, however, so instead we shall take a more realistic figure of 30% industrialisation. The world's annual industrial consumption of O_2 would therefore be

30% of 63,078,137,856 tonnes O_2 = 18,923,442,176 tonnes O_2

To this must be added:
The O_2 consumption of 450,000,000 vehicles assuming, an average use of 5 hours per day per vehicle:

0.02225 t/O_2/hour x 5hrs x 365 days x 450,000,000 vehicles = 18,272,813,056 tonnes O_2

Human O_2 consumption = 0.26 t/O_2 x 5,000,000,000 = 1,300,000,000 tonnes O_2

This makes an annual total of = 38,496,255,232 tonnes O_2

Using the Canadian figure for the O_2 production of conifer forest of 10.0619 tonnes/hectare, or 1,00619 tonnes/km², the area of forest required to satisfy the above oxygen demand would be:

$$\frac{38,496,255,232}{1,006.19} = 38,259,432 km^2$$

The total world land area is estimated at 135,000,000km².

Therefore the percentage of total world land area that would be required to replace the above annual consumption is:

$$\frac{38,259,432 km^2}{135,000,000 km^2} = 28.3\% \text{ wholly devoted to forest.}$$

4. *Our Senseless Toil*, Pt.I, p.28.
5. From an article by Viktor Schauberger, "The Development of Steppeland in Germany" ("Die Versteppung Deutschlands").
6. *The Secret Doctrine*, by H.P.Blavatsky, Adyar Ed. 1971, Vol.2, p.234: Theosophical Pub.Ho., Adyar, India.

3

NEW DIMENSIONS OF ENERGY

3.1 The Origin of Energy

Let us take as an hypothesis that the ur-original[1] source of energy is a radiant emanation from the Cause of Causes, from God, or better still, from the Eternally Creative Intelligence to avoid any gender implications (hereafter referred to as the *ECI*). Of necessity an entity such as the ECI must constantly create in the process of Its own evolution. Energy might then be viewed as an expression of the Will-To-Create, as the agency through which the ideas of the ECI become manifest.

This could take the form of an infinitely high-energy emission of unconditional love or spirit pulsating over a wide range of frequencies at hyperluminal speeds. Radiating from the Central Ur-Cause or the ECI, it operates in the most sublime realms, in all directions to all parts of the unmanifested Universe. Not being limited by the constraints of matter, the speed of light or the conservation of energy law, it is therefore present in all parts of the Universe simultaneously, and because of its total unconditionality or as pure, unpurpose-prescribed energy, it can be freely employed either and equally for 'good' or 'evil'.

This is no straight-line movement, however, for this would imply uniformity. Uniformity cannot beget life, since life is created out of differences, out of a state of non-equilibrium which, in this instance is generated by the radiating pulsation of ethereal mind energies at diverse frequencies. In the process of emission, the interaction between these various frequencies produces certain periodicities or cyclical effects. On the one hand this results in

the formation of more densely concentrated energy domains where their respective cycles or wavelengths converge (field energy densification), and on the other, in regions of diffuse, more rarified energy where they diverge (field energy attenuation).

Due to this now non-uniform energy distribution comprising zones of greater and lesser energy density, the way in which the formerly unimpeded, primary outflow of energy moves, it gradually becomes influenced through the creation of denser vibratory matrices to which it is no longer directly harmonically related. Deflected from its initially linear radiating path on encountering these lower vibratory resistances, the outward movement of energy progressively assumes a more curvilinear configuration in its descent into less spiritual planes. According to the 'angle' at which these emissions impact on the denser domains of resistance, they are imparted a right-hand or left-hand direction of spin. From an originally undifferentiated state, the energetic entity thus created becomes endowed with either a positive or negative charge and enters the lower worlds of duality (fig. 3.1).

The difference between these various levels and dimensions of creative, formative energy may best be illustrated by a simple analogy. By replacing the Eternally Creative Intelligence with the Sun (our principal source of life-energy), one could say that the solar wind (waves of high-energy particles) impinges on the Earth's atmosphere, creating turbulence (air-waves) due to thermal and energetic reactions. This represents the first demodulation from a high energetic state to a

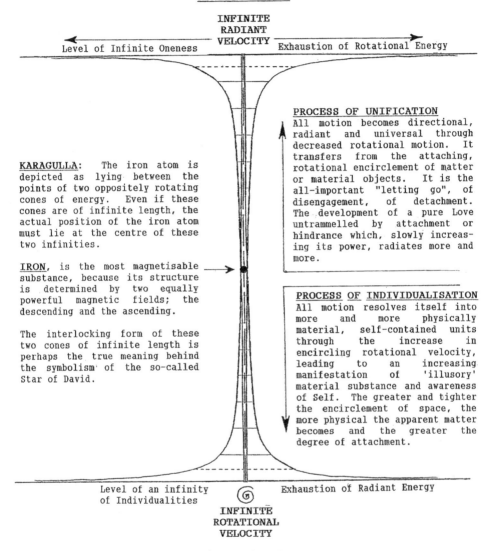

PURE LOVE RADIATING IN ALL DIRECTIONS
PURE SPIRIT = PURE ENERGY = PURE KINETIC ENERGY

No Substance - only Motion
= KINETIC ENERGY =

INFINITE
RADIANT
VELOCITY

← Level of Infinite Oneness   Exhaustion of Rotational Energy →

PROCESS OF UNIFICATION
All motion becomes directional, radiant and universal through decreased rotational motion. It transfers from the attaching, rotational encirclement of matter or material objects. It is the all-important "letting go", of disengagement, of detachment. The development of a pure Love untrammelled by attachment or hindrance which, slowly increasing its power, radiates more and more.

KARAGULLA: The iron atom is depicted as lying between the points of two oppositely rotating cones of energy. Even if these cones are of infinite length, the actual position of the iron atom must lie at the centre of these two infinities.

IRON, is the most magnetisable substance, because its structure is determined by two equally powerful magnetic fields; the descending and the ascending.

The interlocking form of these two cones of infinite length is perhaps the true meaning behind the symbolism of the so-called Star of David.

PROCESS OF INDIVIDUALISATION
All motion resolves itself into more and more physically material, self-contained units through the increase in encircling rotational velocity, leading to an increasing manifestation of 'illusory' material substance and awareness of Self. The greater and tighter the encirclement of space, the more physical the apparent matter becomes and the greater the degree of attachment.

Level of an infinity   Exhaustion of Radiant Energy
of Individualities

INFINITE
ROTATIONAL
VELOCITY

No Motion - only Substance
= POTENTIAL ENERGY =

PURE MATTER = HARMONICALLY STRUCTURED ENERGY = POTENTIAL ENERGY

·   All Manifesting Energy is resolved into Rotational Energy.
There is no other component of motion. It appears static.
This is the illusion of the world of Reality.

Fig. 3.1

motion of lower velocity and intensity. These reactions in turn generate waves of yet lower velocity, but greater physicality, on the surface of the ocean, a denser medium with more harmonically stabilised energy than air. Finally, the ocean waves form nearly static ripples in the sand on the ocean floor.

The whole arrangement not only clearly demonstrates the creative power of higher energies and higher dimensions over lower ones, but also the distinct energetic separations between them in terms of the matter-energy or matter-spirit balance. For the sand-ripple dweller, the fluid movement of the water above it is all it is aware of. The causal dynamics of the air above the water are almost beyond its ken, although it may be dimly aware of this higher state of energy.

As human beings we are immersed in a three-dimensional world, but yet have an inkling of a possible 4th dimension in the form of time. What spacial magnitude is occupied by a 5th dimension, perhaps the dimension of thought and feeling, is well-nigh inconceivable to us. It may indeed possess none of the familiar 3-dimensional aspects of length, width and depth, but all the same it IS.

Although these various levels of being will be elaborated in more detail in the following chapter, a simple computer graphics programme may perhaps give an insight into these other dimensions of energy. With it a circle is drawn, whose centre lies about 50cm above the centre of the screen (fig. 3.2). As the sequence progresses, the initial, visible portion of the circle, represented by a series of arrows, is drawn from the bottom centre of the screen towards the right. After a certain period the line of the circle again appears from the left to close with the point from which it began. What is visible is only part of the circle.

In its operation a computer embodies relatively subtle energetic processes. While the visible part of the circle stops at the right-hand side of the screen, the computer continues to draw it, as is proven when the circle finally re-emerges from the left-hand side of the screen a few moments later. Where is the space in which the circle is being drawn when it is not on the screen? This somewhere, this nowhere,

occupies a dimension which perhaps has no size. It has no physical magnitude.

How big is a thought? What is thought? What is an idea and what is the substance of an idea? What is the process which motivates us to do something? We first get an idea, then we develop the concept and then, and only then, are we in a position to fulfill our desire to implement it. Our natural aspiration is to be creative. The force, the impulse, which is the motivator for us to create, is an unseen energetic process.

There are those who believe that the world came into being purely accidentally. There are others who believe it was created by God or the ECI. The truth, however, probably lies somewhere in between and in a certain sense this could be viewed as a reflective process. That is to say that the ECI, imbued with the desire to create, is constantly seeking for new knowledge gained through the experiences of Its multifarious creations in order to create even better universes. As human beings, we could thus be construed as the creative, cellular organisms within the host entity of the ECI, which contribute to Its overall development, although having no inkling of the spaces and higher planes in which the ECI operates. As a corollary of this, there is therefore no absolute truth as such, for

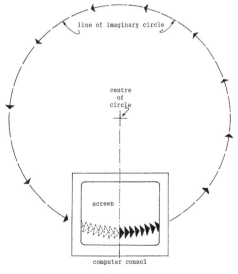

Fig. 3.2

however profound and absolute it may appear to be, such a truth must move and develop as its discoverer, the Eternally Creative Intelligence, Itself evolves.

3.2 Sound as a Formative Force

It could therefore be argued that all physical manifestation develops as the product of focused energy emanating from a seed of desire, of Will-to-create. This manifests itself as vibrations carrying the image or the idea of what is to be created and that form and that form only can arise which corresponds faithfully to the idea of the thing itself or, in other words, the particular pattern of vibrations. Fig. 3.3 taken from Hans Jenny's book Kymatic/ Cymatics[2], gives a graphic example of this in relation to the formative force of sound as the source of the idea or information. Here a 0.5mm thick, square metal plate sprinkled with sand is vibrated at a frequency of 7,560 cycles per second. Following the sequence from Plate 1 to Plate 6, the gradual evolution from the unformed to the final form can be traced. This beautiful image is the one directly associated with the formative influence of 7,560cps.

As a form of energy, sound has long been attributed a form-creating capacity, indeed in the Christian religion the coming into being of the world was ascribed to the 'Word' of God; in the Hindu religion to the 'Beat' of Rama's drum; in modern scientific parlance, to the 'Big Bang', all of which are sound phenomena. Prayers, chanting, Indian ragas, the uttering of mantras are believed to produce various effects, some of which are as concrete in form as the photographs in fig. 3.3 show. That sound also has an effect on the quality of a structure, organic or otherwise, is also subconsciously reflected in our own language. We say that a structure is 'sound' or 'unsound', meaning that it is either safe or unsafe. Similarly a person is said to be of 'sound' or 'unsound' mind, reflecting their creative or destructive propensities. Jericho was supposedly destroyed by destructive sound resonances.

In his book *The Secret Power of Music*[3] David Tame makes a convincing case that the fall of great civilisations was always preceded by the degeneration of popular music, which seems to be about where we are now. In this regard, research carried out by Dr. John Diamond in the field of behavioural kinesiology (BK)[4], yields some interesting insights. A member of the International Academy of Preventive Medicine, Dr. Diamond found that while the deltoid muscle of a healthy adult male can normally resist a force of 40–45lbs, its strength is reduced to 10–15lbs through the negative effect of certain types of rock music, such as heavy metal and hard rock. In contrast to a more natural rhythm, where the beat emulates that of the heart, with emphasis on the first beat, i.e. DA-da-da or 'LUB dup rest', as he puts it, in the above type of music this emphasis is reversed, i.e. da-da-DA, which conflicts with the body's natural pulsation and in poetry is known as an 'anapestic beat'. As Dr. Diamond states:

..one of the characteristics of the anapestic beat is that it is stopped at the end of each bar or measure. Rock music that has this weakening effect appears to have this stopped quality; it is as if the music stops and then has to start again, and the listener subconsciously 'comes to a halt' at the end of each measure. The anapestic beat is the opposite of the dactylic or waltzlike beat, which is DA-da-da, and in which there is an even flow.

He further asserts that these forms of music and unnatural rhythms cause switching in the brain's responses, which induces 'subtle perceptual difficulties' that *may well manifest themselves in children as decreased performance in school, hyperactivity and restlessness; in adults as decreased work output, increased errors, general inefficiency, reduced decision-making capacity on the job, ...in short, the loss of energy for no apparent reason.*

Moreover, exposure to such music also appears to create an addiction for more of the same plus a desire for debilitating foods. To this can be added the deleterious effect of the fashion prevalent amongst young people today, when dark glasses are worn both day and night and even on overcast days. As a result, the eye never receives the full spectrum of natural frequencies for which it is designed and which it requires for the health

Fig. 3.3.
The illustrations show a simple sonorous figure taking shape under the action of crystal oscillators (piezoelectric effect). Steel plate 31 x 31 cm. Thickness 0.5mm. Frequency 7560 cps. The material strewn on the plate is sand which has been calcined to purify it.

and stability of those parts of the brain associated with it. Apart from other factors, this may well account for the alarming increase in violence, disease and mental instability. Sunlight as a vital factor in health is discussed in chapter 16 in relation to the findings of Dr. John N. Ott. One of the reasons for this debilitating effect is that each molecule of the body has its own resonant frequency, which can be stimulated, over-stimulated or suppressed by different light frequencies and vibrations (sounds). What long-term effect the ceaseless bombardment of the body's very sensitive, electrically charged cells by the veritable salad of electro-magnetic emissions in the way of high-tension cables, radio, television, radar, microwave ovens and transmitters, etc. has on the overall health is a matter for serious conjecture.

3.2 The Phenomenon of Resonance

Sound or resonance therefore does seem to be associated with creative or destructive phenomena. Resonance is the free transfer of energy or the sympathetic vibration between one system and another without loss, and is the function of mutually precisely harmonically related frequencies. As such, it and the phenomena, physical or otherwise, that it produces, are the result of the periodic repetition of a given number of impulses, which can be categorised as vibration, oscillation, or rotational periodicity.[5] In fig. 3.3 the formative effects of resonance in the form of sound are clearly apparent and, in other plates in Hans Jenny's book higher frequencies are shown to give rise to increasingly complex perceptual patterns[6]. From this it follows that the state of order of a given physical structure manifested through resonance is dependent on a particular frequency level or standing-wave pattern of vibrations, higher vibrations producing higher forms and vice versa. Therefore if the intensities of those resonant interactions that furnish the idea and energetic basis for more evolved manifestations of life are lowered artificially or by other means, then the general quality of life-forms degenerates, sometimes reaching the extreme condition of extinction. This is because

the overall level of vibration, which contains the formative patterns explicit to the creature or form of life in question, has demodulated to frequencies too low to support these formerly highly complex structures.

As we survey the world around us today this is precisely what appears to be happening – the quantitative thrust of our technology and ideology is pressing downwards towards uniformity, to a vibrationless state, which is equivalent to zero energy and quality. Thus species after species is disappearing simply because the ambient creative energetic matrix, which has to do with upward evolution, has been rendered inoperative. But while it may appear that all we now have left is all that we can still preserve, namely an increasingly limited spectrum of possible life-forms, all that is needed to reawaken the creative urge of Nature is to raise the level of human spirituality and natural awareness, in order to produce an outflow of positive, creatively potentiated energy.

Higher spirituality is synonymous with a higher level of energy. As this energy is renewed in the human psyche it permeates and enriches the noosphere, the immaterial realms of thought, the abode of the Will-to-create, and the complexity of the creative energetic matrix is raised as a result. New species or those previously extinct may then begin to reappear in physical form as a reflection of this higher creative dynamic. Ultimately we therefore have no need to fear for the future on this planet – that the spectrum of life will constantly diminish – because, as we attune our own harmonic vibrations more and more with those of the ECI, then in the process we will reactivate the evolutionary vibrancies through which all life will be revivified and reborn.

Incidentally in regard to resonance *per se* the number 29 seems to have some strange affinity with the Earth and the planetary system for, in the course of my research I discovered some peculiar coincidences, which are perhaps worthy of note and are set out in fig. 3.4.

To return to the theme in hand: As the will-to-create intensifies, the focus becomes more concentrated, extraneous elements are ejected and a channel is opened to the free passage of creative energy, resulting in an increasing charge (life-force), energetic density and

Pure Coincidence?
or
The Manifestation of Resonance?

Speed of light .... = **299**,792.458 km/s

Earth's natural resonant frequency calculated as .... = $\dfrac{\textbf{29.9}79\ 245\ 8}{4}$

= 7.493 1145 cycles/sec

Mean diameter of the Earth's orbit... = **299**,195,742 km

Earth's mean orbital velocity .... = **29.7**99 328 85 km/s

Orbital velocity of the Earth squared... = $(29.799\ 328\ 85)^2$
= **888**

Length of Lunar or Synodic month .... = **29.5**30 59 days

Saturn's orbital period .... = **29.4**6 years

The square-root of the Earth's rotational period or
sidereal day in seconds, i.e. 86,164.090 55 seconds .... = **293**.537 204 7

Jupiter's orbital velocity.. = **29,2**24.048 97 km/hr

Velocity required to maintain a satellite in orbit .... = **29**,000 km/sec.

Best frequency for communication with other realms .... = **29** megacycles[7]

Dividing the orbital periods of all the planets by
365.26 (Earth's orbital period) and multiplying all
the results together gives a value of 19,281,435.35
whose reciprocal value... = 0.00000000**2993**865136

(Earth's equatorial radius = 6,378.164 km) $\dfrac{6{,}378.164}{21.365}$ = **298**.533 302 1
(Earth's polar radius   = 6,356.799 km)

(6.378 164 – 6.356 799   = 21.365 km) $\dfrac{6{,}356.799}{21.365}$ = **297**.533 302 1

Average human consumption of molecular oxygen hour .... = **29.7** grams

The speed of light can also be calculated
as follows, beginning by multiplying the prime numbers – 13 x 23 = **299**
2² x 10² x 299 = $\overline{119{,}600}$
(119,600)² x 2π = 8.987 568 794 x 10¹⁰
$\sqrt{8.987\ 568\ 794\ \times\ 10^{10}}$ = **299**, 792.7416km/sec

Callum Coats, July 1992

Fig. 3.4

ENERGY IS PRIMARY – THE CAUSE.

FORM IS SECONDARY – THE EFFECT.

Energy creates the form in which it wishes to move.
The form is therefore the mirror of the energy flow.

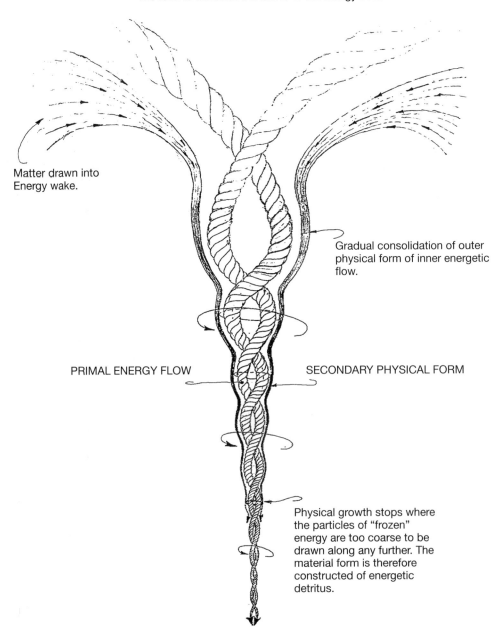

Matter drawn into
Energy wake.

Gradual consolidation of outer
physical form of inner energetic
flow.

PRIMAL ENERGY FLOW   SECONDARY PHYSICAL FORM

Physical growth stops where
the particles of "frozen"
energy are too coarse to be
drawn along any further. The
material form is therefore
constructed of energetic
detritus.

Fig. 3.5   **Energy and Form**

rotational velocity; in other words, a vortex of life-energy evolves, into which more and more and higher qualities of energy are drawn for the generation and development of the form itself (fig. 3.5). Since it is first generated in a particular location or moment in space-time, this vortex bears the imprint of the conditions obtaining at that spot (its reference point in the space-time continuum) and is therefore a totally unique phenomenon with its own individual and characteristic frequency or vibration, or combination of vibrations. Its inherent stability and eventual physical manifestation is assured as long as its originating idea is unchanged and remains concentrated.

These interacting vibrations must be in harmony with each other and also in resonance with the particular conditions of the place of genesis, so that a given life process or creature can actually grow and evolve. This is the function of the various chakras of the human body, which are represented as flower-like vortices whose stems enter the body at various points, such as the heart, in order to conduct the particular variety of higher energies suited to the enhancement and health of the organ in question.

Harmony and resonance are prerequisites for growth and development; lower stages of harmony in the form of lesser individualities providing the firm and stable substructures upon which the higher structures are built. The ECI is thus everywhere at once, and creates all the various levels of existence through the formation and concentration of life-force into harmonic vortices of matter from Its infinite ocean of energy. That Goethe was very much aware of this is evident from the following poem[8]:

All things into one are woven, each in each doth act and dwell
As cosmic forces, rising, falling, charging up this golden bell,
With heaven-scented undulations, piercing Earth from power Sublime.
Harmonious all and all resounding, fill they universe and time!
Amidst life's tides in raging motion, I ebb and flood – waft to and fro!

Birth and grave, eternal ocean, ever-moving, transient flow.
A changing, vibrant animation, the very stuff of life is mine,
Thus at the loom of time I sit and weave this living cloth divine.

In Its universe, therefore, there is no energy crisis!

From this it could be construed that it is due the interaction of manifold harmonic vibrations ultimately manifesting into tight radius and extreme rotational velocity that material existence emerges. A good example of this is the spiralling air masses of our weather systems, in which the very large and extended gyrating air-masses have relatively little dense substance, a large radius of action, very little material form and very slow rotational velocities. As they gradually converge, however, their speed and force increases and their radius reduces.

Ultimately they resolve themselves into almost physically palpable energetic entities such as tornadoes and waterspouts, whose core at the base, where the rotational velocity is greatest, is very nearly hard, physical, matter. From being ephemeral, they have become almost tangible. Their upper roots originate in relatively low-density atmospheric conditions, which can be equated with a less structured and more radially dynamic energy-state, since this zone is more exposed to high-energy solar radiation, whereas the base of the tornado penetrates into greater atmospheric densities which are synonymous with more structured, rotational conditions of energy. The effective density of tornadoes is such that their naturally occurring vortexial energies have been known to bend steel railway lines.

Using this as an analogy for the structural development of the atom, which is of course infinitely smaller and has a much higher rate of rotation and vibration, then it becomes clearer how physical matter could come into being through the focusing of energies at one particular point. Therefore in almost nothing is almost everything. Taken to its extreme, it could therefore be said that in nothing is everything; that all manifestation emerges through the 'eye of the needle' as it were, from

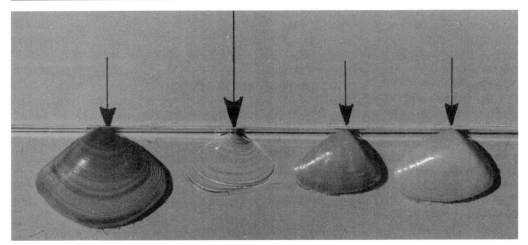

Fig. 3.6   **Sea shells: energy focussing at a point.**

the high-potency, formless void of the ECI. Our world is thus, indeed, a world of illusion!

The sea-shells shown in fig. 3.6 are an example of this focusing of energy, for their gradual growth in size is due to the application of creative energy from and at a point, from the minute ovum in which initial fertilisation took place. On the other hand, the fourth shell-like form indicated by the larger arrow was also created, this time more rapidly, by the application of energy from and at a point, in this case a hammer on the edge of a piece of glass!

3.3 *The Creative Energy-Vortex*

Since we still do not know what energy is and for the purposes of discussion, fig. 3.5 represents a possible energy path. As the energy moves along its desired path, it draws matter into its wake and forms the vessel through which it wants to move. A river does exactly the same thing. The capillaries in our bodies likewise. The blood is the external manifestation of an energy path. What we see is the blood, but we do not see the energy that moves it. The blood is all that matter which is too coarse to be taken to the energy's final destination. Energy therefore creates the form of the path through which it wants to move and along which it can move with the least resistance.

If we desire to build a house, we certainly do not want one in which it is inconvenient to move about. We build it to suit ourselves and our way of living. As has been mooted earlier, all natural systems are evolved as a result of the pattern of energy, or the idea that sought to create them in the first place. All this may reek of metaphysics, but it is difficult to express the notion otherwise.

Once the external form has been created, a point is reached where the matter used to create it is now too coarse to continue along the energetic path and is left behind. Viktor Schauberger often referred to this Earth as a huge dung-heap and said that all the matter, all the living things upon it, were only the fecal matter ejected by the various energies and their forms of movement, because they could not carry the material any further. In other words, whatever energies contribute to an increase in life-force are retained in immaterial form, while the remaining energetic material is expelled as waste, analogous to the daily defecation of human beings. Having been extracted from food, apart from metabolic functions, these often very subtle immaterial energies are used for the production of thought processes. From a certain point of view, the human body could therefore be seen as a hollow energy path, a complex toroidal vortex for the transmutation of matter-energy into physical and intellectual activity.

Fig. 3.7 **A natural vortex**

In line with this view, energy and its movement are unquestionably the primary cause, the prerequisite for physical manifestation. Everything we see around us, the trees, the flowers, all are the outside casing of the formative energy path. According to Viktor Schauberger, while the main body of a tree's energy lies above it, the tree can only grow to a certain height, because the energies are only able to draw up the physical mass of the tree so far in their wake.

Continuing our discussion of the vortexial movement of energy, let us observe just how beautiful such a naturally structured vortex is (fig. 3.7). Such phenomena are not often observed. What a marvellous structure! It is not handmade, but it is the path along which water likes to move. Each of these segmental whorls is fractionally smaller than the one above, the mathematics and proportions of which can be explained using the system developed by Walter Schauberger.

Let us briefly examine various illustrations taken from a book, beautifully penned and printed in 1908[9] (figs. 3.8–3.10). In fig. 3.8 the movement of the fish is shown to be undulating and sinuous, and the woman walks with a swinging gait. What should be noticed in particular is that none of these shapes has any connection with the straight line, circle, point or cylinder, or with any of the mechanical systems we presently employ for the generation of energy. Nevertheless, they are all energy paths. They were all created by a movement of energy and express the way that that particular form of energy desired to move in the manifestation of the original or originating idea of the thing itself.

It is now becoming more and more imperative that we understand how energy moves in order to create conditions similar to those achieved with double-helical pipes in the investigation carried out by Professor Franz Pöpel at the Stuttgart Institute of Hygiene in 1952 on Viktor Schauberger's initiative (see chapter 14 on water supply). It is vital for our survival that whatever methods we adopt in a future technology should always emulate the natural movement of energy and Nature's systems of motion, growth and development. In her systems involving dynamic energetic

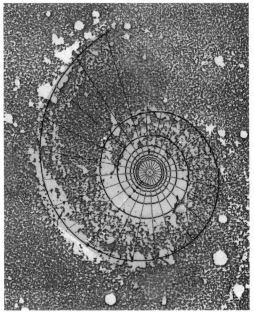

Fig. 3.11   **Spiral galaxy**

processes, she always appears to select a spiral form of movement and its vortical derivatives, which are represented in both macrocosm (fig. 3.11, a galaxy, in this case overlaid by Walter Schauberger's hyperbolic spiral) and microcosm (DNA molecule – fig. 3.12[10]).

Nature's workings could therefore be described not as 'wheels within wheels', but as 'whorls within whorls'. It is all the more extraordinary, therefore, that despite so much

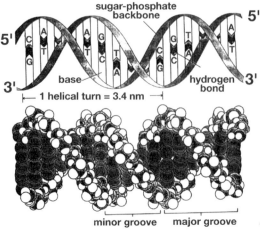

Fig. 3.12   **DNA Molecule**

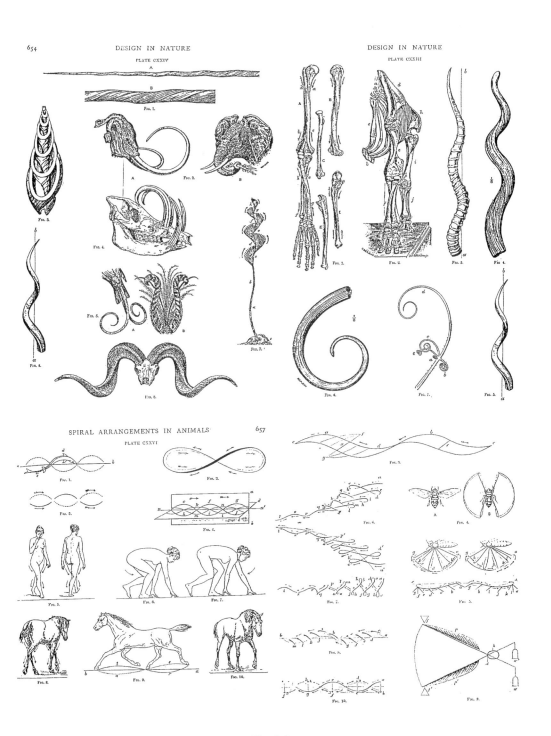

Fig. 3.8

Fig. 3.9

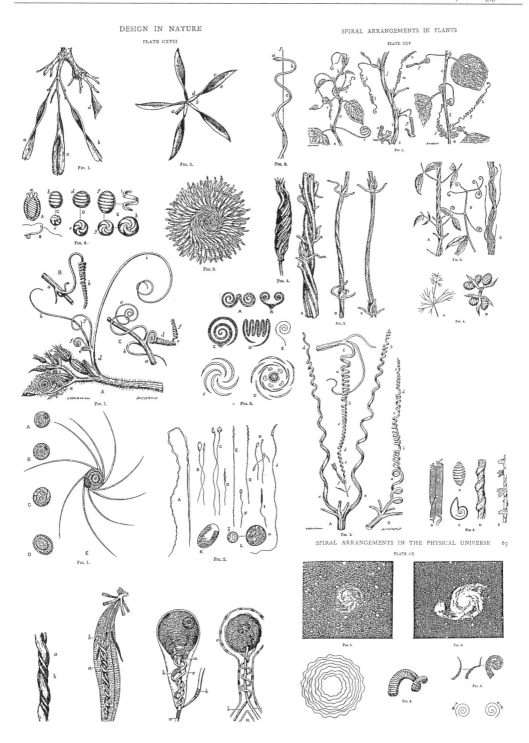

Fig. 3.10

evidence of this vortical, cyclical, helical movement, which lies everywhere in Nature before our very eyes, science has never ascribed any fundamental importance to it or tried to copy it. It has been too immersed in the euclidean elements of mechanics with little knowledge or conceptions of organics. We have never taken the time to understand Nature's dynamics enough to be able to exploit them.

Today, science is only just developing a new (but in all truth, a very, very old) field of research that it now calls 'power fluidics', which is investigating the vortex as a means of controlling the flow of liquids. It is high time that we developed a technology, whereby these processes are truly understood. This should be termed an 'Eco-Technology' rather than 'Biotechnology', the latter having been brought into disrepute through gene manipulation and experimentation. Perhaps $Ec^2otechnology$ would be an even better term, for it embodies Viktor Schauberger's concept '$C^{2'}$', signifying '*Comprehend and Copy Nature*'.

Notes

1. See ftn.5, chap.1, concerning the use of the prefix 'ur'.
2. From *Kymatik/Cymatics* by Hans Jenny, photos by Hans Peter Widmer: Basilius, Basel, Switzerland (now defunct).
3. *The Secret Power Of Music* by David Tame: Inner Traditions, Rochester, VT, USA.
4. *Your Body Doesn't Lie*, (Behavioral Kinesiology) by Dr. John Diamond MD: Harper & Row, New York, 1979.
5. Referring once more to Planck's constant whereby energy can only be emitted or absorbed in whole-numbered quanta, since Nature never seems to lack energy for her various functions, they must therefore be closely associated with resonant states. While the present system of manipulating large numbers using scientific notation, i.e. the first five or so significant figures multiplied by 10 to the power of something, may simplify calculation, the establishment of an exact value or periodicity upon which true resonance at high frequencies is founded becomes rather hit and miss.

   For example, were a given resonant state giving rise to a particular phenomenon to have an actual value of say 6,622,458,316 Hz, then with scientific notation this would be expressed as $6.622\,46 \times 10^9$ Hz. If written out in full, the value of the latter would be 6,622,460,000, slightly higher than the former. Subtracting the original number from this truncated value leaves a deficit of 1,684 Hz from the true state of resonance. If the creation of the above phenomenon was the object of the exercise, then for lack of the missing 1,684 vibrations, it would be impossible to reproduce the original phenomenon exactly. In terms of the achievement of resonant states, in my view it is actually the last few digits that are significant, not the first. With the use of computers, however, this should be a simple matter to rectify.

   With regard to the above whole-numbered harmonical aspects themselves, the value of Planck's constant of 6.62×10^{-34}, i.e. the whole number 6 plus the decimal value of 62, would seem to be at variance with Nature's use of integers. This value was no doubt founded on the calibrated values of the measuring instruments available to Planck at the time. These calibrations were probably quite arbitrary originally in the same way that the standard gauge railway track owes its dimension (4ft 8½in 1.435m) to the distance between the wheels of the first steam engine, 'The Rocket', built by Robert Stephenson. Since Planck's constant is fundamental to the interpretation of physics, it might be extremely rewarding if its present value could be replaced with some fundamental unit or integer value. In so doing some very interesting integer relationships might surface between what are now apparently disparate magnitudes through the conversion of their current values to accord with this new unit value for Planck's constant.

6. Perceptual patterns or structures possessing qualities as a whole that cannot be described merely as a sum of its parts. Collins English Dictionary.
7. *The Ghost of 29 Megacycles*, by John G. Fuller: Signet ed. 1986, New American Lib., New York. Describes research of Dr. George Meek, an American engineer, and the German electronics engineer, Dr. Hans Otto König, into communication with the recently deceased. The optimum frequency for enabling the dead to communicate with the living and vice versa by super-imposing their voices on the carrier wave, was 29 megacycles. On January 15th, 1983 Radio Luxemburg invited Dr König to broadcast a live-to-air experiment in such communication, which much to the consternation of all concerned, was largely successful.
8. From Viktor Schauberger's article, "The Ox and the Chamois", pub. by Prof. Werner Zimmermann in TAU magazine, No.146, June 1936, p.30.
9. *Design In Nature* by J. Bell Pettigrew: Longmans Green, London, 1908.
10. "DNA Double Helix" p.101 of *The Molecular Biology of the Cell* by B. Alberts, D. Bray, J. Lewis, M. Raff, K. Roberts & J.D. Watson: Garland, New York.

4

WHAT IS MOTION?

4.1 The 'Original' Motion

If one observes the Universe as a whole, i.e. from 'Big Bang' to 'Black Hole', as it were, a form of motion is evident that Viktor Schauberger called "cycloid-spiral-space-curve motion". He also referred to it as the "original" motion, not only in a primordial sense, but also as a "form-creating" dynamic. Shown in its quintessential, archetypal form in fig. 4.1, which depicts the creation of three successive universes, the 'cycloid-spiral-space-curve' embodies an initial out-breathing, centrifugal, curving expansion of undiscriminating, creative energy (unconditional love) from a point, which results in the generation of countless individualities and energetic systems. In *The Secret Doctrine*[1] Helena P. Blavatsky describes this phenomenon stating that:

An out-breathing of the 'unknown essence' produces the world and an inhalation causes it to disappear.

Its culmination is an in-breathing, centripetal implosion of the concentrated energies and experience of the created individualities who now seek reunion with their source, the ECI, bringing back with them all the myriad experiences they have gained. Once all has reverted to the ECI via the 'Black Hole', then that universe, or that part of the Universe at the end of the Black Hole, leaves our space-time and enters a highly ethereal continuum, the magnitudes and dimensions of which we cannot conceive. What happens then is open to all manner of speculation. Possibly the new

experiential information is absorbed and digested by the ECI in order then to create a new universe. The very word 'Universe' signifies a single curve (*uni*=one, *versum*=curve). The fact that the configuration of this curve may be a complex combination of descending and ascending, involuting and convoluting, expanding and contracting spiral movements does nothing to detract from its uniqueness or unit quality, since from inception to culmination its path is continuous. This curve is an energy-path and the essence of energy is ceaseless movement. In its eternal trajectory from spirit to matter (outward breath) and from matter to spirit (inward breath) it permeates all creation. It is all creation!

Apart from its inherent pulsation, it would be impossible to dissect this eternal movement into discrete segments, for the point at which one portion of this sublime curve ceases and the next begins cannot be defined mathematically, whatever the subjective view. Therefore this unique, primordial, creative curve embodies the unbroken path of evolution, of cyclical, pulsating *out*-foldment and *in*-foldment, as it spirals in and out of all the myriads of apparently inextricably interconnected and interdependent individual systems in the cosmos, tying and uniting them all in one inscrutable Gordian Knot. We are therefore unequivocally all part and parcel of the One and any harm of whatever kind we inflict on others or to the planet, we not only inflict on ourselves, but the rest of the cosmos as well.

This creative force and its dynamic have already long been known to Eastern

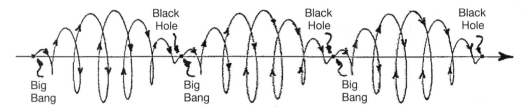

Fig. 4.1   **The cycloid spiral space curve.**

esotericism and is referred to by Mme. Blavatsky as follows[2]:

Kundalini Shakti: *the power or Force which moves in a curved path. It is the Universal life-Principle manifesting everywhere in Nature. This force includes the two great forces of attraction and repulsion. Electricity and magnetism are but manifestations of it. This is the power which brings about that 'continuous adjustment of internal relations to external relations', which is the essence of life according to Herbert Spencer, and that 'continuous adjustment of external relations', which is the basis for the transmigration of souls, punar ianman (re-birth) in the doctrines of the ancient Hindu philosophers.*

Even the tools of common language unwittingly (or wittingly) allude to the character of this spiral movement. When we ex-*(s)pire*, we leave this our 'mortal coil'. When we are in-*spire*-d, we feel drawn to higher ideals. Our *spir(e)it* is raised and we are sucked into the upward spiral. Similarly through re-*spir(e)*-ation the ionisation balance of the body, which varies according to the time of day, is adjusted by the proportional ionisation of the air indrawn through the nostrils, which due to opposite directions of rotation, is negatively ionised by the left nostril and positively by the right nostril. Sneezing, therefore, may perhaps be a compensating process, through which high opposing charges resulting from over-ionisation are reduced to zero.

Interestingly enough, while on the subject of the body, the German word for the spinal column, the fundamental supporting structure of the human body, is 'Wirbelsäule', which translated directly into English, means a 'spiral' column. Similarly each one of the vertebra is referred to as a whirlpool or a vortex. Clearly, the Germans have long had a completely different view of the central structure of our bodies. Whereas we see it as a stiff, more or less rigid, physical structure, they see it more as an energy path. This has obvious associations with the Hindu concept of Kundalini, the name given to the two serpents that dwell at the base of the spine, whose rising energises and spiritualises the various higher chakras (ethereal vortices) of the physical body and whose entwinement on Mercury's staff (the caduceus) empowers him as Messenger of the Gods. Nature too, provides us with countless examples of dynamic spiral growth and movement in the form of galaxies, cyclones, whirlpools and tornadoes, of which we, in our blindness and arrogance, fail to take note in our pursuit of mechanical perfection.

According to the late Dr. Tilman Schauberger, grandson and expert on Viktor Schauberger's works, creative, formative motion is:-

Open, goal-oriented, structured, concentrated, intensifying, condensing, dynamic, self-organising, self-divesting of the less valuable, rhythmical, cyclical, sinuous, pulsating, inrolling, and centripetal = the cycloid-spiral-space-curve.

4.2 Forms of Motion

Within this framework there are four fundamental forms of movement: all natural dynamic motion will comprise one or more of four types – orbital, rotational, toroidal and circulatory (fig. 4.2). All of these are combined in the processes of natural movement as illustrated in the bottom image

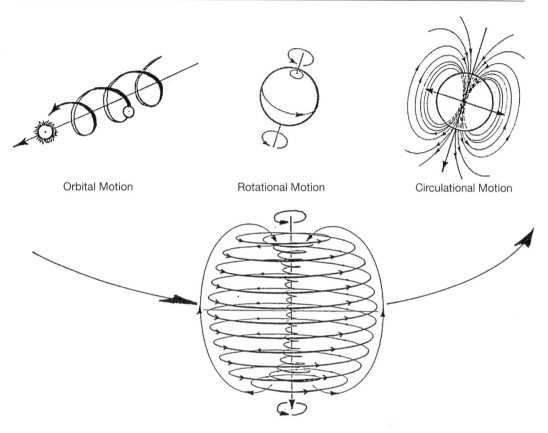

Orbital Motion   Rotational Motion   Circulational Motion

Fig. 4.2 Creative, formative motion according to Dr. Tilman Schauberger.
The open, goal-oriented, structured, concentrated, intensifying, condensing, dynamic, self-organising, self-divesting of the less valuable, rhythmical (cyclical), sinuous, pulsing, in-rolling, centripetal (and out-rolling centrifugal) movement = The Cycloid Spiral Space-curve.
Natural Motion: Natural motion is quadri-partite and comprised of four components.

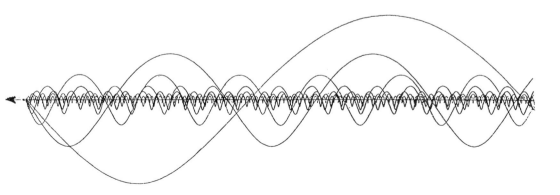

Fig. 4.3   The Planetary Vortex.
The movements of the inner planets viewed over a period of one full Saturn cycle of 29.46 years.

– here the diameter of the internal passage of energy varying according to the pattern of flow. Fig. 4.3 depicts the dynamic body of the solar system over one full cycle of Saturn. It is not the fairly static, disc-like structure we are accustomed to think of, but is actually a vortex with each planet describing its own spiral path about the Sun, which is itself moving in the direction of star cluster 'Hercules' at about 20km per second.

When we come to spiral-vortical motion itself, we can further subdivide it into another two forms. Viktor referred to *radial-axial* and *axial->radial* (actually tangential-> axial and axial->tangential) motion, which are terms of his coinage in this particular context. As illustrated in fig. 4.4 axial->radial motion signifies an initial movement around a centre, which subsequently transfers to a radial movement towards the exterior; it is thus centrifugal and a movement from the inside outwards. At the centre of the wheel, for example, there is no motion but, with increasing distance from the centre, the speed of motion and the tendency towards disintegration also increase. This is why the wooden wagon-wheels of earlier days had a steel band around them to hold them together. It was called a 'tie-er' (= tyre or tire) and tied the wheel together.

In Viktor's theories, also proven practically, with this form of movement the resistance to motion increases by the square of the starting velocity. In other words, if the radial distance from the centre of rotation is 1 and the resistance is 1, when the radius is doubled, the resistance is quadrupled and the rotational period halved. If the radial distance is 3, the resultant resistance is 3^2 (=9) and the rotational velocity reduced to a $\frac{1}{3}$rd, and so on. However if the rotational velocity of such a centrifugal system is to be maintained at a constant level, then a continual, wasteful and expensive increase in the amount of input energy is required to overcome the resistance, and the whole system becomes less and less efficient. Not only this, but it creates discordant noise and the more noise a device makes, the more it operates against the laws of Nature.

The dispersion of energy, therefore, is associated with noise or heat, as the case may be.

This is typical of our forms of technical movement, in which there is initially no motion at the centre, but with increasing distance from this point, velocity and resistance also increase. The axial->radial centrifugal form of motion can thus be defined as divergent, decelerating, dissipating, structure-loosening, disintegrating, destructive and friction-inducing. While the destructive diffusion of energy results in noise, the creative concentration of energy, however, is silent. Indeed, as Viktor asserted on many occasions, *"Everything that is natural is silent, simple and cheap."*[3]

Upon reflection, this statement is quite obvious. All the concentrated energy involved in the growth of the forest, for example, all the innumerable chemical and atomic interactions, are none other than energetic processes, movements of creative energy. The silence of the forest is indicative of the extraordinary concentration of creative energy. Its destruction, however, is always associated with the horrendous racket of chain-saws, heavy machinery and the like.

Whereas our mechanical, technological systems of motion almost without exception are axial->radial and heat- and friction-inducing, Nature uses precisely the opposite form of movement. When Nature is moving dynamically, the slowest movement occurs at the periphery and the fastest at the centre. One only has to observe the dynamics of a cyclone or a tornado. Her form of movement, therefore, is centripetal or radial->axial, moving from the outside inwards with increasing velocity, which acts to cool, to condense, to structure.

Radial->axial motion can therefore be defined as convergent, contracting, consolidating, creative, integrating, formative, friction reducing. If the starting radius is 1 and the initial resistance is 1 on an inwinding path, when the radius is halved, the resistance is $(\frac{1}{2})^2 = \frac{1}{4}$ and the rotational periodicity, frequency or velocity is doubled. The dynamics of evolution must therefore follow this centripetal, radial->axial path, for if the opposite were the case, all would have come to a stop almost before it started.

Force is the application of energy to do work. The magnitude of a force F is the product of a mass m times acceleration a ($F=ma$).

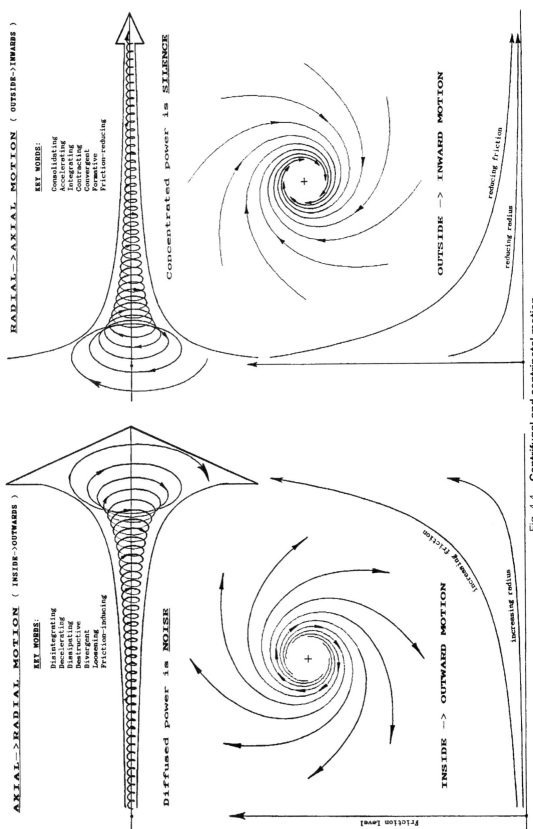

AXIAL→RADIAL MOTION (INSIDE→OUTWARDS)

KEY WORDS:

Disintegrating
Decelerating
Dissipating
Destructive
Divergent
Loosening
Friction-inducing

Diffused power is NOISE

RADIAL→AXIAL MOTION (OUTSIDE→INWARDS)

KEY WORDS:

Consolidating
Accelerating
Integrating
Contracting
Convergent
Formative
Friction-reducing

Concentrated power is SILENCE

INSIDE → OUTWARD MOTION

increasing friction

increasing radius

Friction Level

OUTSIDE → INWARD MOTION

reducing friction

reducing radius

Fig. 4.4   Centrifugal and centripetal motion

As it stands, this equation is not particularly interesting, because it tells us nothing about the all-important type of acceleration, for one form leads to destruction and the other to creation. It is therefore necessary to differentiate between them, which is most simply done by superscripting the acceleration a with either a positive or negative sign, i.e. a^+ or a^-. This would indicate whether the radius of rotation is expanding or the form of acceleration is pressure- and friction-intensifying ($^+$ = axial->radial, centrifugal acceleration) or conversely whether the radius of rotation is reducing, creating a form of acceleration that is suction-increasing and friction-reducing ($^-$ = radial->axial, centripetal acceleration). The equation derived using the latter Viktor Schauberger considered to be the one for determining creative force. Whereas with centrifugal acceleration a^+ more power must be applied in order to accelerate or to maintain the same velocity, in the case of centripetal acceleration a^- the velocity and energy increase automatically. This produces Viktor's formative force, or those upbuilding energies from which all life is created.

In this context we could usefully re-examine the Hasenöhrl-Einstein equation ($E = mc^2$) in connection with other energy-determining equations. While their general premises apply to mechanical systems, there is some doubt as to their relevance to living systems. As presently interpreted $E = mc^2$ requires that the amount of energy in the Universe to be finite and assumes the speed of light to be constant. Here, however, we are reminded of Walter Schauberger's contention that the absolute speed of light is not constant (p.24), but dependent on the frequency-related radius of its spiral path; the smaller the radius of rotation (frequency of periodicity), the greater the velocity and intrinsic energy of the radiation (light) and *vice versa*. Such a nonconstancy in the speed of light – as a factor in quantifying energy or mass – would seemingly negate the doctrine of universally finite energy and the conservation of energy law. Leaving this aside for the moment, let us now consider the standard, textbook equation for kinetic energy or work

W, where W is the product of (mass m x velocity v^2) divided by 2 ($W=\frac{1}{2}mv^2$), we discover something very interesting. This equation also relates to energetic activity and, analogous to the Hasenöhrl-Einstein equation, determines the quantity of energy used in our technical, mechanical systems. Here however we suddenly find that the amount of available energy in the form of work W is halved. In this equation mass is still represented by m, whereas c is replaced by v – both terms relating to the time and speed taken to travel a given distance. The expression mc^2 can thus be equated with mv^2. In the Hasenöhrl-Einstein equation, however, there is no division by 2, so the amount of available energy always remains undiminished.

But when intrinsically the same energy equation is applied to technical energetic processes and purposes, the amount of useful energy is apparently halved. From textbooks we learn that energy is indestructible, but merely changes form, this reduction being attributable to the encounter with a resistance of some kind (deceleration) or through the conversion of energy into heat, or both. In consideration of what has been stated above, and, Walter Schauberger's reinterpretation of C^2, perhaps the real reason for this loss is the exploitation of wasteful axial-radial, centrifugal motion. In contrast, radial-axial dynamics operate according to the law of the anti-conservation of energy mentioned in chapter 1, wherein friction – and therefore heat – constantly reduces and velocity increases automatically, because the type of motion is in conformity with natural energetic (spiritual) law and not the mundane, physical laws of mechanics.

4.3 Thesis, Antithesis and Synthesis

With vortical motion still fresh in our minds, let us begin our appraisal of the elements of thesis, anthesis and synthesis by examining the dynamics of a tornado. The tornado descends from a lower to a higher atmospheric density and generally takes the form of a hyperbolic funnel or cone (fig. 4.5). The smaller

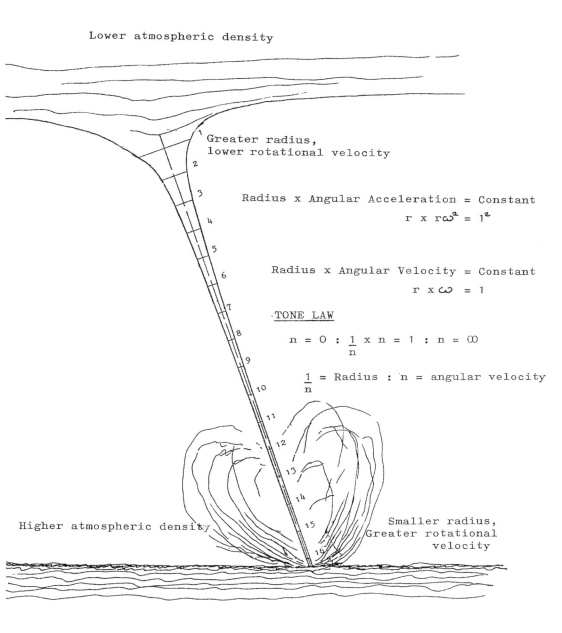

Lower atmospheric density

Greater radius,
lower rotational velocity

1
2
3

Radius x Angular Acceleration = Constant
$$r \times r\omega^2 = 1^2$$

4
5
6

Radius x Angular Velocity = Constant
$$r \times \omega = 1$$

7

TONE LAW

8
9

$$n = 0 : \frac{1}{n} \times n = 1 : n = \infty$$

$$\frac{1}{n} = \text{Radius} : n = \text{angular velocity}$$

10
11
12
13
14

Higher atmospheric density

15

Smaller radius,
Greater rotational
velocity

16

Fig. 4.5   **The tornado as a hyperbolic funnel**

the radius, the higher the rotational velocity. It is another example of how Nature moves from the outside inwards in terms of increasing energetic effect and of generating power. In the eye of the tornado or a cyclone, there is an upward movement – suction. Suction and pressure are the two forces here interacting, each being the counterpart of the other, the opposite sides of the same coin which, taken together represent the wholeness or united, undivided phenomenon. They could thus be viewed as two discrete entities emanating from a single generative principle.

In terms of dialectic thinking, which seeks to fathom the extremes of logical thought, they could also be interpreted as the two counter-concepts of argument (thesis) and counter-argument (antithesis). According to the German philosopher, George W. F. Hegel (1770–1831), dialectic thinking refers *"to the process of thought by which such contradictions are seen to merge themselves in a higher truth that comprehends them"*.[4] The existence of this higher truth or unifying principle, however, appears to have eluded general scientific thinking, which conceives of reality more in terms of laws than **mutually interactive reciprocities.**

Perhaps therefore we need to adopt a more dialectic approach to our appraisal of the dynamics and forces of reality. This should encompass both thesis and antithesis, the two apparently conflicting elements that find their synthesis or wholeness in their mutual combination and interaction. However, there seems at present to be what might be called a 'scientific Berlin Wall' separating these opposing, but complementary magnitudes (see fig. 4.6), which in the light of the above should perhaps be advantageously dismantled as its namesake already has.

Dialectically speaking we could therefore say that: **heat x cold = unity = the wholeness.**

Indeed it requires no great stretch of the imagination to realise that the condition of health, reproductive and otherwise, of all life-forms is founded on the delicate balance between heat and cold specific to the organism in question. Some types of fruit and seeds cannot germinate properly unless they have been exposed to frost. Life therefore is

not merely a question of heat, but also of its inseparable counterpart – *cold*.

Fig. 4.6 lists a few examples of such reciprocities, in which, generally speaking, thesis is the quantifiable aspect and antithesis the qualifiable aspect, both of which are represented in the equation formulated by Walter Schauberger, which incidentally is the simplest equation for the rectangular hyperbola (see fig. 11.4):

$$\frac{1}{n} x\, n = 1 = unity = wholeness$$

where $1/n$ stands for the quantitative aspect, n for the qualitative aspect and n itself is equal to any integer or whole number from zero to infinity.

$$\text{Thus if } n = 2, \text{ then } \frac{1}{2} x\, 2 = 1$$

$$\text{or if } n = 3: \frac{1}{3} x\, 3 = 1$$

$$\text{or if } n = 1,000,000: \frac{1}{1,000,000} x\, 1,000,000 = 1$$

The answer is always 1, echoing Albert Einstein's observation that *"Nature is the embodiment of the simplest conceivable mathematics"*, and indeed the actual mathematics could not be simpler, representing as it does the reciprocal relationship between the two terms. Viktor Schauberger maintained that any given phenomenon always has its counterpart or counter-aspect, and both components should always be taken into account. The manifestation of all natural forces is the result of the interaction between two opposites, neither of which ever reaches totality in the lower realms of duality (the physical world), for they can only become total when they unite within their unifying, non-physical, governing principle.

In the physical world each component of a pair of forces can only attain 96% of its boundary or extreme condition. Once this point is reached, then its opposite force gradually begins to gain strength. It is an action similar to the Chinese concept of Yin and Yang. When Yang reaches the point of exhaustion (96% of its capacity), then Yin intervenes and gradually increases in strength. As a case in point, in the creation of

DIALECTIC UNITY
or
WHOLENESS

THESIS x ANTITHESIS = SYNTHESIS

Dialectic thinking is *imperative* for comprehension of the whole.

Such thinking may best be represented by the simplest equation for the hyperbola, formulated by Walter SCHAUBERGER:

[n = zero] $\dfrac{1}{n} \times n = \boxed{1}$ (*) = DIALECTIC UNITY   [n = infinity]

The scientific BERLIN WALL dividing what are *not* LAWS, but RECIPROCAL CONSTANTS

$\frac{1}{n}$		n		
MATTER _____	x	SPIRIT (Energy) ___	= (1)	= dialectic unity.
EGOISM _____	x	ALTRUISM _____	= (1)	
ZERO _____	x	INFINITY _____	= (1)	
CHAOS _____	x	ORDER _____	= (1)	
QUANTITY _____	x	QUALITY _____	= (1)	
SPECIALISATION	x	GENERALISATION ___	= (1)	
ANALYSIS _____	x	SYNTHESIS _____	= (1)	
CONSERVATION OF ENERGY _	x	ANTI-CONSERVATION OF ENERGY _	= (1)	
GRAVITATION ___	x	LEVITATION _____	= (1)	
CENTRIFUGENCE	x	CENTRIPETENCE _____	= (1)	
ELECTRICISM ___	x	MAGNETISM _____	= (1)	
EXPANSION _____	x	IMPANSION _____	= (1)	
PRESSURE _____	x	SUCTION _____	= (1)	
LIGHT _____	x	DARKNESS _____	= (1)	
HEAT _____	x	COLD _____	= (1)	
OXYGEN _____	x	CARBONES _____	= (1)	
YANG _____	x	YIN _____	= (1)	
MALE _____	x	FEMALE _____	= (1)	
POSITIVE _____	x	NEGATIVE _____	= (1)	
POSITIVE T-G _	x	NEGATIVE T-G _____	= (1)	T-G = temperature gradient
DISTANCE _____	x	INFORMATION DENSITY	= (1)	
STRINGLENGTH _	x	PITCH _____	= (1)	
WAVELENGTH ___	x	FREQUENCY _____	= (1)	
STRAIGHT LINE	x	POINT _____	= (1)	Extreme values of the circle
RADIUS _____	x	CURVATURE _____	= (1)	
RADIUS _____	x	ANGULAR VELOCITY __	= (1)	
TANGENT Ø° ___	x	COTANGENT Ø° _____	= (1)	

On the left margin, vertically: O C T A V E S
Parallel on the right margin, vertically: O C T A V E S

(*)The symbol (1) represents a sometimes inexpressible unity.

In the physical universe, each of the above aspects can only attain 96% of its extreme potential. Were one ever to reach its extreme, transcendental state, then its counterpart would cease to exist in the physical world also. Both would then become transcendental and thus mutually indistinguishable and inseparable.

Callum COATS, July 1992

Fig. 4.6

a vacuum, there is always a residual 4% left of the medium to be evacuated, a figure that can only be further reduced by an enormous expenditure of energy; 100% − 4% = 96%! Thus Chaos x Order = 1. Without chaos (undifferentiated, unstructured matter or energy, or unordered, unmetamorphosed unconditional love) there could be no basis for the creation of order (differentiated, harmonically-structured matter or energy); therefore the foundation of order is chaos. Recently chaos theory has come very much to the fore.

Matter and Spirit or, as they are more commonly expressed, Matter and Energy are also a unity. While a human being or a living system represents a certain quantity, it also possesses certain energetic and other immaterial characteristics, and the totality is the combination of both aspects. Then there is also the conservation and anti-conservation of energy, which was touched on earlier. The so-called 'Law of the Conservation of Energy' requires that energy be indestructible; that the amount of energy in the universe is finite and at all times constant; that there can neither be more, nor less energy. It is merely transformed from one form into another.

On the other hand, according to Viktor Schauberger, the cycle of interactive pulsation between opposite forms of energy can actually be interrupted through the application of radial-axial dynamics, in which one form of energy or element, be it cold or oxygen, is taken to its extreme, non-spacial condition. In this case the law of anti-conservation of energy applies, i.e. power is virtually unlimited as it is obtained from higher realms.

Egoism and altruism are also dialectic opposites, thesis and antithesis. On examination of the above table, however, the antitheses of Quantity and Quality are probably the most important in their ramifications because, through our contemporary development, through our logical, ideological, philosophical development, we have today come to attach a great deal of importance to quantity at the expense of quality, of greed at the cost of generosity, even to the extent of proffering the philosophy of greed as something totally acceptable morally and ethically.

However, it is always the qualities which are the defining factors. In itself quantity is relatively unimportant. In its simplest form it is unformed, amorphous mass − just weight. This quantitative drive has led us into a mass-production mentality. It has also taken us into the mode of reducing diversity and increasing uniformity principally for economic and control purposes. And herein lies a very great danger, for as Montesquieu stated in the 18th century, *"The inner corruption of liberty shows itself first in uniformity"*.

We therefore need urgently to develop a system where the emphasis is far more on the qualitative side, for quality is the differentiator and animator of life.

Another pair of antitheses, not considered by science, are Gravitation and **Levitation**. Levitation is not taken into account at all, consideration being given only to gravitation, although a levitational force is basic to Nature. Viktor Schauberger once commented wryly that instead of asking himself what caused the apple to fall to the ground, Sir Isaac Newton should have asked how it got up there in the first place! What else if not levitation enables a tree to grow upwards against the action of gravity? Were there no levity, the tree would just spread out horizontally over the ground in a green amorphous mass. It does thrust skywards, however, and does so in response to another force operating in the opposite direction.

This is life-force, the quickening and uplifting energy; the force responsible for uprightness and right-side-upness of things. It is the rising power that imbues all healthy living things, particularly the more youthful, with a feeling of lightness, of relative weightlessness, removing all sensation of ponderousness of the limbs. With increasing age it gradually weakens, making the more elderly conscious of the weight of their bodies and the greater difficulty of movement. When this levitational force is extinguished, so too is the life-force of the body, which then dies.

When we consider these interdependencies and the illustrations of spiral forms in Nature (see figs. 2.10–2.12, chapter 2), we can see that the dynamics of the universe are therefore caused by an inherent imbalance, since movement is always occurring somewhere between one extreme and the other. There can be no state of stable equilibrium, which would signify immobility, uniformity and stasis. Were such the case neither development, nor evolution would be possible and the whole condition of the Universe would be unchanging and unproductive, which is manifestly not the case.

4.4 *Phi or the 'Golden Section'*

The eminent biologist Ilya Prigogine once stated that all natural movement arises out of a state of imbalance, of non-equilibrium. Non-equilibrium is a pre-requisite for movement and evolution in all its forms, and a state of equilibrium is therefore impossible in Nature. Yet we find that certain symmetries do occur, nevertheless. The pine cone shown in fig. 4.7 represents a condition of 'balanced imbalance'. The apparent symmetry of the pine cone at the same time embodies a dissymmetry in that from the left-hand side to

the right, its form encompasses five spirals descending and eight spirals ascending.

In terms of integers or whole numbers themselves, uneven numbers are generally considered male and even numbers female, since even numbers are divisible by two (mother + offspring). In the pine cone this gender aspect or duality on the one hand is represented by the five descending spirals of male energies or higher rotational velocities, since within the overall length, or cycloid-spiral-wavelength as it were, of the pine cone, they achieve more rotations. The eight ascending spirals of female energies, on the other hand, gradually being aroused by the male forces, are slower moving, making only one full rotation over their common wavelength. Between them a state of harmony, or resonance, comes into being in relation to their respective energies. Where the two systems of spirals cross; where they combine or negate each other, the seed of future pine trees, the new life, is formed.

The actual proportion of five male spirals to eight female spirals or 5:8 forms part of the

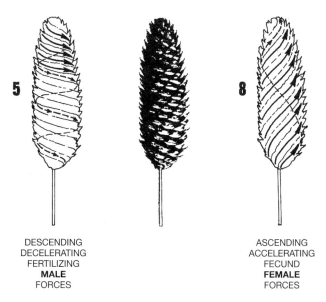

5	**8**

DESCENDING   ASCENDING
DECELERATING   ACCELERATING
FERTILIZING   FECUND
MALE   **FEMALE**
FORCES   FORCES

Fig. 4.7   **The Pine Cone:**
The symmetry of the pine cone demonstrates the condition of "Balanced Imbalance" which arises out of the harmonic interaction of two antithetical, complementary, but oppositely charged forces. The **5** positive male spirals of energy descend towards the **8** rising negative female spirals of energy. Where these cross each other a union of both forces occurs and there the seed of the new life is to be found. The **male forces decelerate** and the **female forces accelerate** to arrive at a mutual state of resonance.

so-called Fibonacci series, which progressively and with increasing accuracy, mathematically defines the proportion of the 'Golden Section', also known as *Phi*, or φ, which becomes almost constant in the ratio of 1:1.618033988. Together with *Pi* (π), the 'transcendental number' describing the circumference of the circle, this is one of the so-called 'Perfect' or 'Divine Proportions'.

Pi has been given the term 'transcendental', because no end to the sequence of numbers after the decimal point has yet been found, even though computers have been working on it for years. It is assumed to be of infinite length and therefore in this sense is a magnitude beyond time and space. Phi on the other hand, is more down to earth and is also found in the linear proportions of the pentagon (fig. 4.8). *Phi* is frequently expressed in many of Nature's creations, and by varying the angle between the adjacent radii (their relative lengths conforming to the *Phi* proportion), a number of natural spirals (fig. 4.9) and leaf-shapes (fig. 4.10) can be created.

Phi is also manifested in the structure of the human body. If the length of the hand has the value of 1, for instance, then the combined length of hand + forearm has the approximate value of 1.618033988. Similarly the proportion of upper arm to hand + forearm is in the same ratio of 1:1.618033988, or 1:φ. In my studies of *Phi* from an energetic point of view, it seems always to be associated with the transmutation of energy into form, since this proportion is reflected in so many of Nature's creations. In recognition of this peculiarity, I have come to call it the **'Transmutation Number'**.

From another angle, the two spiral systems in fig. 4.11 have a common wavelength, dynamically viewed as cycloid-spiral-space-curves, since they curve out from their common axis and eventually return to it over the full length of the pine cone, the eight female spirals having a slower rotational period than the five male spirals. Within this wavelength, there are points where they interconnect creatively. Such a point I call the zero-point, since it is the point where both male and female energetic attributes die or are temporarily suspended in order that new life can be created.

The zero point is where all motion ceases and where all motion begins. It is a point of extremely high potential in the same way that the string of a musical instrument is still in a state of tension, of sound-creating potential, even though it is not vibrating.

Here, therefore, we have two systems of opposing, but complementary energy which create a symmetry, although this is created out of unequal forces. Referring to the function of the dialectic magnitudes set out in fig. 4.6 (p. 63), generally speaking those in the right hand column should prevail over those on the left for evolution to proceed productively. That is to say, the effect and function of the right hand aspects of each dialectic unity should predominate. Viktor estimated the correct proportion between them to be ⅓rd to ⅔rds respectively. The ancient Chinese also considered an unequal relation to be the one most propitious for the harmonious unfoldment of life, their ratio being ⅖ths Yin to ⅗ths Yang. However in view of the manifestation of *Phi* in so many of Nature's creations, the proportion of 1:φ is probably the more correct, since as a proportion of slightly more than 1:1⁶⁄₁₀ it lies between the two other ratios of ⅖:⅗ (= 1:1½) and ⅓:⅔ (= 1:2). In fig. 4.12 the relative magnitudes of these forces are represented by Weight B = 1kg (left hand column aspect) and Weight A = 1.618033988kg (right hand column aspect). Weight A is at a distance of 1/φm or 0.618033988cm from the pivot and weight B is 1m away. Weight B exerts a moment about the pivot calculated as 1kg x 1m = 1kg/m. Weight A exerts the same moment, however, since 1.618033988kg x 0.618033988m also equals 1kg/m. The seesaw of life, as it were, is thus in a state of balance even though the absolute force of one magnitude is greater than the other. The resultant downward force is the sum of these two weights and equals 2.618033988kg, which equals (1.618033988)² or *Phi*².

Through the interaction of these two proportions the unstable dynamic balance in Nature and her energetic processes is achieved. Were it not for this tentative balance no forward progress would be possible, much in the same way that tightrope walkers cannot actually put one foot in front of the

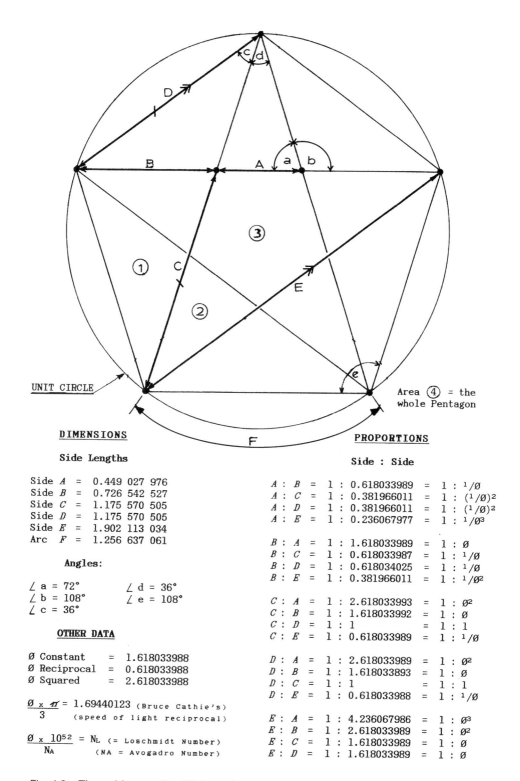

UNIT CIRCLE

Area ④ = the whole Pentagon

DIMENSIONS

Side Lengths

Side A = 0.449 027 976
Side B = 0.726 542 527
Side C = 1.175 570 505
Side D = 1.175 570 505
Side E = 1.902 113 034
Arc F = 1.256 637 061

Angles:

∠ a = 72°   ∠ d = 36°
∠ b = 108°   ∠ e = 108°
∠ c = 36°

OTHER DATA

Ø Constant   = 1.618033988
Ø Reciprocal = 0.618033988
Ø Squared   = 2.618033988

$\dfrac{Ø \times \pi}{3}$ = 1.69440123 (Bruce Cathie's)
(speed of light reciprocal)

$\dfrac{Ø \times 10^{52}}{N_A}$ = N_L (= Loschmidt Number)
(NA = Avogadro Number)

PROPORTIONS

Side : Side

A : B = 1 : 0.618033989 = 1 : $^1/Ø$
A : C = 1 : 0.381966011 = 1 : $(^1/Ø)^2$
A : D = 1 : 0.381966011 = 1 : $(^1/Ø)^2$
A : E = 1 : 0.236067977 = 1 : $^1/Ø^3$

B : A = 1 : 1.618033989 = 1 : Ø
B : C = 1 : 0.618033987 = 1 : $^1/Ø$
B : D = 1 : 0.618034025 = 1 : $^1/Ø$
B : E = 1 : 0.381966011 = 1 : $^1/Ø^2$

C : A = 1 : 2.618033993 = 1 : $Ø^2$
C : B = 1 : 1.618033992 = 1 : Ø
C : D = 1 : 1 = 1 : 1
C : E = 1 : 0.618033989 = 1 : $^1/Ø$

D : A = 1 : 2.618033989 = 1 : $Ø^2$
D : B = 1 : 1.618033893 = 1 : Ø
D : C = 1 : 1 = 1 : 1
D : E = 1 : 0.618033988 = 1 : $^1/Ø$

E : A = 1 : 4.236067986 = 1 : $Ø^3$
E : B = 1 : 2.618033989 = 1 : $Ø^2$
E : C = 1 : 1.618033989 = 1 : Ø
E : D = 1 : 1.618033989 = 1 : Ø

Fig. 4.8   **The golden section (Ø) from the pentagon in the proportion of 1:1.618033988**

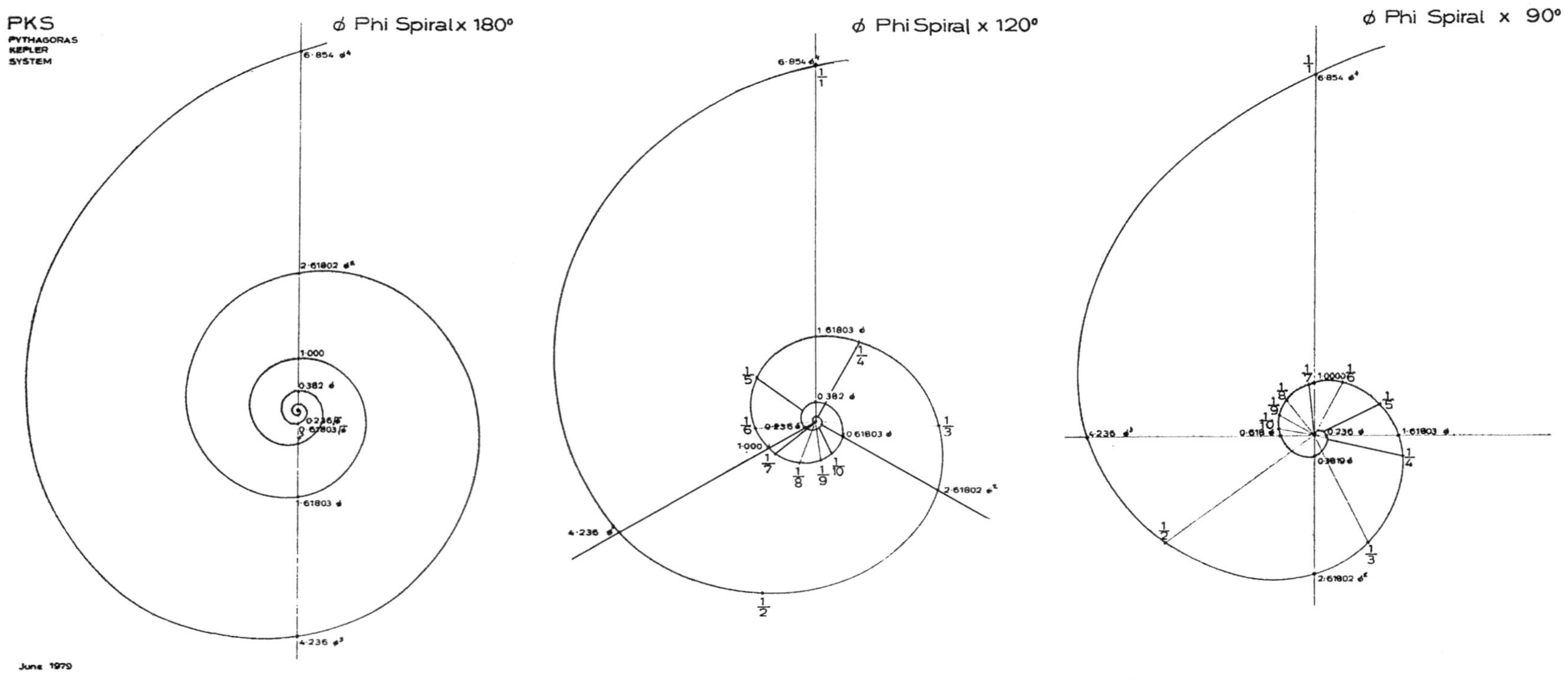

Fig. 4.9 Phi spirals on three different angular axes

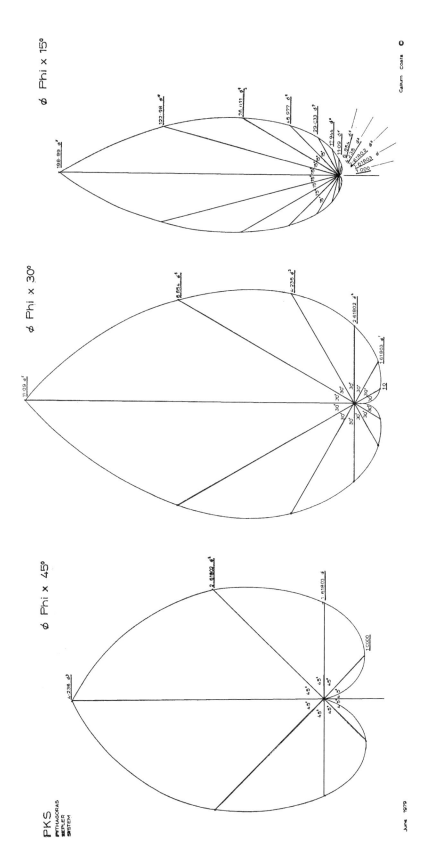

Fig. 4.10 *Phi* leaf patterns on different angular axes

other unless they are in a state of balance. At a more sublime level this also represents what the Buddhists call the 'Golden Middle Way', the path of tranquillity, compassion and contemplation unassailed by the vissitudes and extremes of life.

Viktor Schauberger attached a great deal of importance to this relation, stating that the extreme egg-form suited to his apparatuses was to be found within the pentagon, which is the *Phi* polygon. Viktor never actually stated how he obtained this egg-shape. Fig. 4.13 shows how it may be drawn using six pins and a loop of string, although any variety of egg-shape can be precisely determined using Walter Schauberger's hyperbolic mathematics.

4.5 *Magnetism and Electricism*

Electricism and magnetism are two other complementary, but antithetical forces, the latter being the one that circulates through and around the Earth on the polar axis

(fig. 4.14).[5] In Viktor's view, however, no true magnetism as conceived today existed in the physical world. What did exist was 'bio-magnetism'. Viktor saw magnetism and its higher aspect as the uplifting, upbuilding, creative and levitative form of energy. Therefore, wherever magnetism is mentioned later, the properties of bio-magnetism are also inferred. However, in the physical world neither magnetism nor bio-magnetism are permitted to reach their extreme values because, at the same time the destructive, dismantling, disintegrative, debilitating energy of electricity (similar to electrolysis) applies the necessary brake. Viktor termed this form of energy 'electricism', its higher aspect being 'bio-electricism'.

Overall, however, bio-magnetic energy or bio-magnetism must be slightly in excess of the electrical energy, or electricism, in order that evolution can proceed. Were it otherwise, there would always be less and less creative energy. Viewed in this light, the so-called Van Allen radiation belts girdling

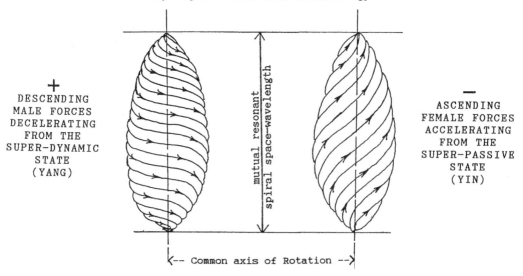

Super-dynamic state "cool" kinetic energy

+
DESCENDING
MALE FORCES
DECELERATING
FROM THE
SUPER-DYNAMIC
STATE
(YANG)

mutual resonant
spiral space-wavelength

–
ASCENDING
FEMALE FORCES
ACCELERATING
FROM THE
SUPER-PASSIVE
STATE
(YIN)

<-- Common axis of Rotation -->

Super-passive state "cool" potential energy

At all points where male and female spirals cross and where radius and angular velocity are equal or in a harmonic relationship, both charges (positive-male and negative-female) cancel each other out, or fuse together to create new life, to bring forth seed, which is the encapsulation of the DNA/RNA gene programme for the structuring of the new manifestation. Such a point is the "ZERO-POINT", the eternal place where all motion ceases and from which all life springs forth.

Fig. 4.11

the Earth therefore represent the electrical component of this symbiotic interaction between bio-magnetism and bio-electricism, which together produce the necessary pulsation, the hallmark of life and living things. Although in this diagram their respective magnitudes are shown to be constant, neither achieves its maximum value at the same time as the other. When the electrical energies expand to their maximum, relative to the system as a whole, the bio-magnetic energies are reduced to their minimum. They can therefore be seen to be reciprocal and their mutual interaction can thus be interpreted by the equation

$$\frac{1}{n} \times n = 1$$

where $1/n$ = electricism or bio-electricism, and n = magnetism or bio-magnetism. According to Viktor Schauberger this oscillation between magnitudes is of such high frequency that it appears as a state of rest.

Referring to fig. 3.1 in chapter 3, "New Dimensions Of Energy", concerning the ur-original source of energy, electricism and bio-magnetism and their respective allied forces of gravitation and levitation, also have their counterparts in the field of human experience

and the slow development of higher consciousness. Analogous to the full dynamic cycle of the tornado described earlier, a young, evolving soul's initial evolution lies in the progressive spiralling descent from its spiritually highest self down through the mental and emotional planes, finally entering the physical body.

Here in its primitive, undeveloped physical state, the ego becomes involved in self-aspected activities, in self-awareness, in self-ishness, wherein it succumbs to the ego-centric drive for the acquisition or 'encirclement' of material attributes. Possession and physical sensation become the all-important purpose of life, to the extent that some earlier societies 'encircled' their opponents, as it were, by eating them, in the belief that the consumer would thereby acquire the additional attributes of its victim. Although unconsciously connected to its spiritual origins, but having meanwhile become oblivious of them, the ego's immaterial energy and driving force (mind), still sourced from its higher self, is devoted towards greedily accumulating material illusions of well-being, drawing them all into its tight personal orbit. Now in intimate contact with and closely surrounded by the objects it has a-mass-ed, a feeling of dissatisfaction, of something miss-

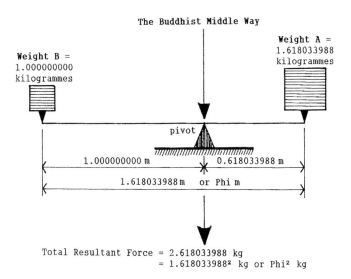

Fig. 4.12 **The dynamic balance of PHI**

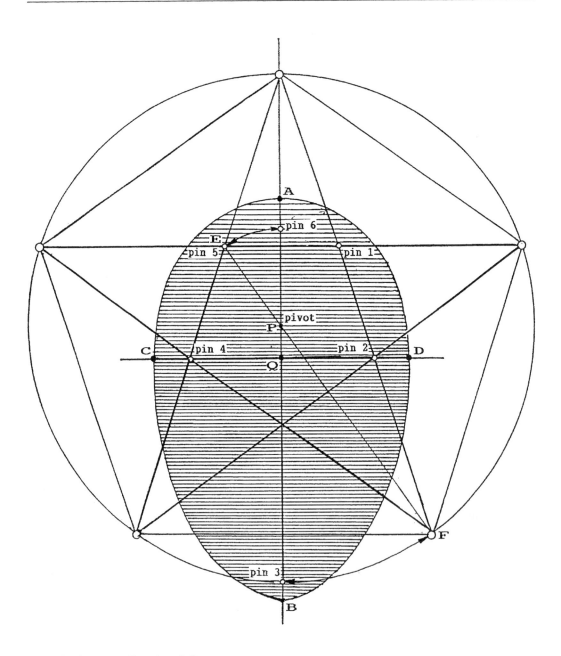

Ratio AQ : QB = 1 : 1.5

Ratio CD : AB = 1 : 1.5277778

Ratio CQ : QB = 1 : 1.8333333

Callum Coats, August 1992

Fig. 4.13   **The cosmic egg in the pentagon of Viktor Schauberger**

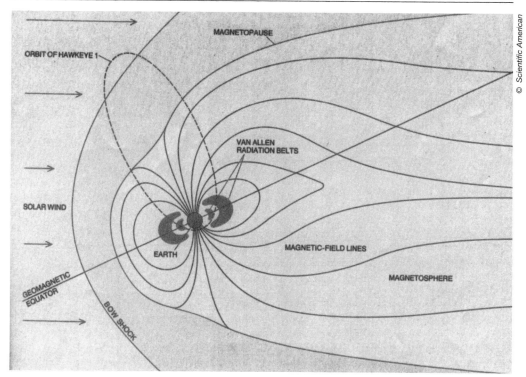

Fig. 4.14 **The Earth's magnetic field**

ing, gradually surfaces from the unconscious and the soul eventually discovers them to be hollow and devoid of actual tangible substance, as is the centre of the tornado. All at once the former static security of physical matter vanishes and the realisation slowly dawns that true reality, security and peace lie in the dynamics of the higher immaterial realms.

In the soul's descent into matter, the bio-magnetic forces, while acting to maintain stability and life, were not uppermost and contributed only to the tightening of the circle around the Self. Once the boundary condition of materiality is reached; once the acquisitive, gravitational impulse is exhausted, the soul begins to resonate more and more with its higher aspects as the ever-present bio-magnetism finally and inevitably must gain the upper hand. In the same way that it creates the updraught in the centre of the tornado, these bio-magnetic forces begin to draw the soul upward. As its power increases, bio-magnetism accelerates this

uplifting process and levitates the soul to the source from whence it came. As it rises up through the various planes of higher energy and spirituality, the soul's vibrational rate or frequency progressively increases and its motion reverses direction. It now changes from axial, self-centred rotation to radial expansion and in the process enters into an increasingly harmonic relationship with the rest of the Universe.

Finally reaching the level of infinitely high vibration, which is synonymous with a state of infinite harmony, it becomes one with everything; it loses its individuality as it once again unites with its originating source. Having now completed its long, arduous and often painful journey into matter; having become aware of the vacuity of physical substance, it has become filled with the selfless love arising from total non-attachment and adds its small contribution to the eternal radiation of unconditional love throughout the manifested and unmanifested universe.

4.6 *Other Dimensions of Energy*

Amongst the antitheses listed on the table on p. 63, Viktor viewed certain pairs such as heat and cold, pressure and suction, expansion and impansion, electricism and magnetism, centrifugence and centripetence, gravitation and levitation, as being similar provenances of energy, but separated by octaves. Therefore cold, suction, impansion, centrifugence, magnetism (actually bio-magnetism) and levitation are all related magnitudes. Endowed with specific vibrational energies and powers, these antitheses are the agencies or self-organising, intermediate, vibratory matrices of immaterial energies by which the gap between Will-to-create and creation, spirit and matter, and idea and manifestation is bridged. In *The Secret Doctrine* these forces are comprised in the concept of 'Fohat'.

Fohat is the 'bridge' by which the 'Ideas' existing in the 'Divine Thought' are impressed on Cosmic substance as the 'laws of Nature'. Fohat is thus the dynamic energy of cosmic ideation; or regarded from the other side, it is the intelligent medium, the guiding power of all manifestation. Fohat is the mysterious link between mind and matter, the animating principle electrifying [or bio-magnetising – C.C.] *every atom into life.*[6]

In the attempt to describe these subtle energetic essences with terminology more familiar to readers than sanskrit, it became necessary to coin various new terms under the collective term of 'ethericities', the word 'ethericities' itself referring to those supra-normal, near non-dimensional, energetic, bio-electic, bio-magnetic, catalytic, high-frequency, vibratory, super-potent entities of quasi-material, quasi-etheric nature belonging to the 4th and 5th dimensions of being. These ethericities are further categorised as *'fructigens', 'qualigens', 'dynagens'*.

These respectively represent those subtle energies whose function is the enhancement of fructification (fructigens), the generation of quality (qualigens) and the amplification of immaterial energy (dynagens). According to their function or location these may be female

or male in nature. There are thus female fructigens and male dynagens, for example. The female attributes, however, are principally related to the magnitudes in the right hand column in fig. 4.6. In their aggregate these are the primary prime movers of creation and in the human mind enthusiastic or inspired thought gives rise to the formation of the immaterial dynagens that ceaselessly provide the motivating energy for external activity, thus totally confuting the Energy Conservation Law which requires that the amount of available energy be finite. To obtain some insight into what may be the relative magnitudes of the various levels of energy or vibratory energetic matrices here involved, it may be enlightening to refer to comments in *The Secret Doctrine*[7] concerning the 'Keely Motor', a free-energy device constructed by John Worrell Keely, which operated through the creation of a 'neutral centre', or in Viktor Schauberger's terms, a *'biological vacuum'*.

We are told that Mr.Keely defines electricity 'as a certain form of atomic vibration'. In this he is quite right, but this is electricity on the terrestrial plane, and through terrestrial correlations. He estimates:-

		per second
Molecular vibrations	*at*	*100,000,000*
Inter-molecular vibrations	*at*	*300,000,000*
Atomic vibrations	*at*	*900,000,000*
Inter-atomic vibrations	*at*	*2,700,000,000*
Aetheric vibrations	*at*	*8,100,000,000*
Inter-aetheric vibrations	*at*	*24,300,000,000*

The vibrational level of the so-called ethericities would probably lie somewhere between the inter-atomic and inter-aetheric in the above table. Moreover they may well function at frequencies that can be beneficially or detrimentally affected by human thought. It is a known fact, for instance, that the level of white blood corpuscle production can be significantly influenced by the positive or negative attitude towards life of the human host. The extent to which the collective human psyche may influence these ethericities and their proper function may well be far greater than we imagine.

Imprisoned – as we have been led to believe – within our physical reality by the speed of light (299,793,000 metres per second or *m/s*), and since we are also here concerned with certain dimensionalities, it might be more useful were we to attempt to express what may be even vaster differences between the various planes of the higher realities by using squared, cubed, quadrupled, etc. multiples of the speed of light *c* expressed in metres per second. At the same time we might also begin to get some notion of the primary, creative and formative supremacy of such high, yet extraordinarily subtle energies, for the higher the frequency of a given vibration, the shorter its wavelength and the greater its intrinsic energy and power. In this regard I have deliberately avoided using scientific notation as many readers will find it confusing.

Recalling the brief discussion of the effect of sound in chapter 2, let us for the moment equate c^1 above with simple vibration as the agency of physical manifestation. Energy on the other hand, through which the physical manifestation is animated, is determined using c^2. In striving to obtain a more graphic concept of the possible structure of the various energetic and spiritual levels of reality, we could therefore say that: Vibration (= c^1) cannot take place without energy (= c^2), but energy cannot manifest itself without form (= c^3). Having certain 3-dimensional connotations, here c^3 brings to mind the morphogenetic fields of Rupert Sheldrake[8] which, as vibratory matrices possessed of certain properties and potential, are the immaterial energetic agencies that engender the emergence of a new species.

As the configuration of the formative patterning (the design) of a given progenerative matrix becomes 'hardened', as it were, or perfected through its frequent reiteration, each successive reproduction of the entity in question becomes increasingly easier, its character and appearance at the same time becoming more and more well-defined. Such a form, however, cannot be created without a design (= c^4) and the design cannot be conceived without the idea (= c^5). As Plutarch states:

An idea is a being incorporeal, which has no subsistence by itself, but gives figure and form unto shapeless matter, and becomes the cause of the manifestation. (De Placit. Philos).

The existence of the idea demands an intellect (= c^6) and intellect requires a higher consciousness (= c^7), all of which are enclosed one within the other like Russian dolls. c^7, the Eternally Creative Intelligence, must necessarily lie at the very centre, the hub, in order to regulate and be aware of all it surveys, always ready to develop new systems to fill new needs or to gain new experiences.

As an architect I have long been associated with processes of design, the end-product culminating from recurrent movements between the dialectic opposites of analysis and synthesis. A building does not just happen, but is the physical outcome of a great deal of mental activity in realms of unknown dimension. What eventually results is the synthesis of the interaction of various immaterial energies and imagery, themselves vibrations of a kind. For example, a kitchen is not merely an assembly of various elements, although viewed purely theoretically if all the elements of sink, stove, refrigerator, etc are placed in one space, then the material parameters of a kitchen are fulfilled. If by accident they were disposed in a certain configuration, then the space as a kitchen might actually work. However, to ensure as far as possible that this space is both aesthetically pleasing as well as functional, then it must be designed.

vibration c^1	= 299,793,000*m/s*
energy c^2	= 89,875,842,840,000,000*m/s*
form c^3	= 26,944,148,550,000,000,000,000,000*m/s*
design c^4	= 8,077,667,127,000,000,000,000,000,000,000,000*m/s*
idea c^5	= 2,421,628,061,000,000,000,000,000,000,000,000,000,000,000*m/s*
intellect c^6	= 725,987,141,300,000,000,000,000,000,000,000,000,000,000,000,000,000*m/s*
higher consciousness c^7	= 217,645,863,200,000,000,000,000,000,000,000,000,000,000,000,000,000,000,000,000*m/s*

Here we come up against the long-held materialistically founded conviction that every creature on this planet evolved solely through processes of natural selection: that whatever shape, colour or form it has, is merely the result of accidental interactions and the influences and demands of the environment in which it has to exist. Although natural selection may play a certain role in the physical evolvement of the genetic base, any intelligent direction or control of evolution and development is totally excluded. Some creatures, fish, birds and flowers for example, are particularly breathtaking in their beauty, in the various proportions of shape and colour they embody, and seem to refute this hypothesis entirely. Their physical appearance is very hard to explain in terms of purely mechanistic and environmental demands.

The intricate geometry and exquisite form of many flowers speak far more about intention than random happenstance. The sheer magnificence of the peacock, for example, defies all rational explanation from a natural selective point of view. Its colour could not have evolved for purposes of concealment and self-protection, because the gleaming turquoise iridescence of its breast-feathers loudly declares its presence to all predators. Its tail too, with several superimposed layers of variously patterned feathers, capped with single quills upon which the famous 'eyes' flutter and sway, is difficult to construe as having evolved merely for the purposes of courtship. As far as the peahen's attraction to the male is concerned, it seems unlikely that one or two fewer layers of tail feathers would make much difference. So why all the layers?

What, apart from increasing the diversity and majesty of life, is the purpose of a peacock, if not purely for the sake of introducing exquisite beauty into this world for the delight of those entities whose immaterial sensitivities can appreciate it in all its aesthetic splendour? How else would evolving human beings be able to develop any aesthetic sense or learn what beauty and proportion is unless some examples were provided for the purpose?

Today new species are continually being discovered whose form, behaviour and other characteristics are totally suited – and with such perfection – to the surroundings in which they live. Each has its ecological niche, as it were, and fulfils a function contributing to the enrichment of the whole panoply of life and yet all this apparently happened by accident of Nature, a Nature, however, to whom we have ascribed certain laws. What formulated these sublime and mathematically elegant laws, if not some form of intelligence far beyond our own? For laws cannot evolve by accident or by themselves. What entity other than such as the ECI could have a high enough overview of affairs in order to perceive yet another space, yet another possibility, into which it could infuse new experiential life in the form of an ideally suited creative design?

Let us try, therefore, to think at least one octave higher and instead of developing extremely complex theories based on the morbid logic of random interactions, let us entertain the notion that things are perhaps much simpler than we perceive, for as Albert Einstein is reputed to have stated, *"The simpler a theory is, the more it is to the point"*.

Notes

1. *The Secret Doctrine* by H.P. Blavatsky, Adyar Ed.1971, Vol.1, p.71.–1971), Theosophical Pub. Ho., Adyar, India;
2. *Ibid*, Vol.1, p.333.
3. From list of Viktor Schauberger quotations in the Schauberger archives.
4. *The Compact Edition of the Oxford English Dictionary*, Oxford Univ. Press 1971.
5. *Interplanetary Particles and Fields* (diagram by Dan Todd), by James A. van Allen, © 1975 by Scientific American, Inc.
6. *The Secret Doctrine* above, Vol. 1, p.81.
7. Ibid, Vol.2, p.286.
8. *The New Science of Life*, by Rupert Sheldrake: Blond & Briggs, London, 1981.

5
THE SUN

5.1 The Light and Temperature of the Sun

The source of energy that supports all life on this Earth, our Sun[1], needs to be examined. In a sense it is also the spiritual centre of our planetary system. Johannes Kepler, the great astronomer famous for his three laws of planetary motion, not only considered it to be a magnet (which has connotations with the attributes of centripetence, cold and levitation mentioned in the previous chapter), but also believed that as an immaterial body its energy, and by extension that of the whole planetary system, was derived from and governed by the realm of the spirit.

In theosophical teaching the Sun is the abode of the Logos, the spiritual entity that administers and orders the planetary system. Viktor Schauberger held similar views about it, but in its relationship to the Earth he also considered it to be the male fertilising impetus for life on this planet, as will be shown later. In addition he made assertions about the Sun, which are Copernican in their ramifications.

As part of the Pleiadean system our Sun, a fairly average star, revolves around Alcyone, taking about 180 million years to complete one orbit. Its speed in relation to the largely hydrogen-filled space through which it passes is around 48,280km/hr and it is presently moving in the direction of the Hercules system. It has a diameter of 1,392,530km, roughly 110 times greater than that of the Earth. Its magnetic poles also swap over every 11.2 years as part of the well-known magnetic sun-spot cycle and it pulsates, like something alive, expanding and contracting by about 3km every 160 minutes (see analogous description of a dipole in fig. 6.11, chapter 6). All this data, however, can be gleaned from various textbooks and therefore will not be elaborated further here.

One aspect concerning the Sun and our conception of it does need to be examined, namely the question of **temperature**. In our understanding of temperature, we generally consider it to be a measure of heat. For most of our customary purposes this is indeed the case. However, when speaking of the temperature of the Sun, for instance, which is supposed to be about 6,000°C at the surface and 20,000,000°C at the centre, we may no longer be concerned with thermal temperature, but rather with energetic activity, for according to Isaac Asimov:

Temperature here has to be distinguished from heat. The temperature is a measure of the kinetic energy of the atoms or particles in the gas, but since the particles are few, the actual heat content per unit of volume is low.[2]

In the light of previous discussions concerning the contrasting characteristics of axial-> radial (inside-outward) and radial->axial (outside-inward) motion, it is therefore not kinetic activity per se that generates heat, but it is the type of motion that produces either heat or cold. In the context of the Sun, therefore, temperature may be merely a measure of kinetic energy and may have little or no thermal content at all. Indeed viewed thermally, and since we cannot actually visit the Sun, the conditions applying to such activity may actually be icily cold. This proposal would represent a gigantic paradigm shift. It would be against all reason and apparent logic, just as was Copernicus' assertion in 1543 that the Earth actually orbited the Sun at a time when the opposite was held to be the case, although as early as the 3rd century BC, Aristarchos of Samos, a Greek astronomer, had already advanced the theory that the planetary system was heliocentric. Copernicus' daring declaration, however, proved to be true.

And this is perhaps the moment to drop Viktor Schauberger's bombshell! Viktor considered the Sun to be a cold, dark body, expressing this view in the introductory remarks to "Questions for Science" in his book *Our Senseless Toil* published in 1934, in which he states:

Since the very beginning of time the Sun has stood above everything, staring down in icy silence at the frenzied activities of humankind, who regard it as a fiery orb. How could it be otherwise, such is their direct mental approach towards life! The closer we approach this source of light and heat, the colder and darker its face will become. The nearer we are to it, the brighter the stars will be and as its light diminishes, heat, atmosphere, water and life will also disappear.[3]

Astonishing as this may be, let us not reject the proposal out of hand, for as was mentioned in chapter 1, Viktor made many of his discoveries by despatching his "free consciousness into those places the eyes cannot see". These assertions are not further elaborated in the documents in my possession, but in view of the number of other practicable discoveries he made in this way, they should not be merely discounted as foolish conjecture. We shall therefore examine the two claims of darkness and cold more closely. Let us begin with the aspect of darkness, for there is some evidence to support his view that, without any atmosphere, no stars would be visible.

In the last sentence of the above quotation there appears to be a slight conceptual inconsistency, because the Sun is also a star.

However, since we cannot know the exact sequence of Viktor's train of thought or imagery before he committed it to paper, in order to make sense of it in line with known facts it may be more appropriate to reverse the order of the last two sentences in the above quotation. Let us examine the last sentence first:

*The **nearer** we are to it, the brighter the stars will be and as its light diminishes, heat, atmosphere, water and life will also disappear.*

In this statement the keyword is 'nearer', which does not define how much nearer we have to be, whether half way towards the Sun or merely at very high altitudes above Earth's surface. According to available information, once free of the denser atmosphere and the lack of clarity caused by the presence of atmospheric dust, water-vapour, etc., the stars do increase in brightness and more of them are visible than from the surface of the Earth.

Indeed in the documentaries showing the various space-shuttle flights it is quite evident that there is a great deal of light at the altitude at which the shuttle orbits, i.e. about 800km or 500 miles. The visual clarity at orbital altitude is phenomenal, the intensity of light extreme; doubtless the Hubble space-telescope was sent into orbit to take advantage of this super-clarity. Instead of the normal graduations of shade that occur on Earth, however, in orbit the areas of light and shade are sharply defined with little graduation, being reduced to almost pure light and shadow. This is because the density of the particles of the surrounding gas is insufficient to cause any significant lateral diffraction or scatter, which would vary the direction in which the light is propagated, thereby lightly illuminating the areas in shade.

From this it would appear that it is upon the density of the gas particles in the space surrounding the Earth that deceleration, diffraction and scattering of radiation and the overall luminosity depend. Relative to space, the Earth's atmosphere is extremely dense and would most certainly have a braking effect, causing the very high frequency of the incoming radiation to be reduced to the frequency levels of visible light. The greater the density, the greater the scattering, which in its aggregate at lower levels of the atmosphere acts like a magnifying glass, producing an enlarged image, a phenomenon which explains why the Sun and the Moon appear larger when just above the horizon at dawn or dusk. In this sense therefore, the *"nearer we are to"* the Sun at a small scale, *"the brighter the stars will be"*.

At a larger scale, however, the picture may well change markedly, for as we proceed from the Earth's surface towards deep space, the particle density gradually decreases from about the Loschmidt constant[4] of 2.68719 x 10^{19} (or 26,871,900,000,000,000,000) particles per cubic centimetre at standard temperature and atmospheric pressure until it equals the density of the interstellar hydrogen gas, estimated at 1 gas atom per cm^3 which, relative to conditions on Earth, represents an extreme vacuum.

While high-frequency electromagnetic radiation can be made to manifest itself as visible light in a cathode ray tube under conditions of very low pressure or a moderate vacuum, if this is increased to an extreme vacuum, then the light disappears. As far as the generation of light is concerned, therefore, the decisive factor here would be the specific particle density required to produce it which, at a certain distance from the Earth may be too rarefied to do so. Assuming for the moment that there is such a boundary condition of density, the sky would then gradually darken as it is approached, in keeping with the assertion in the penultimate sentence in the above quotation, namely; *"The closer we approach this source of light and heat, the colder and darker its face will become,"* and in regions lying beyond it the sky would be totally black.

If this is actually the case, then whence did the light come that enabled the astronauts to be filmed during their visit to the Moon, which is supposed to have no atmosphere? In his book *The Awesome Life-Force*[5] Joseph H. Cater, a physicist and engineer who studied data from the American Apollo missions to the Moon very closely, discusses amongst other things the presence or otherwise of an atmosphere and strong gravitational field on the Moon. The scientifically proffered view of the absence of any significant lunar gravity he contests, stating that:

...A strong Moon gravity, of course, is not compatible with orthodox physics. Other powerful evidence of a dense Moon atmosphere came from statements made by astronauts during Apollo missions. The following case is a typical example. Prior to the publicized excursions to the Moon, early astronauts had stated that the stars were not visible above the atmosphere. This is to be expected. There is little or no diffusion of light in outer space and therefore the only stars that could be seen would be those whose discs could be resolved. This could only be done with powerful telescopes. An atmosphere functions in a manner analogous to a lens. The light from a distant star is diffused and spread out. Consequently, stars are visible because of a greatly enlarged and distorted image of the disc caused by the atmosphere.

On the Apollo 11 mission shortly before reaching the Moon, Armstrong stated that he could see the crater Tycho clearly and that he could see the sky all around the Moon, even on the rim of it where there is no earthshine or sunshine, Collins then stated, 'Now we're able to see stars again and recognise constellations for the first time on the trip....The sky's full of stars...it looks like its night side on Earth.' This means that after leaving the Earth the astronauts could not see any stars until they got close enough to the Moon to view them through the Moon's atmosphere!

If this transcript of the astronauts' commentary is authentic – and there is no reason to suppose that it is not – then light is a function of the atmosphere without which no stars can actually be seen. By extension, this invisibility could obviously also apply to the Sun, its actual degree of visibility as a much larger, far closer and more powerfully radiant object being dependent on the ultimate extent and attentuation of the Earth's atmosphere. In this sense, therefore, the face of the Sun could indeed be dark. All of this would appear to confirm Viktor's proposition.

Because no-one apparently has as yet been far enough away from this planet physically, i.e. far beyond the Moon, the extent to which the atmosphere and visible light actually reaches into space is not known. It could reasonably be assumed, however, that there is a very gradual attenuation of both until the atmosphere equals the degree of rarefaction of the hydrogen gas that fills interstellar and intergalactic space. Alarmingly, we might find, were we able to go far enough away, that upon looking back at our own planet we could not even see it! It would be black; it would be dark! We would find ourselves engulfed by a particularly Stygian blackness in which there was nothing to be seen at all. There would be no up, no down, no right, no left, no sideways, just total disorientation and isolation.

Let us turn now to the question of cold, for as we approach the Sun, as we climb higher, it certainly does get colder. In actual fact the temperature varies with height as can be seen in fig. 6.1 in chapter 6, although in connection with Isaac Asimov's definition of temperature above, it is a matter of conjecture whether the values indicated in the upper regions of the atmosphere in the above fig. are to be interpreted as thermal or kinetic.

If there is an outpouring of heat from the Sun as is presently believed, then why do these various regions of extreme cold exist within the atmospheric envelope? Perhaps they lie within the zones where the Earth's magnetic or bio-magnetic field lines are strongest (neutron concentration), the heat being generated in the Van Allen radiation belts (see fig. 4.14 – concentration of electrons and protons) or where the electrical component of the Earth's electromagnetic field predominates. Moreover, if interstellar space is a near absolute vacuum with a thermal temperature of $-273.15°C$ ($0°$ Kelvin), then how does the Sun's supposed heat ever reach us, since, being unable to pass through an extreme vacuum, a denser medium is therefore necessary for the propagation of heat-rays or infra-red rays?

Curiously enough, while the Sun's outer envelope rotates about its axis in 25 days at the Equator, towards the poles it rotates considerably more slowly, taking 34 days to complete one revolution. Recalling the earlier discussion of radial-axial motion – the movement from outside inwards – and the centripetal interrelationship between cold, suction and biomagnetism, this may perhaps be due to the concentrative effect of the greater density of the magnetic field lines entering the current (in time) north pole radially-axially, i.e. vortically, and leaving from the current south pole axially-radially. It could therefore be mooted that as the particles of the more rarefied equatorial gases draw nearer to the solar north pole, they would tend to become increasingly contracted and concentrated spacially owing to the cooling and densifying effect of radial->axial motion and its attendant biomagnetism. As a result of exposure to this extremely intense biomagnetic field the particles would *implode* isotropically[6]. This would effectively remove some of their outer (that is, detectable) translatory velocity, thus producing the apparent deceleration in lateral movement, a deceleration that could not happen if we were here concerned with heat, since heat causes expansion. With immense heat, therefore, expansion would be immense. At the solar south pole on the other hand the process would take place in reverse order; the supercooled, biomagnetic particle constriction gradually being released as the magnetic lines diverge and the field intensity decreases, thus permitting the particles to 'breathe' and expand, giving rise to the faster rotation observed about the equator.

Should this proposition concerning the deceleration of lateral motion towards the poles be correct, then a corollary would be that, thermally speaking, the Sun is at least a relatively cold body, despite a high kinetic temperature. In terms of its radiant qualities, it is known that the superconduction of electricity, that is, the resistanceless transport or propagation of energy, takes place at extremely low thermal temperatures. In view of the fact that the Sun has been radiating vast amounts of energy over billions of years, that it is able to do so may well be due to an effect similar to superconduction. By extension the energies given off by the Sun, which deluge the Earth with about 100,000 trillion watts of energy, would therefore be the result of cold fusion, representing the aggregate mass defect ensuing from the cold fusing of myriads of pairs of hydrogen atoms into helium atoms.

Should Viktor's hypothesis that the Sun is both dark and cold prove to be correct, it would without doubt have far-reaching implications for all human intellectual endeavour, science, religion, etc., and the resultant upheaval would be gargantuan in its ramifications. As in the earlier case of Copernicus, suddenly all accepted doctrine, all that had previously been held to be true, would be overturned. The whole system of education, textbooks and religious documents would have to be rewritten.

Two other sources known to me also allude to the limits of the Earth's and the Sun's light and heat. While not widely known, they are presented below because in Viktor's writings there is no specific explanatory detail of this remarkable reappraisal of reality. It would be a serious omission if these far-seeing perceptions of Victor's were left wholly unsupported by other available data and merely considered to be the delusions of a madman, which he most certainly was not.

The first quotation is from James Churchward's book *The Lost Continent of Mu*[7], which is a largely anthropological study examining the folklore, legends and myths of the peoples of the Pacific basin and the Indian subcontinent who survived the cataclysm of the subsidence of Mu, a land which according to his research occupied most of what is now the Pacific Ocean. In it there is a translation of the Naacal Tablets, reputed to have been written by the Holy Brothers, the Naacals, who had been sent from the motherland of Mu to teach in the colony of Burma. On these tablets are recorded the seven intellectual commands of the seven superlative intellects of the Seven-headed Serpent, together with nine explanatory diagrams describing the manner in which the Earth was formed. The story told therein is analogous to the seven days of creation recorded in Genesis. The third intellectual command states the following:

The third command was: 'Let the outside gases be separated and let them form the atmosphere and the waters.' And the gases were separated; one

part went to form the waters, and the waters settled upon the Earth and covered its face so that no land anywhere appeared. The gases that did not form the waters formed the atmosphere, and:

- *The light was contained in the atmosphere.*
- *And the shafts of the Sun met the shafts of the light in the atmosphere and gave birth to light. Then there was light upon the face of the Earth;*
- *The heat was also contained in the atmosphere.*
- *And the shafts of the Sun met the shafts of the heat in the atmosphere and gave it life. Then there was heat to warm the face of the Earth.*

The second quotation is taken from *The Life and Teaching of the Masters of the Far East* by Baird T. Spalding[8], written as a record of his three-year visit to Tibet in company with ten other Americans at the invitation of high lamas, and which began in 1885. Here it was explained to Spalding that:

If we take the science of things, we know there is a legend told here that all the heat and light and many other natural forces are contained right within the Earth itself. The Sun, of itself, has no heat or light. It has potentialities that draw the heat and light from the Earth. After the Sun has drawn the heat and light rays from the Earth, the heat rays are reflected back to the Earth by the atmosphere that floats in the ether. The light rays are drawn from the Earth in about the same manner and are reflected back to Earth by the ether.

As the air extends only a comparatively short distance, the effect of the heat rays varies as you leave the Earth's surface and ascend toward the outer limit of the atmosphere. As the air becomes less dense, there is less reflection; consequently as you ascend into the higher altitudes the heat becomes less and the cold increases. Every heat ray, as it is drawn out and reflected, drops back to the Earth, where it is regenerated. When you have reached the limit of air, you have reached the limit of heat.

It is the same with the light rays. They are drawn from the Earth and reflected back by the ether. As this ether extends much farther from the Earth than the air, the light rays extend much farther before they are all reflected. When you have reached the limit of ether, you have reached the limit of heat and light. When you have reached the limit of heat and light, you have reached the great cold. This cold is far more solid than steel, and it presses down upon the ether and the atmosphere with almost irresistible force and holds them together.

Now that we have disposed of the (them) above, let us take the other scientific legend and go below. According to this legend, the Earth a short distance from the surface is a molten mass. It is so hot that it melts any substance. This molten mass at the centre revolves more slowly than does the crust at the outer, and the belt where the two meet is the place where the natural forces are generated and there, again, the hand of God rules all.

If all these quotations represent the truth and should Viktor Schauberger be right, then it makes our Mother-Earth, this lonely capsule of light amidst the darkness, all the more precious to us. What we do to the atmosphere enveloping our planet and to the life-sustaining environment of water, trees and warmth within which we live and to which we owe our very existence, then becomes of crucial, vital importance. It is that special medium that gives us light and allows us to marvel at all the beauty that surrounds us and to experience what earthly life is. For this reason the worsening pollution of the skies becomes of even greater concern, not only for its more immediate thermal and climatic effects, but also for its overall luminosity. If we do nothing, if we do not act effectively and quickly, then perhaps the light on this planet will slowly and irrevocably go out and all life will be painfully extinguished.

5.2 *The Sun as a Fertilising Entity*

Viktor Schauberger considered the Sun to be the entity responsible for impregnating the Earth – Mother Earth – thereby creating the myriads of different life-forms that inhabit this planet. Its life-activating rays penetrate through the atmosphere and deep into the ground to awaken the sleeping, passive princess (the elements and substances of the Earth) and stimulate them into an evolutionary union. The dynamic motion of the Sun's radiant and fertilising energies, the bearers of in-*form*-ation and the stimulators of activity, must **decelerate** through external

or internal resistances in order to modify their rate of vibration and intensity to such a point that they harmonise with the rate of vibration of the now slowly, but increasingly **accelerated** and more stimulated, receptive and passive female forces. They must attain a mutual level of interaction, a state of reciprocity in order to be able to combine with one another, an example of which was shown in chapter 3, figs 3.7 and 3.12. Without this modification or change in the state of both forces, no growth or evolution can take place. When they are in a state of resonance, however, reproduction or regeneration occurs, the Earth-ovum is fertilised and the processes of incubation, birth and growth begin (in-*cube*-ation means to evolve in three dimensions).

All life can thus be seen to evolve through the interaction of male and female entities, energies and essences. Each has its own special direction or orientation of action and operates perpendicularly to the other. As energies of contrasting gender they are also imbued with opposite, but yet complementary, properties and potentialities, which function on diverse planes varying from the gross material to the ethereally subtle, as was explained in the previous chapter.

This is a pulsating process which varies according to the time of year and the elongation or reduction of the respective developmental paths of the upwardly-radiant earthly subtle energies and the downwardly-radiating solar ones as they alternate between the extreme and the mean, from differentiation to integration. In winter when there is the highest solar luminosity (greater percentage of blue and ultraviolet light) and the greatest passivity on the Earth, with low temperatures and the cold, bright, white, winter sunlight, the vegetation is dormant and much animal life hibernates. At this time reproduction, fertilisation and growth are reduced to a minimum.

But in spring and summer, when the angle of the Sun's rays increases, the thermal intensity of its radiation rises as the intrinsic power of the ultraviolet increases and the ultraviolet-infra-red balance shifts more towards the red end of the spectrum. This stimulates the passivity of the Earth and the high-frequency energy of the Sun is moderated through their mutual interaction. Acting along their mutually perpendicular paths, both come into a state of reciprocal resonance and an expulsion of the waste products of this energetic exchange occurs. This outfall is what Viktor Schauberger saw as the discharged precipitates of higher, bipolar subtle energies which result in what we commonly call 'growth'. A third entity is thus created, the offspring of the marriage between male and female potentialities.

With the exception of oxygen and hydrogen, Viktor grouped all the known elements and their compounds under the general classification of 'female', although some, such as silver, zinc and silicon, were endowed with paternally-oriented characteristics and powers, whereas gold, copper and limestone were more maternally oriented (these will be discussed in more detail in chapter 20). All these elements he called 'carbones' ('carbone' or 'carbones' is my English interpretation of the original German expression 'Kohlestoffe', normally spelt Kohlenstoffe, the additional 'e' in the English word redefining and enlarging the scope of the usual term 'carbon'), reflecting the predominance of carbon and carbonous matter in the formation of the physical structures of life, the various living bodies and organisms created in the womb of Mother-Earth. In terms of her procreative psyche Goethe called her the *'Eternally Female'* and the *'All-uplifting'*. To endow the Earth with this attribute, Goethe must have had some inkling of the forces of levitation.

Oxygen, on the other hand, Viktor deemed to be male and a lower form of solar energy, seeing both Sun and oxygen as the means by which these female, fecund, fructifiable potencies are fertilised, for without the Sun there would be no life at all, and without oxygen there would be no organic growth and development. Hydrogen, however, is in a category of its own, for Viktor viewed it as the carrier substance of both oxygen and carbone, often writing it down in the hieroglyphic form in fig. 5.1. If we look at the world from space this concept is quite factual, because we can see that our planet, composed as it is of carbones and fertilised by oxygen, is floating in the carrier ocean of the hydrogen gas filling all space.

Fig. 5.1

As mentioned above, each of these two potentialities of opposite gender has its own characteristic orientation or axis along which it moves in a particular direction. So the Sun's paternal energies are propagated vertically with respect to the Earth's surface, whereas the Earth's maternal energies are propagated horizontally. This 'horizontality', as it were, depends on the scale at which it is observed. At a small scale this lateral extension appears flat and planar whereas, viewed over the Earth as a whole, it is actually curvilinear and spherical, and is coupled with a certain expansive movement. The Earth-ovum is therefore fertilised through the Sun's seasonally pulsating, male impulses from a direction perpendicular to the Earth's surface and embodies the most ethereal and sacred act of coition (fig. 5.2b). In its *modus operandi* it is comparable to the fertilisation of the female ovum by the male sperm (fig. 5.2a) and, without in any way wishing to offend, the human sexual act is perhaps the best way to explain it.

Analogous to the penile penetration of the female (Earth) by the male (Sun), this pulsating movement along its characteristic, straight (vertical) axis subsequently metamorphoses into a movement perpendicular to it; into a spherical expansion of the Earth's matter-energy field, like the rotund expansion of the womb. In human beings (and many animals) the growth of the foetus produces a lateral stretch-expansion of the outer tissues, namely a horizontal movement that occurs when the outwardly-radiating, formative energies reach the physical limits of their radial extension. They are then propagated parallel to the outer surface. Equally applicable to the Earth, both movements of energy are caused by the expansion of the internal pressures resulting from the conversion of the combined energies of the two genders into physical mass (the baby).

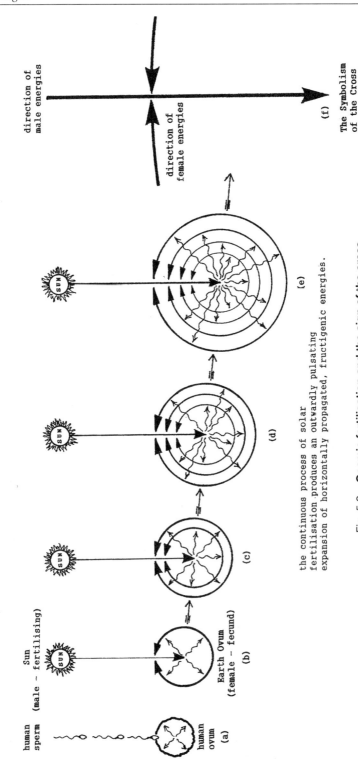

Fig. 5.2 **Cosmic fertilisation and the sign of the cross**

The same applies to solar fertilisation. During the winter months, those fertilising solar ethericities, which have not been metamorphosed into physical growth by fusing with their female counterparts present in the higher strata of the Earth, continue their inward penetration and encounter the embryonic female energies lying deep below the surface. Here their union gives rise to the procreative energies that produce the burgeoning blossoms of springtime. Since this process of impregnation is repeated continually, there is an almost continuous outward- and upward-moving, pulsating flux of maternal fructigenic and qualigenic matter radiating from the centre, which forms and concentrates at the ground surface (figs. 5.2b, c, d & e) providing the creative impulse for renewed growth.

Reduced to their simplest form, the paths these two ethereal energies follow could be represented by the Cross (fig. 5.2f), symbolising the ennobling creative power of the ECI in both material and immaterial dimensions. When the sign of the cross is made by a priest during Mass, for instance, the first gesture is a strong, blade-like downward movement of the hand reflecting the Sun's primary downward fertilising impulse. This is then followed by the softer, flatter sideways movement of the palm, which alludes to the horizontal motion of female, fructigenic energies.

At a physical level, loving coition between man and woman should be a very sacred act, never to be debased, for as entities with opposite charge and potential, in their true, exalted union of mind, body and soul, man and woman fulfil the function ordained by the ECI for the furtherance of material life and higher spiritual evolution on this planet. In its highest sense and performance this union is the closest that two human beings can approach the essential nature of the selfless outpouring of the Divine on the physical plane of existence, for it is through the intermingling of their characteristic energetic essences that the eternal ur-procreative spark of new life is thrust forward into the future. The symbol of the cross predates Christianity. That earlier peoples understood the deeper occult significance of these two axially different movements may well be the reason why the Cross has long been held not only to be a symbol of spiritual perfection, but also of the sublime marriage between spirit (the father) and matter (the mother).

The feminine nature of physical substance is further affirmed by the fact that the two words *matter* and *material*, both have their root in the Latin word *mater*, meaning *mother*. Thus all physical elements of whatever kind (with the exception of oxygen and hydrogen) can be viewed as the progenitive essences of 'Mother-Earth' and therefore innately maternally-oriented. This explains more completely Viktor Schauberger's concept of the 'Mother-Substances' from which all physical structures, all new living entities, come into being through the marriage between these elementary substances and the inseminating spirit, predominantly oxygen.

This affords us an insight into what fire may actually be. Also associated with spirit, it is one of the four arcane, alchemical elements of *earth, air, fire* and *water*, and over the ages the quintessential nature of flame has long been the subject of much study and speculation by both chemist and alchemist alike. Frequently ascribed a purifying function, the physical effect of fire is to reduce a given substance to its elementary constituents; to its maternal potentialities, in a process which, from this point of view, could be described as 'de-insemination', namely the withdrawal of paternal potencies. This could also be interpreted as the retraction or release of spirit from matter, wherein light is again manifested in the form of flame as the departing spiritualising essences are freed from material confinement and rise once more to reunite with their spiritual origins – the Sun.

To return to the theme, however, it is these female fructigenic ethericities (subtle energies) in their outward spiralling desire for fertilisation that give rise to the generation of levitational energies. On their vortical ascent these forces draw up matter in their wake. In this way they are responsible for the expansion of the Earth-ovum, whose further outward movement is restrained by the opposing forces of the Sun as sunlight and the atmosphere. The former exerts a mild pressure of about $4kg/km^2$ and the latter of about 10.683 tonnes/m² or 14.72lbs/in², a large component of which is the weight of water vapour. The extent of the Earth's present diameter or girth is therefore the result of the attainment of an unstable state of equilibrium between these counter-directional forces. This echoes the assertion from the second quotation above, in which the great cold of space was described:

This cold is far more solid than steel, and it presses down upon the ether and the atmosphere with almost irresistible force and holds them together.

If, indeed, the above immense pressure is actually resisted by a levitational counterforce as Viktor Schauberger maintains, that it can expand at all suggests that, in keeping with all other globular cell-structures, the Earth is hollower than we presently think, which may be the reason why it resonates like a bell when seismic charges are set off. Solid bodies do not resonate so readily. A similar, apparently unaccountable resonance was also detected on the Moon at the time of the lunar landings.

In his writings Viktor also refers to the Rig-Veda, the most ancient and most important of the four Vedas comprising the sacred Hindu scriptures, in which air battles are described that were fought from flying machines referred to as 'vimanas'. He suggests that not only were these machines powered with levitational energy, but that the forces of implosion and levitation were also known to the high priests of Atlantis. Moreover it was through their overstimulation by the priesthood that Atlantis was first torn upwards from the Earth, before being flung back, its levitational forces disintegrated, to create the basin that is now the Atlantic ocean, giving rise to the Great Flood recorded in the Old Testament and the myths of other peoples.

Notes

1. I have given the Sun, the Earth and the Moon capital letters, for as living, spiritual entities, in my view they are as equally deserving of capitals as the rest of the planets, which are named after gods.
2. *Guide to Science: 1 The Physical Sciences* by Isaac Asimov, Chap.2, p.88, Penguin Books, Harmondsworth, England.
3. Published by Krystall Verlag, Vienna, 1934 – defunct in 1938.
4. The Loschmidt Constant or Loschmidt Number (N_L) determines the number of particles per unit volume of an ideal gas at standard temperature and pressure and has a value of 2.68719×10^{25} particles per cubic metre. First calculated by Joseph Loschmidt (1821–1895).
5. *The Awesome Life-Force* by Joseph H.Cater: Cadake Industries, P.O.Box 9478, Winter Haven, FL, USA, 1984, ISBN 0-86540-274-0.
6. ISOTROPIC = Exhibiting equal physical properties or actions (e.g. refraction of light, elasticity, conduction of heat or electricity) in all. (Compact Edn.Oxford English Dict.)
7. *The Lost Continent of Mu* by James Churchward: Neville Spearman, London, 1959.
8. Volume 2, p.50: De Vorss, Marina Del Rey, CA, U.S.A. ISBN 0-875516-085-9.

6

The Earth's Atmospheric Envelope

6.1 *The Atmosphere*

Let us now come down to Earth as it were, and examine the planet on which we live. We have seen how life, movement and energy are synonymous; therefore for life to exist on our planet, as anywhere else for that matter, there must be a number of natural processes and functions which promote the concentration of the energetic matrix within which physical life can evolve. According to Viktor Schauberger these are created by the 'original' motion of the Earth as it rotates about its own axis and circulates its bio-magnetic and bio-electrical energies through itself during its 365.26-day, orbital waltz around the Sun.

Contrary to common belief the Earth is not actually a true sphere, but is slightly oblate. That is to say, there is a slight flattening at the poles. According to best measurements the polar diameter is 12,639.648km and the equatorial diameter, 12,682.176km, the latter being 42.688km greater. Due to the effect of centrifugal forces acting on the greater landmasses of the northern hemisphere, it bulges slightly more above the Equator, making the world pear-shaped, the southern hemisphere being the more 'pointed' end.

This has the effect of displacing the Earth's centre of gravity marginally north of true centre, producing the so-called 'Chandler Wobble', which is akin to the wobble of a spinning top. One revolution of this wobble takes 26,000 years to complete and in the process causes a variation in the inclination of the Earth's axis to the ecliptic, the plane in which all the planets orbiting the Sun lie, with the exception of Pluto.

Viktor viewed the Earth as a living organism, a being possessed of intelligence. The word 'organism' actually originates from Aristotle's concept of 'Organon', meaning an 'instrument of reason'. This throws a whole new light on everything we consider organic, in that all physical forms are seen to be the creation of mind or an ordering principle. As an animate being, the Earth also breathes, pulsating its fundamentally female energies outward in tune with its gyration and in response to the energy received from the Sun.

This concept of a *breathing* planet is not new. The word **'atmosphere'** and its associated concepts are interesting and originate *inter alia* from the Ancient Greek and Sanskrit. From the *Oxford English Dictionary*[1] we discover the following meanings, opinions and data, which are relevant to the discussion that follows. Words in bold type are to draw the reader's attention to their further significance.

Atmosphere

GREEK:	ATMOS = Vapour
	SPHERE = Ball.
SANSKRIT:	ATMAN = Breath
OLD HIGH GERMAN:	ATUM = Breath

1) The spheroidal gaseous envelope surrounding any of the heavenly bodies. The name was invented for the ring or orb of vapour or **'vaporous air'** *supposed to be* **exhaled** *from the body of a planet, and so to be part of it, which the air itself was not considered to be. It was extended* *to the portion of surrounding air occupied by this, or supposed to be in any way 'within the sphere of activity' of the planet (Phillips 1696) and finally, with the progress of science, to the supposed limited aeriform environment of the Earth, or other planetary or stellar body. (It is curious that the first mention of an atmosphere is in connection with the Moon, now believed to have none.)*

2) 1677 PLOT: That subtile Body that immediately incompasses the Earth and is filled with all manner of **exhalations**, *and from thence commonly known by the name of the atmosphere.*

3) 1751 CHAMBERS: Among some of the more accurate writers, the atmosphere is restrained to that part of the air next the Earth, which receives **vapors** *and* **exhalations** *and is terminated by the refraction of the Sun's light.*

4) 1867 E.DENISON ("Astronomy without Mathematics"): *The Earth's atmosphere decreases so rapidly in density, that half its mass is within 3.5 miles above the sea; and at 80 miles there can be practically no atmosphere.*

5) 1881 STOKES: In the solar atmosphere there is a cooling from above.

6) 1727–51 CHAMBERS: Atmosphere of Solid or Consistent Bodies, is a kind of sphere formed by the **effluvia**, *or* **minute corpuscles** *emitted from them.*

7) 1871 EMERSON: A man should not go where he cannot carry his **whole sphere** *or circle with him, not bodily, but atmospherically.*

While several of these quotations underscore some of the comments made in the previous chapter about the Sun, in the main they affirm an apparently earlier held view that the Earth is a living organism, namely an entity that breathes. Viewed from outer space, the atmosphere itself could also be construed as the vital amniotic fluid that surrounds an Earth pregnant with life, in which it floats and which shields it from the potentially destructive forces of the Sun and Cosmos.

When the Earth was first formed, supposedly from a molten mass of condensing gases, it is believed to have been totally covered by water before the dry land eventually came into being. Apart from volcanic emissions, in the main these 'vaporous

exhalations' are the water vapour present in the atmosphere. Due to the heating effect of the interaction between solar radiation and atmosphere, the water covering the Earth's surface gradually evaporated and became dispersed through the atmosphere, ultimately charging the atmospheric envelope with water vapour, though mainly in the troposphere which extends to an altitude of about 6km at the poles and 18km at the equator. According to H.L. Penman's paper, "The Water Cycle"[2], water has the greatest specific heat known among liquids (=1) and also has the greatest thermal conductivity of all liquids, whereas iron, which heats and cools more rapidly, has a far lower specific heat of 0.107.

Its great specific heat means that, for a given rate of energy input, the temperature of a given mass of water will rise more slowly than the temperature of any other material. Conversely, as energy is released its temperature will drop more slowly.

Owing to its high specific heat and its capacity to retain heat, the water vapour gradually absorbed the heat of the Sun, and in doing so raised the general level of temperature. Because it absorbs heat strongly in the infrared portion of the spectrum and is transparent to (i.e.unaffected by) ultraviolet light, during the night when there is no heat input, heat losses are kept to a minimum. Had water not this capacity, if this water vapour buffer did not exist, then the Earth would have remained cold, lifeless and barren. Water, initially in its vaporous form, is therefore responsible for the emergence of all life.

When water vapour reaches extreme altitudes, however, it then becomes so rarefied that it is dissociated into its constituent atoms of oxygen and hydrogen through the action of strong ultraviolet radiation. Being the heavier element, the oxygen then sinks back to Earth, while the lighter hydrogen atoms rise to rejoin their peers in space. Now separated from the hydrogen, the oxygen is exposed to high levels of ionising radiation through which the now single oxygen atoms are made to combine with the molecular oxygen (O_2) into an allotropic form of oxygen, O_3 or ozone, which is responsible for the absorption of otherwise dangerous levels of ultraviolet radiation, a process is vital for all life on Earth. The result is a net loss of water. The greater the amount of water vapour propelled into the atmosphere through the overheating resulting from excessive deforestation, the greater the consequent losses; losses indeed that can never be recovered (see pp. 121 & 123).

What differentiates water from all other liquids, a factor that will be discussed in more detail later, is its so-called 'anomaly point' or 'point of anomalous expansion'; that is to say, water's volume does not decrease continually with increasing cold. Its behaviour is anomalous, and hence the term 'anomalous expansion' or 'anomaly point'. This point of reversal is reached when the water attains its greatest density and energy content at a temperature of +4°C, below which it eventually crystallises as ice at 0°C, a process greatly assisted if so-called 'impurities' are present which provide the nucleus around which the ice forms.

Another important factor is water's dielectric value. The base dielectric value for calculating all other values is based on the permittivity of a vacuum and has a value of 1. Permittivity is the extent to which a substance can be penetrated or traversed by an electric current or charge. Apart from a vacuum, a dielectric can be formed of an electrically neutral, interstitial membrane separating positive and negative electric charges, i.e. a non-conducting substance such as paraffin wax.

The dielectric value of pure water (distilled water) is 81 ($=9^2$) and is therefore 81 times more effective as a charge separator than a vacuum and almost the highest dielectric value there is. $1mm^3$ of the purest water at room temperature, for example, has an electrical resistance equal to a $1mm^2$ copper wire, 15,000,000km long. It thus possesses a tremendous innate resistance to the transfer of charge. Pure water will only freeze at temperatures of around –40°C or in clouds at about –10°C, which again is fairly important, as we shall discover later. In comparison with a temperature of –273.15°C (= absolute zero or 0°Kelvin), supposedly the lowest possible

temperature to be found anywhere in the Universe, the temperature of 0°C, or freezing point, is relatively warm.

Lying between approximately +40°C and –10°C, the temperature range in which we live is not very large. In fact it is a fairly narrow band-width between extremes to which we are are not normally subjected. Our radius of action, our living space, as it were, lies within the upper and lower boundaries of the troposphere, itself a stratum or 'sphere' within the overall atmospheric envelope and defined by temperature and water vapour content.

To glean more facts about the structure of the atmosphere, from the *Phaidon Concise Encyclopedia of Science and Technology*[3] we are provided with the classifications shown in fig. 6.1, which should be viewed in conjunction with fig. 6.2. My own questions and comments are printed in bold type.

6.2 The Terrestrial Bio-Condenser

Keeping in mind water's dielectric value of 81 and its enormous resistance to the transfer of charges, let us now examine the thermal structure of the atmosphere (fig. 6.2), for this may explain to us another way in which, apart from the accumulation of heat, the Earth could become charged with life energy.

The portion of the atmosphere most important to us and which affects us most is the troposphere, which from fig. 6.2 can be seen to terminate at the tropopause between 6km and 18km up. Curiously enough, we also find that the temperature neither decreases nor increases constantly (shown as wavy broken line), but fluctuates as we ascend through the various atmospheric layers, so that at a certain altitude, at 29km for instance, the temperature is –60°C, whereas at a height of 80km it is +10°C. Somewhere between these two temperatures, therefore, there is a layer where the temperature is +4°C. According to my calculations there are at least four such levels where the temperature equals +4°C, at altitudes of about 3.5km, 77km, 85km and 175km.

EXOSPHERE: *The outermost layer of the Earth's atmosphere extending from about 400km-500km above the Earth's surface, where terrestrial gravitation is too weak an effect to prevent the escape of uncharged particles.*

THERMOSPHERE: *An atmospheric layer lying between the mesosphere and the exosphere, reaching an altitude of about 400km, where the temperature is over 1000°C.* **[Is this thermal or kinetic?** – CC]

IONOPAUSE: *The transitional zone in the atmosphere between the ionosphere and the exosphere about 644km (400 miles) from the Earth's surface.*

IONOSPHERE: *A region of the Earth's atmosphere extending from about 60km to 1000km above the Earth's surface in which there is a high concentration of free electrons formed as a result of ionising radiation entering the atmosphere from space.*

F-REGION: *150km-1000km. Highest proportion of free electrons and most useful for long-range radio transmissions, also called the Appleton Layer.* [**+4°C stratum at about 175 km** – CC]

E-REGION: *90km-150km. Reflects radio waves of medium wavelength, also called the Heaviside Layer.* [**+4°C stratum at about 85km** – CC]

D-REGION: *60km-90km. Lowest region of the ionosphere – Low concentration of free electrons and reflects low-frequency radio waves.* [**+4°C stratum at about 72km** – CC]

MESOPAUSE: *The zone of minimum temperature between the mesosphere and the thermosphere.*

MESOSPHERE: *The atmospheric layer lying between the stratosphere and the thermosphere characterised by a rapid increase in temperature with height. The atmospheric zone immediately above the stratosphere marked by a* **temperature maximum of +10°C** *between altitudes of 48km and 53km.*

STRATOPAUSE: *The transitional zone of maximum temperature between the stratosphere and the mesosphere.*

STRATOSPHERE: *The atmospheric layer lying between the troposphere and the mesosphere in which the* **temperature generally increases with height**. *The atmospheric zone immediately above the tropopause, including the Ozone layer.*

TROPOPAUSE: *The plane of discontinuity between the troposphere and the stratosphere characterised by a sharp change in the lapse rate[4] and varying in altitude from about 18km (11 miles) above the equator to 6km (4 miles) above the Poles.*

TROPOSPHERE: *The lowest atmospheric layer about 18km thick at the equator and 6km thick at the Poles in which* **air temperature decreases with height** *at about 6.5°C/km. Most meteorological phenomena occur in this layer. The innermost zone of the Earth's atmosphere extending from the surface to the tropopause.*

Fig. 6.1   **The Structure of the Atmosphere**

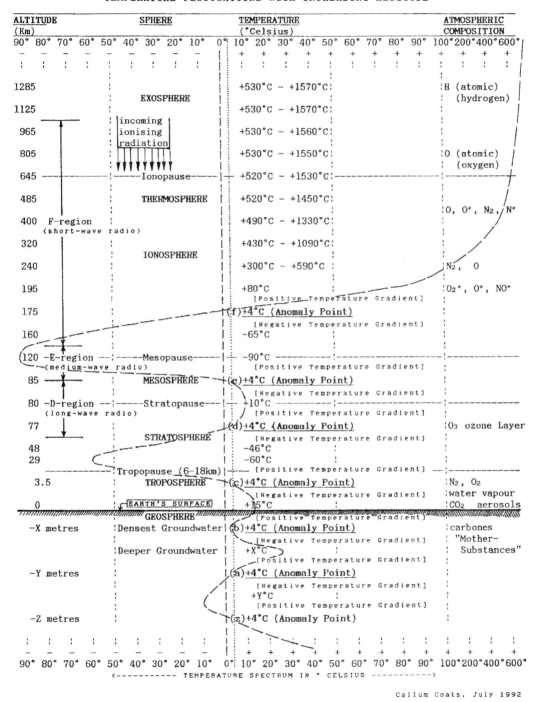

TEMPERATURE FLUCTUATIONS WITH INCREASING ALTITUDE

Callum Coats, July 1992

Fig. 6.2   **Section through Earth's atmosphere showing temperature fluctuations**

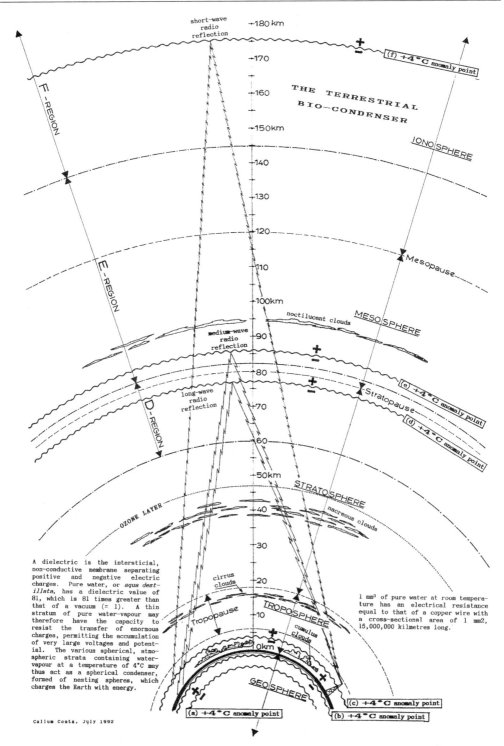

A dielectric is the intersticial, non-conductive membrane separating positive and negative electric charges. Pure water, or *aqua destillata*, has a dielectric value of 81, which is 81 times greater than that of a vacuum (= 1). A thin stratum of pure water-vapour may therefore have the capacity to resist the transfer of enormous charges, permitting the accumulation of very large voltages and potential. The various spherical, atmospheric strata containing water-vapour at a temperature of 4°C may thus act as a spherical condenser, formed of nesting spheres, which charges the Earth with energy.

1 mm³ of pure water at room temperature has an electrical resistance equal to that of a copper wire with a cross-sectional area of 1 mm2, 15,000,000 kilometres long.

Callum Coats, July 1992

Fig. 6.3   Earth's inner atmosphere showing possible levels for natural bio-condensers

Since there is water vapour in the atmosphere near these various altitudes in the form of cumulus and cirrus clouds (troposphere), nacreous clouds (stratosphere) and noctilucent clouds (mesosphere) as shown on fig. 6.3, we have a situation where a thin stratum of pure water may exist at each of these levels, which has a high resistance to the transfer of an electric charge. In view of the presence of these various +4°C strata and water's high dielectric value of 81, it could be postulated that their combined effect would act to create a natural bio-condenser, a condenser being a device with which an electric charge can be accumulated and stored.

Before elaborating further on this hypothesis, however, it is necessary here briefly to explain the principles of an electrical condenser. In its most elementary form, a condenser consists of two electrically charged plates, one with a positive charge equal to the other's negative charge. If the positive charged is raised on one side of the dielectric then the negative charge automatically rises to the same level on the other. In fig. 6.4 these two charged plates are separated by the intervening dielectric (the largest element), which in this case we shall deem to be pure water. The charges themselves are distributed uniformly over the surfaces of the two plates.

In order to increase the charge density on one side of the dielectric, the surface area of the respective plate is reduced. If this plate is reduced to a quarter the size of the other, then its charge density is four times that of the larger plate (fig. 6.5). The force with which the two opposite charges try to equalise or attract each other is known as the potential. The smaller the separation between the charges, the smaller the distance between them, the greater the potential, which increases by the inverse square of the separation. Therefore, if the separation is 10mm, for example, then the potential is 1^2. If the separation is reduced to $\frac{1}{2}$, i.e. 5mm, then the potential is 2^2 (=4) and so on, as shown in fig. 6.6. The smaller the separation, therefore, the greater the corresponding potential, which could be unleashed once the permittivity of the dielectric has been overcome.

If the charge surface on one side and the separation are decreased simultaneously, then both charge density and potential increase exponentially relative to the initial magnitude of the charges and sizes of the charge-plates (fig. 6.7). If we now recompose these plates in the form of concentric cylinders as shown in fig. 6.8, then as the surface area of the inner cylindrical plate is necessarily smaller, the charge and potential increase automatically from the outside inwards. The greater the number of nested plates, therefore, the more intense the potentiation.

Referring once more to fig. 6.3, we can see that from the outside inwards, like an onion, each succeeding layer has a smaller surface area owing to their concentricity. In other words, these layers form a condenser with concentric spherical plates (fig. 6.9). It could therefore be construed that, on encountering each successive, concentric, spherical +4°C dielectric stratum, the potential of the energy coming from the Sun is gradually magnified. As the Sun's energy passes from the outside towards the inside, it becomes increasingly concentrated as it approaches the Earth's surface, due to these enveloping layers of +4°C water, which as noted earlier does not freeze at temperatures of –40°C.

Viewed from a more cosmic perspective these strata are extremely close together, producing a very high potential. Relative to the average diameter of the Earth – 12,660.912km – the height of the highest of these +4°C strata represents only 0.0138%. In other words, if the Earth were depicted as a sphere with a diameter of 1 metre, then these four or

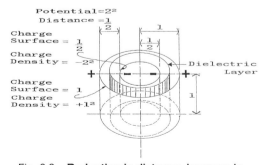

Fig. 6.8 **Reduction in distance, increase in potential**

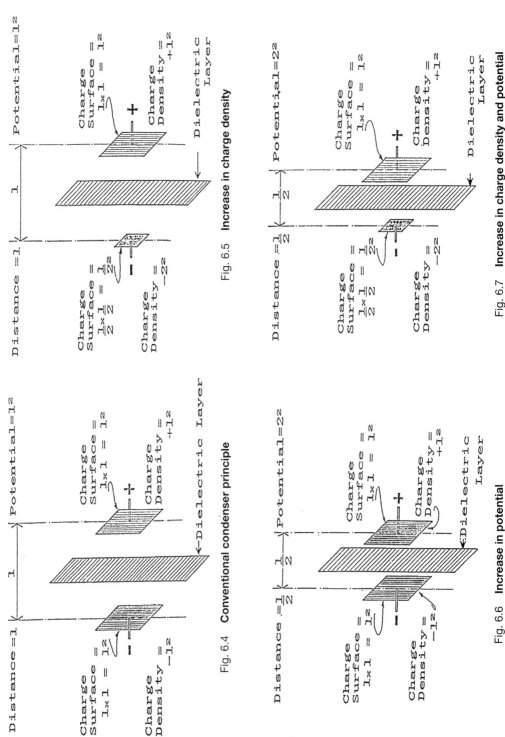

Fig. 6.4   **Conventional condenser principle**

Fig. 6.5   **Increase in charge density**

Fig. 6.6   **Increase in potential**

Fig. 6.7   **Increase in charge density and potential**

so strata would lie within 13.8mm of the surface. From this arises the concept of the Earth as an accumulator of energy within whose volume a charge is progressively built up. This accumulation of energy naturally enhances the emergence of life because, without energy, without differences in charge, gender, potential or a suitable energy field any form of life is impossible.

As charge-resisting layers, these mooted dielectric strata could also in part contribute to the reflection of long, medium and short-wave radio transmissions from different altitudes as shown on fig. 6.3, normally attributed to different ionisation levels for in each of the so-called D-, E- and F-regions water vapour is present at different densities. Being in a lower dynamic and more harmonically stabilised energetic state, the greater density of water vapour at increasingly lower altitudes may well correspond through resonance to the lower wavelengths of the incident radiation, whose frequency has been reduced by contact with the braking effect of

the atmosphere, thus creating the medium with which radio-waves are reflected back to Earth.

6.3 *The Development of Electricity*

Once the preconditions for life were established, then the development of another form of energy – electricity – became necessary, although it was probably almost simultaneous. Through its agency the ozone layer could be additionally reinforced. How this is done is demonstrated by a very simple experiment, in which energy in the form of an electric charge is generated by falling water (fig. 6.10[5]).

First carried out by Lord Kelvin (1824–1907) in the latter part of the 19th century, it consists of two needle-jets of water falling through two insulated brass collector-cylinders into two similarly insulated collector-cylinders below, each of which contains a metal funnel. Each of the upper collector-cylinders A and A^1 is

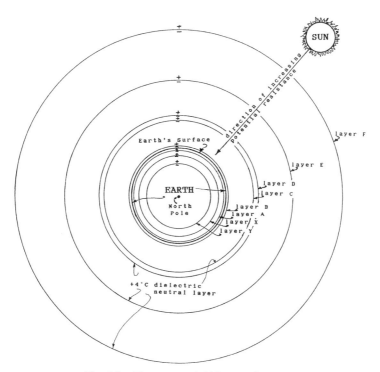

Fig. 6.9   **The terrestrial bio-condenser**

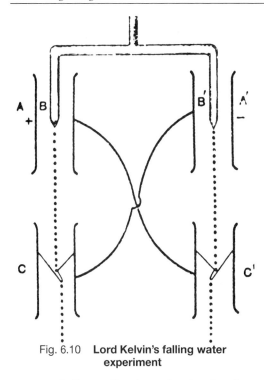

Fig. 6.10   **Lord Kelvin's falling water experiment**

with paraffin wax to prevent any charge leakage to earth. These vessels are labelled *V–* and *V+* on the apparatus I built shown in fig. 6.11, and each contains a brass strip diagonally connected with an insulated copper rod to the respective insulated, hollow collector-cylinders denoted by *C–* and *C+*. Instead of the finest hypodermic needles at *A* and *B*, which I used to create the jet, Viktor Schauberger used needle-jets in which the configuration and volume of flow could be adjusted by the extent to which the central needle was inserted through the jet. With very fine adjustment, the water could be made to stream out in spirals around the needle tip, endowing it with a greater energetic potential.

In order to detect the presence of an electrically charged field, an electroscope is required, the first of its kind being invented by Professor Wilhelm Exner at the University of Vienna, which he lent to Viktor Schauberger for his Nuremberg experiments. Exner's electroscope consisted of a cylindrical metal casing sealed with glass at each end into which a thin flat metal plate, insulated from the surrounding metal casing, was inserted through the top. Attached to each side of this and hanging vertically were two thin foils made of gold leaf. When a wire connected to one of the collector-cylinders was held near the protruding tip of the metal plate or touched it, the two strips of gold leaf flapped. Endowed with like charges, they repelled one another. Upon touching the metal casing at their furthest extent, the charges were earthed and gold-leaf foils once more hung vertically.

The structure of water is formed of dipole molecules (molecules with negative and positive poles) and when falling each of the water droplets generates a charge. To give a more detailed idea of a dipole let me quote from H. Lindner's book, *Das Bild der Modernen Physik*[6] (fig. 6.12).

connected diagonally via an insulated rod to collector-cylinders C^1 *and* C respectively, positioned under the opposite water-jet. Each drop of water falling from nozzle *B* through cylinder *A* towards lower cylinder *C* is negatively charged, due to the inductive influence of cylinder *A*. Upon coming in contact with the funnel, this negative charge is transferred to cylinder *C* and the water drains away through the bottom of the funnel free of charge. Since cylinder *C* is connected to upper cylinder A^1, A^1 also becomes negatively charged. Now negatively charged, cylinder A^1 induces a positive charge in the water falling from nozzle B^1 into cylinder C^1, thus reinforcing the positive charge in cylinder *A* via the insulated diagonal connection, the combined effect of which is a constant increase in both positive and negative charges which may well be without limit.

In 1937 this experiment was also carried out by Walter Schauberger in Nuremberg at Viktor Schauberger's behest in order to study the energies in water, but with some modifications to the experimental arrangement vis-a-vis Lord Kelvin's. Instead of funnels, the water fell into collector-vessels heavily insulated

For the generation of electromagnetic waves a 'transmitter' is necessary, which in many instances is a very expensive apparatus technically speaking. That such apparatuses, despite their diverse construction, can propagate electromagnetic waves, in the final analysis is founded

on one feature only: *Electrical charges are forced to perform accelerated movements. Electrons are usually employed for such purposes. They pendulate to and fro in oscillating circuits created by coils and condensers. The particular part of the apparatus in which the waves are generated, contains an open oscillating circuit, which is so constructed that the fields evolving within it are radiated into space via the attached antenna.*

Let us take a simple example and one of a type Heinrich Hertz also used in his experiments. This consists of a metal rod with a sphere at each end. The electrons, which were originally distributed through it uniformly, will subsequently be stimulated into rapid oscillation, into an alternating current of the highest frequency by the remote emitter. What happens in the vicinity of this dipole emitter is shown in the diagram below and is briefly described in the following:

1. Each end of the dipole is either positively or negatively charged. In the same way as occurs between the plates of a condenser, an electric field is propagated between them. This extends much further into space than can be shown in the diagram.

2. The charges equalise, the electrons flow through the connecting rod towards the positive pole. This swelling current generates a magnetic field, during which the electric field disappears in the vicinity of the dipole. In relation to Maxwell's equation, it can just as well be said that the changing electric field creates the magnetic field.

3. After completion of the charge equalisation, the electric field has vanished. The widely extended magnetic field has reached its maximum strength.

4. The spheres at the poles become oppositely charged, plus becomes minus and vice versa. The magnetic field begins to disappear, a new electric field evolves with reversed polarity, ultimately regaining its original strength.

Incidentally, this also explains more graphically why the Sun's poles swap over every 11.2 years as mentioned in chapter 5. The Earth's poles are also known to have shifted periodically, the mechanics of which are the same and the way the electric fields shown in fig. 6.12c come into being is virtually identical to the formation of the Van Allen radiation belts surrounding the Earth in fig. 4.14.

But to return to the theme in hand, for the same reason that the gold leaf foils of the electroscope diverge, the fine jet of water particles soon splits apart as the charge intensifies and the negative or positive field builds. Finally the electric field, generated in and filling the space below the jets, becomes so great that the particles are forced to rise (fig. 6.11). When the water pressure is very slight and after the charge has built up, no falling water can be heard, nor is any seen below the

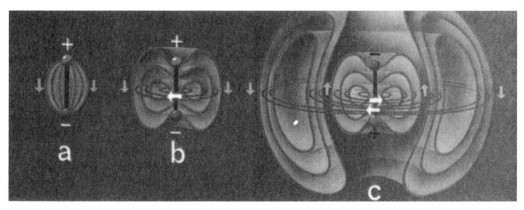

(a)	(b)	(c)
Starting condition	Equalisation of charges, formation of magnetic field-lines (blue)	Outer-lying portions of the electric and magnetic field-lines migrate outwards into space.

Fig. 6.12 **The formation of electro-magnetic waves in the vicinity of an oscillating electric dipole**

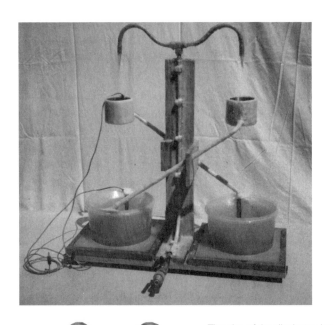

Water, expressed from a very fine needle, falls from jet A through an open-ended insulated brass-foil cylinder C+ into an insulated collecting vessel V–, incorporating a charge collecting brass strip. It is assumed that cylinder C+ is positively charged and as the fine water-droplets pass through it, they are endowed with a negative charge, imparting this charge to the collector strip in vessel V–. This negative charge is then passed on to cylinder C– via an insulated copper rod, imbuing it with a negative charge. As the water from jet B falls through negatively charged cylinder C–, it receives a positive charge, which is passed to cylinder C+ via the collector strip in vessel V+ . The charge in each collector vessel constantly intensifies the charge in the diagonally opposite cylinder.

The size of the discharge between terminals X and Y, connected to cylinder C– and vessel V+ respectively, is dependent on a combination of altitude and the moisture content of the atmosphere. As a rule of thumb, a discharge across a gap of 1mm represents 2,000 volts.

In the process of such an electric discharge, ozone O_3 is created.

The water-droplets falling from jets A and B, are endowed with positive and negative charges respectively. As like charges repel each other, each of these droplets migrates away from its neighbours, resulting in their splayed, outward distribution through the positively or negatively charged fields. In this ionised state, they begin to rise upwards, those water droplets nearest the cylinder with the opposite charge, being attracted back into the water-jet above it.

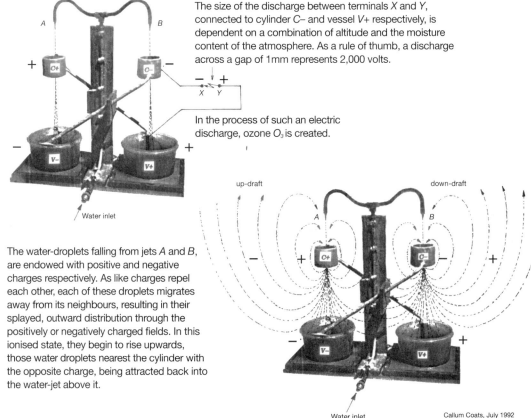

Callum Coats, July 1992

Fig. 6.11 The double water-jet experiment

First carried out by Lord Kelvin at Cambridge, England in the 1890's and later by Walter Schauberger at Nürnberg, Germany in 1938.

upper collector-cylinder. However, when holding one's hand about 50cm away from the jet, after a while icy-cold pin-pricks can be felt as the droplets encounter the skin and discharge into it. An insulated high-tension lead can be connected to each collector-cylinder and when the ends of the two leads are brought closely together, a spark suddenly jumps between them, which can be in the order of 60,000 volts. The rule of thumb for determining the magnitude of the charge is 2,000 volts per millimetre jumped. With the device that I built, a charge was generated sufficient to arc across a gap of 2cm, producing a sharp snap as a result of the passage of about 40,000 volts. This relatively large charge was generated by an extraordinarily small quantity of falling water.

This explains, for instance, why rainwater is much more productive, regenerative and growth-enhancing than irrigation water. While rainfall does not always culminate in a discharge of lightning, which depends (as discussed later) on the prevailing conditions and density of water vapour, as this little dipole falls, it rotates, building up both an electric and a magnetic, or bio-magnetic field, the formative energetic field. When this now highly-charged raindrop encounters a living organism, in this case a leaf, its accumulated energy is discharged into the plant and is made directly available for the plant's use. This is the reason for the more vigorous reaction of plants to rainwater vis-a-vis irrigation water, because the latter does not have the same fall-distance, and therefore cannot accumulate any significant charge.

If this experiment is carried out in the dark, then with a powerful torch, the water droplets can be seen to rise upwards above the upper collector-cylinders. If horizontally disposed spirals of copper rod are installed in lieu of the upper collector-cylinders, this apparently gives rise to another phenomenon namely the appearance of vertical plumes of bluish and white, cold light above the water-jet the result of intense ionisation and the horizontal propagation of a reddish glow below the copper

spirals. The blue light is associated with bio-magnetism – the upbuilding, levitational life-energy – and the reddish light is the product of electricism and has a degenerative effect.[7]

Apart from his interest in the actual generation of charges, Viktor Schauberger also made use of this apparatus to test the quality and vitality of water. One litre of good, mountain springwater had to pass through the needle-jets about 150 times before the gold-leaf foils ceased flapping. Experimenting with varying water temperatures he also found that at +37°C the oxygen in the water became aggressive and the water almost undrinkable. Its charge also decreased with increase in temperature. Whether the colour of the ionised glow described above, similar to the Aurora Borealis, varied with temperature, has not been reported. One could however assume with some confidence that different temperatures would produce different emanations.

6.4 Storms, Water Vapour and Climate

This experiment has many implications. It shows, for instance, that as a result of the gradual accumulation of water vapour, the atmosphere became sufficiently saturated to permit the aggregation of individual water molecules into macro-molecules, or raindrops. In the process of falling, these droplets of water generate a charge, and suddenly the phenomenon of electricity appears in the form of lightning. All at once a form of pure energy is made available for the planet's use.

In the course of an electrical discharge, ozone is created and, due to the often intense temperature- and ionisation-induced, high-velocity updrafts in thunderstorms, this ozone can be borne aloft to form or reinforce the ozone layer, which protects us all from excessive ultraviolet radiation. At any given moment the number of thunderstorms world-wide has been placed at about 1880 with an estimated 100 lightning strikes per minute. At an average of 15,000,000kw per strike, this amounts to 1,500,000,000kw/min or 13,000,000,000kw/hrs per year[8].

Lightning strikes can be up to 9km long and sheet lightning can extend up to 100km. All of these strikes are associated with the production of ozone due to the intense ionisation caused by the electrical discharge. In view of the fact that thunderstorm clouds can reach altitudes as high as 12km or so and contain extraordinarily powerful upcurrents, as demonstrated on a small scale in the experiment described above, it is possible that this newly produced ozone is carried up to augment the protective ozone layer.

If thunderstorm activity should decline, however, then this contribution will also drop commensurately. Indeed, over recent years the author has noticed a fall in the usual number of thunderstorms in the area where he lives and it may well be that this is a trend world-wide. Should this be the case, then it may have serious consequences for us all. Remembering that the water molecule is a dipole, for rain to produce an electrical discharge the water particles must be very fine in order to be able to spin fast enough to generate a high charge.

According to research by Kenneth S.Davis and John Arthur Day[9] the amount of water evaporated annually from the oceans amounts to about 333,000km³, the contribution from lakes, river and land surfaces being in the order of 62,000km³; the latter representing 18.6% of the total of 395,000km³ that returns to Earth as rain every year. Relative to the total area of rivers and lakes, the land surfaces covered by forest are far greater and therefore the major part of land evaporation is derived from the forest. As a percentage of the whole the contribution from the forest is therefore critical to the maintenance of stable climatic conditions.

However, owing to our massive deforestation activities, principally for agriculture and beef production, the area of natural forest has decreased enormously from its original state. This massive enlargement of hot, sun-exposed surfaces has resulted in an enormous increase in the evaporation rate, which

has been greatly assisted by an increase in temperature caused by the effects and products of our technology. A 1°C rise in temperature causes the retention, but not necessarily an even distribution, of an additional 1,000 million cubic metres of water vapour in the atmosphere.

In consequence the whole of the Earth's water balance has been seriously disturbed, resulting in very disorderly agglomerations of atmospheric water; a fact we are daily made aware of. In some places there is an overload, causing repeated catastrophic rainfall and large-scale inundation, such has been occurring in recent years in Bangladesh, while in others there is little or none at all, i.e. severe drought conditions prevail, as in the Sudan and Ethiopia, all of which are associated with extreme suffering and enormous loss of life. Due to the sheer volume of excess water vapour, instead of the creation of the small water particles mentioned above, much heavier drops are formed which fall as deluging rain and generate considerably lower charges.

In many such rainstorms, cyclonic and monsoonal storms there is no thunder at all. While this additional water vapour will increase the general atmospheric temperatures, due to the movement of the upper air streams it graduates towards the poles, there to fall as snow, adding to the volume of water fixed almost permanently as ice. Moreover the area of cloud cover also increases owing to this abnormal water-vapour content, which in turn amplifies the so-called albedo effect of the Earth. The albedo is the term for the overall whiteness of the Earth's atmosphere caused by the reflection of light off the white cloud areas. This obscures the Sun's rays and prevents the water vapour below the clouds from being further warmed.

On the other hand, as most of the water vapour has been accumulated in the clouds, where there are none relatively little vapour is present and so the Sun, where it can shine through, no longer warms the atmosphere. Assisted by the increasing pressures in the lower atmosphere caused by the temperature-induced expansion of abnormal quantities of water into vapour, more and more water-molecules are forced to higher altitudes, there to be subjected to the dissociative processes mentioned earlier and the irredeemable loss of water increases. In the long-term all of these effects act to reduce the general ambient temperatures and the presence of atmospheric water and while initially the temperature in parts of the Earth will rise, in the end it will inevitably cool off dramatically as the precursor to a new ice-age.

Historically no-one has ever experienced the initial stages of an ice-age. But perhaps the recent, totally unseasonal fall of snow in Australia at Christmas 1993 (hottest time of the year) is the first outstretching of the icy tentacles of an incipient ice-age. Viktor Schauberger already foresaw all this in 1933, long before anyone had any idea of global warming, and described it in detail in his book *Our Senseless Toil – The Source of the World Crisis*. The major causes in his view being the overclearing of the forest, coupled with heavy-handed, mechanistically-oriented agricultural practices and unnatural, misguided systems of water resources management, all of which are due to a total incomprehension of natural energies and processes.

Notes

1. *The Compact Edition of the Oxford English Dictionary:* Oxford Univ. Press, Oxford, 1980.
2. "The Water Cycle", *The Biosphere*, Scientific American, 1970: W.H. Freeman, New York, U.S.A.
3. *Phaidon Concise Encyclopedia of Science and Technology*, © 1978 Andromeda Oxford Limited, 11–15 The Vineyard, Abingdon, OX14 3PX, England.
4. *ibid.* LAPSE RATE: The rate of change of any meteorological factor with altitude, especially temperature, which usually decreases at a rate of 0.6°C per 100m (environmental lapse rate). Unsaturated air loses about 1°C per 100m (dry adiabatic(*) lapse rate), whereas saturated air loses at an average of 0.5°C per 100m (saturated adiabatic lapse rate).
   ibid. (*) ADIABATIC: Of a thermodynamic process occurring without loss or gain of heat.
5. *Electricity & Magnetism*, Cambridge Univ. Press, 1908.
6. *Das Bild der Modernen Physik* by H.Lindner, p.108, fig. 51/1, "The formation of electromagnetic waves": Urania-Verlag, Leipzig, Germany.
7. Why blue above the red below one might ask? For an explanation of the principles rather than the specifics we must refer to the table in figure 4.6, where we are reminded that gravitation, centrifugence, electricism, expansion, pressure and heat are all octavely related. It could thus be interpreted that as the dipole droplets fall due to *GRAVITY* they develop like *ELECTRIC* charges, giving rise to mutually repulsive *PRESSURES*. These in turn cause the *CENTRIFUGAL* axial–> radial and horizontal *EXPANSION* of the *ELEC-* TRIC field, which has a relatively low potential due to increased charge separation. In consequence it produces a discharge, whose colour lies at the lower frequency, longer wavelength, *HOT* end of the spectrum, i.e. red. We also know from fig. 4.6 (p. 63) that levitation, centripetence, magnetism, impansion, suction and cold are equally octavely related. As the continuing flow of spinning dipole molecules with like charges encounter the now fully developed electric field, they are repelled aloft in what might be described as an 'upward fall'. Along this longer U-shaped fall-path each gradually develops its *MAGNETIC* charge. As the *BIOMAGNETIC* field develops gravity rapidly gives way to *LEVITY*. Mutual attraction *(SUCTION)* increases, producing a *CENTRIPETAL RADIAL–>AXIAL IMPANSION* that converges the coiling *MAGNETIC* lines of force into an accelerating *LEVITATIONAL* vortex. Reaching extreme intensity at the pinnacle of this vortex, a plume-like, high frequency, bio-magnetic, bluish-white, COLD light soars upward as the biomagnetic field discharges. In a sort of backhanded confirmation of this phenomenon, the human psyche appears already to have been unconsciously impressed with the respective colours of magnetism and electricism, because coloured diagrams in most text books show magnetic fields in blue and electric fields in red!
8. Leopold Brandstätter, *Implosion statt Explosion*, Self-publication, Linz 10, Fach 20, Austria.
9. *Water – The Mirror of Science*, by K.S.Davis & J.A.Day, p.149: Heinemann Educ., London, 1964.

7

TEMPERATURE

7.1 Other Forms of Temperature

We shall now turn our attention to more familiar concepts of temperature. The movement of temperature in its eternal cycles is also the activator of life and death, of increase and decrease, decomposition and renewal. It is temperature, or rather the innate energies functioning under the banner of temperature, that produce the pulsations which punctuate and control all life's processes. We think of evolution as a continuous process, which it is on the whole, although it also has an important discontinuous aspect. If it were not for these energy pulsations which at one moment act to dissociate and at another to recombine both energy and matter, there would be no ordering instruments by which the countless individualities and qualities could be created that make up life as we know it. Thus the cyclical movement of temperature can be viewed as individuality-evoking motion which creates episodal conditions conducive to the evolution of new life forms or the renewal of existing ones.

The defining factors of temperature are the two antitheses of heat and cold, their extreme limits being the transcendental aspects of infinite heat and infinite cold. As we have seen, the achievement of either limit is impossible in the physical world, since the attainment of one would totally negate the existence of the other, while at the same time negating itself. It would then have no counterpart, no polarity, no duality, and the wholeness comprising the interaction of heat and cold at a physical level would cease to exist. Through the neglect of dialectic thinking in science, through which both sides of the coin, as it were, are taken into account, it would then have become a 'Law' in the same way that science speaks of the 'Law of Gravity' while discounting the counter-aspect of Levity (see fig. 4.6, chapter 3).

While there may indeed be very high temperatures elsewhere in the Universe, here on Earth the temperatures conducive to growth and development are relatively low and lie within a fairly narrow band-width. In the main, natural growth takes place in moderate temperature conditions, large or abrupt variations being harmful to most organisms. Owing to our blinkered education and the technology arising from it, we are accustomed to think of, and accept as natural, temperatures of an extremely high order. We generate our power using combustion and hot fission. Our form of chemistry is *coercion-chemistry*, in which we create compounds and power our machines using heat, often under extremely high pressures. Nature, on the other hand, has little constructive use for high pressures and temperatures, except as a means of relieving stresses, e.g. volcanoes and earthquakes, and instead employs cold fusion in her *cooperation-chemistry*. This is the cool chemistry of mutual suction or attraction between opposite polarities and charges, in which under a partial vacuum – the spacial and energetic vacuity between attracting bodies – various elements come together to create life.

Were it not for such a vacuum, we would not be able to breathe. In 1908 the Viennese surgeon, Prof. Ernst Ferdinand Sauerbruch, discovered this region of low pressure between the pleura and the surface of the lungs and explained it to his superior, Professor Mikolitsch, as follows:

In the enclosed and healthy lung a low-pressure zone exists, which maintains the pulmonary cavity and enables the lungs to expand with inhalation and contract with exhalation. Were there no vacuum between the surface of the lungs and the pleura, no intake of breath, no resistanceless expansion of the lungs would be possible. Without this partial vacuum, which causes the lining of the lungs to cling to the interior of the rib-cage, the lungs would collapse and death would follow. Should this biological vacuity be filled with normal, atmospheric pressure through any form of perforation, then everything would suffocate.[1]

When Sauerbruch had finished speaking, Mikolitsch told him he was out of his mind and dismissed him without notice. So much for Mikolitsch's open, objective, scientific opinion, a response many other discoverers have suffered at the hands of orthodoxy!

The currently accepted and one-sided view of this heat-cold duality, however, is that heat rises and expands, and cold falls and contracts. This is certainly valid for all technical systems and where this applies we shall call them technical heat and technical cold, for want of a better definition. However, this view is only part of the truth for Nature also uses the opposite form, namely rising and expanding cold and falling and concentrating heat.

Relative to the vast expanse of the Earth, we humans are little more than viruses, if that. Our general perspective therefore borders on the analytical, since from our low vantage point we cannot observe the whole, but only the smaller parts in our immediate vicinity. By raising our station, as it were, we can see that this other, opposite temperature relationship also exists. Viewed from space, a high-energy state of risen and expanded cold, we can see that a condition of falling and concentrating heat gradually evolves as we approach the Earth's surface, where it supposedly reaches its maximum in the Earth's interior, depending on whether the Earth is viewed as a solid or a hollow body. So far neither of the latter propositions has been proven incontrovertibly.

The difference between these two forms of temperature most commonly experienced,

relates to the temperature inversions that occur between night and day, between winter and summer, or a combination of both diurnal and seasonal temperature fluctuations. During the daytime increasing warmth is experienced as we descend to the bottom of a valley (falling and concentrating heat), whereas it gradually becomes cooler (rising and expanding cold) as we ascend. At night the process reverses (it is more apparent in winter). As we descend the air becomes chillier and denser (falling and concentrating cold), whereas when we ascend the air warms (rising and expanding heat).

It is therefore evident that two different forms of natural temperature/density relation exist, one of which has as yet neither been recognised nor investigated by science, although according to Viktor Schauberger it is the predominant form and the one that makes life possible. Our present technology is therefore completely unbalanced as a result.

These two different forms of temperature, or temperament as Viktor says in reflection of their ethereal origins, have opposite functions and are both active in Nature simultaneously. For evolution and development to proceed unimpeded, however, the higher, uplifting form must predominate. This we will call Type A, representing the collective attributes of rising and expanding cold and falling and concentrating heat, which acting together have an integrating, life-affirming function, leading to cold, formative, metabolic processes. It arises through the 'original' motion of the Earth and can be induced mechanically through the artificial, but naturalesque creation of the cycloid-spiral-space-curve motion (radial-axial) discussed in previous chapters. By this means bio-magnetism can also be generated, a form of energy of which science is presently ignorant.

Conversely, Type B temperatures where heat rises and expands and cold falls and concentrates, have a disintegrative, life-negating function and give rise to *warm*, decomposive, metabolic activity. Being associated with the analysing energies of electricism, when generated naturally, Nature makes use of Type B for the proper organic decomposition of previously living matter, i.e. for decay without putrefaction.

Through his understanding of the interaction

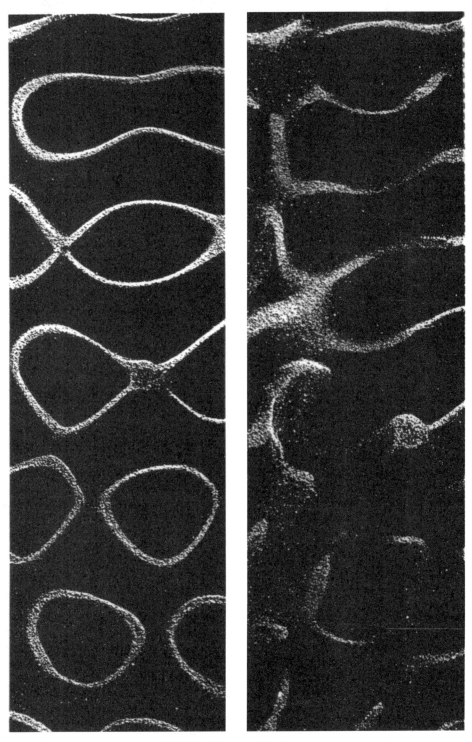

Fig. 7.1 **Sonorous figure.**
Plate 24.5 x 32.5 cm, thickness 0.5mm, frequency 1580 cps before the effect of heat (detail).

between these two types of temperature, in the latter years of the 1930s and early 1940s Viktor Schauberger developed the 'Klimator', a space-heater/cooler that functioned according to natural law and was the size of a hat. With the use of this machine, instead of the usual conditions of cold feet and hot head experienced in winter and symptomatic of technically controlled environments, warmer air was generated at lower levels and cooler air higher up. It was also able to create the reverse conditions in summer. In the later chapter 21 on implosion this will be addressed more fully.

Type B temperature can be generated by excessive heat - man-made creation of deserts and overclearing of forests. When exploited mechanically in machines or devices not constructed according to Nature's system of dynamics, it gradually disturbs the delicate balance of health in all organic bodies, making them susceptible to cancer and other diseases. This is mainly due to disturbances in the metabolism and therefore in the healthy formation of the life-fluids of water, blood or sap. Unfortunately for us and the rest of the environment, today it is Type B that is exclusively in widespread use.

7.2 Temperature – Health & Disease

With present methods of energy generation and creation of motion, large amounts of unnatural, technical heat, noise, noxious fumes and vapour are dissipated into the atmosphere, while soil and water are subjected to massive doses of poisonous materials. All of this is orchestrated according to a mechanistic, centrifugal and therefore divisive ideology which, driven by purely materialistic motives, arrogantly upsets the delicate thermal balance and preconditions required for the health and vitality of every living thing. These misguided practices all have a tendency to raise the general level of temperature above the naturally normal, thus bringing about subtle and sometimes lethal changes in cellular function. In other words the anomaly state of health, the state of 'indifference' as Viktor called it, peculiar to all organisms, macro and micro alike, is disturbed.

Cumulatively this has very serious consequences for all those organisms constantly exposed to it. In the process, all the natural conditions for creating and maintaining health are disrupted and the afflicted organism eventually falls victim to disease. In addition to the reduction in available oxygen due to over-consumption by vehicles (see chapter 2), which in humans produces a mild anoxia (oxygen starvation) coupled with a marginal rise in overall body temperature, the permanent establishment of slightly higher and therefore abnormal, unnatural ambient temperatures creates conditions suitable for the propagation of pathogenic bacteria.

A graphic example of the damaging effect of excess heat on structure is shown in fig. 7.1, where a flame was applied to a metal plate upon which an orderly pattern of sand had been formed through vibration[2]. To further illustrate the effect of a rise in temperature here are some pertinent quotations from Viktor Schauberger[3].

TO BE OR NOT TO BE: In Nature all life is a question of the minutest, but extremely precisely graduated differences in the particular thermal motion within every single body, which continually changes in rhythm with the processes of pulsation.

This unique law, which manifests itself throughout Nature's vastness and unity and expresses itself in every creature and organism, is the Law of Ceaseless Cycles *that in every organism is linked to a certain timespan and a particular tempo.*

The slightest disturbance of this harmony can lead to the most disastrous consequences for the major life forms.

In order to preserve this state of equilibrium, it is vital that the characteristic **inner** temperature *of each of the millions of micro-organisms contained in the macroorganisms be maintained.*

The fact that temperature plays a role in the development of cancer, however, has now at least been recognised in the sphere of mammography. According to a recent report[4] concerning the detection of breast cancer in women, the milk-ducts in healthy women are regular, whereas in cancer-prone breasts (about 1 in 10 women) the milk-ducts are lumpy and irregular. Strange to relate, the degree of cancer risk is determined by temperature! Using a Chronobra scanning device, the daily changes in breast temperature are measured at 1 minute intervals. It was determined that there was a different rhythm for high-risk breasts and that their overall temperature was higher than healthy ones. Now what did Viktor Schauberger just say?

While on the subject, on average there are 85,000 dust particles in a litre of city air. Not only that, but in France, for example, investigations determined that the street-air (warmer than normal air) in Paris contained 36,000 pathogenic bacteria per cubic metre, whereas in the forest and over the fields this reduced very sharply to only 490 airborne germs per cubic metre, 0.0136% of the above figure. Other data also infer a correlation between green space and disease, as exemplified in the comparative levels of tuberculosis in relation to the population of three major European cities set out below[5].

London	14.0% green space	1.9% tuberculosis
Berlin	10.0% green space	2.2% tuberculosis
Paris	4.5% green space	4.1% tuberculosis

Under the direction of Dr. John Whitelegg at Lancaster University, England, a recent two-year scientific study[6] of 1,000 households fronting on major traffic arteries and the health of their occupants has established a direct connection between respiratory diseases and traffic fumes (corollary of traffic heat). It was found that these people had a higher incidence of disease, the most common complaints being headaches, sore throats, breathlessness, itching eyes and a general lack of energy. What is surprising here is that it has taken so long to confirm scientifically what would appear to be quite obvious.

In their aggregation all the various factors mentioned above change, accelerate, retard or otherwise inhibit the normal healthy metabolism of any organism constantly exposed to them. This changes the natural movement of energy associated with the metabolism in question which inevitably alters the state of 'indifference' (temperaturelessness) peculiar to it.

Another interesting facet, which relates to a conversation I once had with an experienced glider pilot, further highlights the differences in the forms of temperature produced by forest and city respectively and is indicative of the inferior quality and dynamics of the rising technical heat from factory chimneys, car exhausts, concrete surfaces, metal roofs, etc. As the gaining of altitude is the most crucial factor in gliding, I asked where the best thermals (rising air currents) were to be found. Expecting him to say that these occurred over obvious heat sources, such as towns, I was surprised to learn that it was large areas of natural forest that produced them.

With the continued use of present methods, it is therefore no wonder that the incidence of cancer and other diseases is rising so quickly. But worse than this, they are infecting younger and younger age groups. Acute suffering and previously unheard of ailments are increasing alarmingly and all manner of cures are attempted – surgery, radiation, chemotherapy – and yet no-one perceives that it is inherent in the heat-generating and health-debilitating systems of technology, forestry, land and water resources management that we have contrived and with which we have managed to debase all life.

Thorough knowledge of these two forms of temperature and their application will in time put an end to this dreadful scourge. There is therefore no time to be lost in implementing a programme of in-depth investigation of the theories put forward by Viktor Schauberger leading to their practical application, for therein may lie the main chance for our ultimate salvation.

Notes

1. "The Biological Vacuum – The Optimal Driving Force For Machines", by Viktor Schauberger: *Implosion* No.53, p.28.
2. From *Kymatik/Cymatics* by Hans Jenny, photos by Christiaan Stuten: Basilius, Basel, Switzerland (now defunct), ISBN 3-85560-009-0.
3. "The Forest and its Significance" ("Der Wald un seine Bedeutung"), by Viktor Schauberger: *Tau* magazine, Vol.146, p.2.
4. "Beyond 2000", Channel 7 Television, Australia, 25th June 1991.
5. *Our Common Future*: Oxford Univ. Press, Oxford/New York.
6. BBC 9.00pm news broadcast, Monday 17th December 1993; and *The Times* newspaper, p.9, 14th December 1993.

8
THE NATURE OF WATER

How blossomingly I rejoice! All hail to the new!
All is born of water and upheld by water too!
Transpierced thus am I by beauty and by truth!
Oh great ocean, grant us thine eternal ruth!

For wouldst thou not send clouds, nor bounteous
  streams endow,
Nor perfect the currents, nor rivers here and there
  bestow,
Then where would mountains be and what of
  plains and world?
For thou alone it is that keeps this freshest life
  unfurled.

Johann Wolfgang von Goethe

8.1 Water – a Living Substance

WATER! Where do we begin our quest in search of the true nature of this remarkable substance, this wondrous, many-facetted jewel, which is both Life and liquid? So primordial, primeval and fundamental is the function of water that it begs the question as to which came first, life or water. Thales of Miletus (640–546BC) described water as the only true element from which all other bodies are created, believing it to be the original substance of the cosmos. It was the only real substance, because it was imbued with the quality of Being.

This view was also firmly held by Viktor Schauberger, who saw water as the 'original' substance formed by the subtle energies called into being through the 'original' motion of the Earth, itself the manifestation of even more sublime forces. Being the off-

spring or the 'First Born' of these energies, as he put it, he maintained and frequently asserted that **"Water is a living substance!"** a notion to which Goethe also subscribed in the above poem.[1]

As a living entity, Viktor saw water as the accumulator and transformer of the energies originating from the Earth and the Cosmos, and as such was and is the foundation of all life-processes and the major contributor to the conditions which make life possible. Not only that, but once mature, water is a being invested with the power of extraordinary giving and gives of itself to all things requiring life in the ECI's Great Plan. It is the ECI's faithful life-messenger and, in its eternal cycles, coils and twists in its natural movement about the path of evolution, like the serpents on Mercury's staff.

*The **Upholder of the Cycles** which supports the whole of Life, is WATER. In every drop of water dwells a Deity, whom we all serve; there also dwells Life, the Soul of the **'First'** substance – Water – whose boundaries and banks are the capillaries that guide it and in which it circulates.[2]*

Viktor Schauberger

Water is therefore a being that has life and death. With incorrect, ignorant handling, however, it becomes diseased, imparting this condition to all other organisms, vegetable, animal and human alike, causing their eventual physical decay and death, and in the case of human beings, their moral, mental and spiritual deterioration as well. With this awareness we can see just how vital it is that water should be handled and stored in such a way as to avoid such disastrous consequences. When we fail to perceive water as a living entity which nurtures all life, we arrest water's creative cycles, we stop life and water is transformed into a dangerous enemy.

Viktor Schauberger's understanding of water and what he achieved as a result is well exemplified in this quotation from his book, *Our Senseless Toil*, written in 1933:

It is possible to regulate watercourses over any given distance without embankment works; to transport timber and other materials, even when heavier than water, for example ore, stones, etc., down the centre of such water-courses; to raise the height of the watertable in the surrounding countryside and to endow the water with all those elements necessary for the prevailing vegetation.

Furthermore it is possible in this way to render timber and other such materials non-inflammable and rot resistant; to produce drinking and spa-water for man, beast and soil of any desired composition and performance artificially, but in the way that it occurs in Nature; to raise water in a vertical pipe without pumping devices; to produce any amount of electricity and radiant energy almost without cost; to raise soil quality and to heal cancer, tuberculosis and nervous disorders.

... the practical implementation of this ... would without doubt signify a complete reorientation in all areas of science and technology. By application of these new found laws, I have already constructed fairly large installations in the spheres of log-rafting and river regulation, which as is known, have functioned faultlessly for a decade, and which today still present insoluble enigmas to the various scientific disciplines concerned.[3]

But before going further, let us acquaint ourselves with some of the more commonly known facts about water. First of all, whence did water come? Obviously it cannot have come from the upper atmosphere, since as we saw in chapter 6 the water molecule is actually dissociated at high altitudes. Where else do we look then? If not above then perhaps below, because the atmosphere does not seem conducive to its formation. If below then where? Has it been contained in a crystalline state in ore-bearing rocks since the Earth began? There is some evidence to suggest that it has.

In *The Divining Hand*[4] Christopher Bird describes the pioneering theories and discoveries of Stephan Riess in the United States, which like Viktor Schauberger's, completely contradicted established hydraulic theory. According to Stephan Riess under certain conditions the oxygen and hydrogen gases present in certain types of rock can be released due to the effects of geothermal heat and a process akin to triboluminescence, a phenomenon relating to the light given off by crystalline rocks under friction or violent pressure. This glow is attributed to the energy given off by the electrons contained the rocks as they return from a pressure-induced, excited state to their rest orbits. As a discharge it imparts free energy to the surrounding material, which could be sufficient to cause the hydrogen and oxygen released by the pressure to form new water under a process of cold oxidation.

Riess called this *virgin water*, and as a result of his knowledge he was able to tap straight into formations of hard rock of the right composition and obtain very large quantities of water, in some cases as much as 3,000 gallons per minute. All this right out in the middle of the desert, where no water could be expected. Unfortunately, his efforts to provide needy areas with copious quantities of superb quality, fresh water were sabotaged. As happened to Viktor Schauberger before him, Christopher Bird relates how Riess was slandered and his ideas brought into disrepute through the scurrilous activities of certain high officials in the state of California, whose interests were threatened by Riess' discoveries.

As a liquid, water is chemically described as H_2O and is a dipole molecule comprising two hydrogen atoms, one positive and one negative, and one negative oxygen atom containing two positive charges. Due to the distribution of the charges around the nucleus, the angle between the two hydrogen atoms is 104.35°, as shown in upper right-hand inset in fig. 8.1. According to Kenneth S. Davis and John Arthur Day, pure water is actually a mixture of 18 different molecular compounds and 15 different kinds of ions, making a total of 33 different substances[5]. In this regard *The Secret Doctrine* comments:

THE WATER MOLECULE
A Dipole

H_2O

Hydrogen
Oxygen
Hydrogen
104.23°

WATER

a) Is **specifically most dense at +4°C** and at this temperature has its greatest energetic content.

b) Is chemically described as H_2O with 2 hydrogen atoms, 1 positive and 1 negative, and 1 negatively charged oxygen atom.

c) Has its **lowest Specific Heat at +37.5°C**, which has great significance for human beings with a **normal Blood Temperature of +37.0°C** in that it requires greater amounts of heat or cold to change the temperature of the **blood consisting of up to 80% water**.

d) Has a **Dielectric Value of 81**, which is 81 times greater than that of a vacuum

e) $1mm^3$ of Pure Water (H_2O) has an **Electrical Resistance = to a 15,000,000 km** long copper wire $1mm^3$.

f) Has as many varieties as there are human beings, animals and plants.

g) Is the "**BLOOD OF THE EARTH**" and performs the same function in the Earth as does blood in animal life and sap in plants. Sap, blood and water are synonymous.

h) There are two different TEMPERATURE GRADIENTS which have a **decisive effect** on the action and energy of water.
POSITIVE Temperature Gradient = a motion of temperature **towards +4°C**.
NEGATIVE Temperature Gradient = a motion of temperature **away from +4°C**.

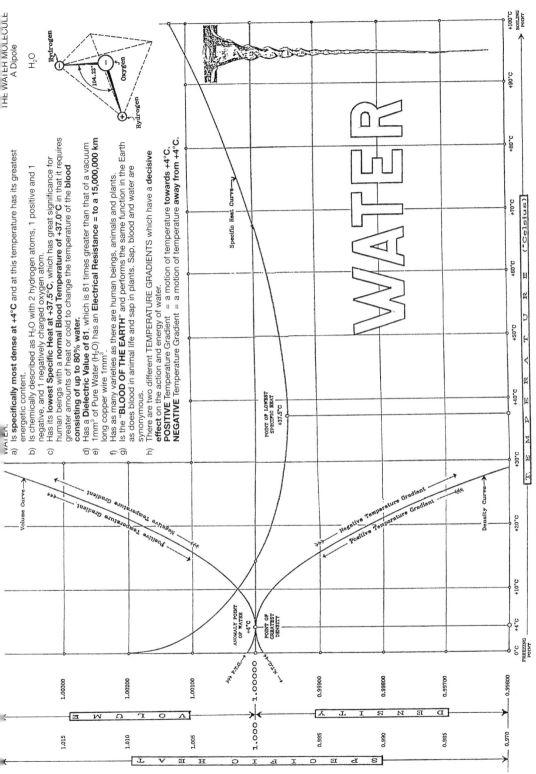

WATER

Specific Heat Curve

POINT OF LOWEST SPECIFIC HEAT +37.5°C

Volume Curve

Positive Temperature Gradient

Negative Temperature Gradient

ANOMALY POINT OF WATER +4°C

POINT OF GREATEST DENSITY

Negative Temperature Gradient

Positive Temperature Gradient

Density Curve

T E M P E R A T U R E (°Celsius)

0°C FREEZING POINT | +4°C | +10°C | +20°C | +30°C | +40°C | +50°C | +60°C | +70°C | +80°C | +90°C | +100°C BOILING POINT

V O L U M E
1.00300
1.00200
1.00100
1.00000
0.99900
0.99800
0.99700
0.99600

D E N S I T Y

S P E C I F I C   H E A T
1.015
1.010
1.005
1.000
0.995
0.990
0.985
0.970

Fig. 8.1   **Water – some important physical facts**

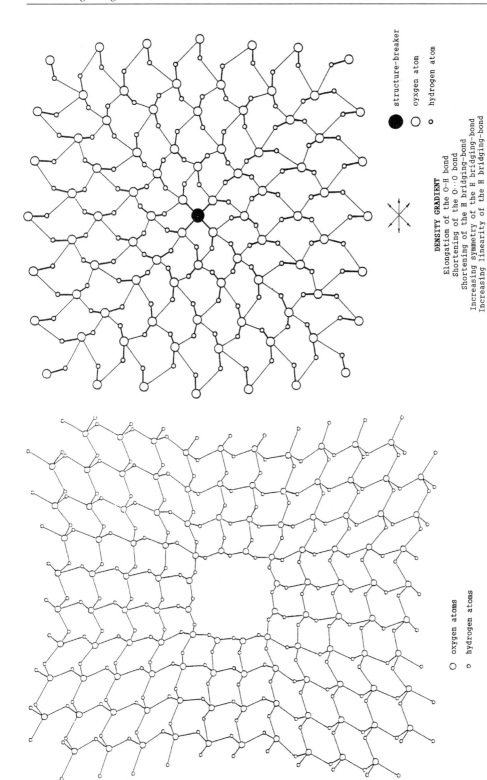

structure-breaker

◯ oxygen atom

∘ hydrogen atom

DENSITY GRADIENT
Elongation of the O–H bond
Shortening of the O··O bond
Shortening of the H bridging-bond
Increasing symmetry of the H bridging-bond
Increasing linearity of the H bridging-bond

Idealised illustration of the static aspect of the structural order of water in the vicinity of a so-called structure-breaker.

Fig. 8.3

◯ oxygen atoms

∘ hydrogen atoms

Idealised illustration of the static aspects of the structure of water in the vicinity of a void in the structure, whose size corresponds to that discovered experimentally in acid hydrates.

Fig. 8.2

Even on the next higher plane, that single element which is defined on our Earth by current science, as the ultimate undecomposable constituent of some kind of matter, would be pronounced in the world of a higher spiritual perception as something very complex indeed. Our purest water would be found to yield, instead of its two declared simple elements of oxygen and hydrogen, many other constituents, undreamt of by our terrestrial modern chemistry.[6]

In its pure form, being a compound of the two gases hydrogen and oxygen, water could technically be described as an oxide of hydrogen. Water is no self-contained, isolated substance, however, for it possesses other characteristics according to the medium or the organism in which it resides and moves. As a molecule, water has an extraordinary capacity to combine with more elements and compounds than any other molecule and is sometimes described as the universal solvent. As such it is able to provide the basis for an intimate intermixture of substances which Viktor referred to as an 'emulsion'. The more complex the make-up of constituents dissolved or suspended in water, the more complex the emulsion and the broader the spectrum of its properties. Carbon, its so-called inorganic counterpart, has a similar capacity above and beyond all other elements. At a physical level water is to be found in three states of aggregation, solid (ice), liquid (water) and gaseous (water vapour) and in terms of its structure as a liquid, it tends more to the crystalline, as it continually forms and re-forms nodes of temporary crystallisation, exhibiting a space-lattice structure, such as is shown in figs. 8.2 & 8.3 taken from a homeopathic study of water by Dr. Gerhard Resch and Prof. Viktor Gutmann[7].

8.2 The Anomaly Point of Water

The anomalous expansion of water is also a factor of major importance. While this has already been partly covered in chapter 7, further elaboration is necessary. To recapitulate briefly: As a liquid, the behaviour of water differs from all other fluids. While all fluids become consistently and steadily denser with cooling, water, alone reaches its densest state at a temperature of **+4° Celsius** (39.2° Fahrenheit). This is the so-called '**anomaly point**', which is decisive in terms of its potency and has a major influence on its **quality**. Below this temperature it once more expands. At +4°C water has a density of 0.99996 grams per cubic centimetre (g/cm^3), has the least spacial volume and is virtually incompressible (fig. 8.1).

Plus 4°C also signifies the temperature where water has its the highest energy content and is in what Viktor called a state of 'indifference'. In other words, when in its highest natural condition of health, vitality and life-giving potential, water is at an internal state of energetic equilibrium and in a thermally and spacially neutral condition. In order to protect water's health, energy and life-force, certain precautions must be taken, which will be addressed later. For the present it is important to realise that the +4°C anomaly is crucial to water's diverse functions. Viktor's theories about the temperature gradient and their implementation will be elaborated in the following section.

If water's temperature rises above +4°C, it expands. When it cools below this level then it also begins to expand and becomes specifically lighter. This anomalous expansion below +4°C is vital to the survival of fish life, for as the water expands and cools further it eventually crystallises as ice at 0°C, thus providing a floating, insulating sheath, which protects the aquatic life underneath from the harmful effects of severe external cold in winter. The specific gravity of water at +0°C = $0.99984 g/cm^3$, whereas the specific gravity of ice at the same temperature = $0.9168 g/cm^3$. As 1 spacial unit of water expands into ice, its volume increases in the ratio of 0.9168:0.99984, or 1:1.09058, which is equivalent to an increase in displacement of about $^1/_{11}$th of its former volume as water. This is why ice floats.

8.3 Dielectrics and Electrolysis

While pure water's high dielectric value of 81, namely its capacity to resist the transfer of an electric charge, has already been mentioned in chapter 7, there is another aspect to this which, in the light of Viktor Schauberger's concept of hydrogen as the carrier of oxygen and carbone (fig. 5.1, see p. 83), needs to be looked at in relation to one of the major fallacies of science. Still taught as Gospel truth in all schools and universities, electrolysis is supposedly the process by which water is dissociated into its constituent atoms of hydrogen and oxygen. However from the above we know that pure water will not transmit an electric current and this factor is also used to measure the pollution of water using what are called electro-conductivity units or ecus. The greater the content of dissolved and suspended matter in water, the greater its capacity to carry an electric current and the higher the values in ecus registered.

In order to set the process of electrolysis in motion, however, it is necessary to add some acid, such as sulphuric acid – H_2SO_4 – to the distilled water, the acid here always being referred to as the 'catalyst'. A catalyst is an element or agent which inaugurates a given reaction, but is not itself affected or changed in any way by it. This can be learnt from any physics textbook. From time to time, however, if electrolysis is to continue, more acid must be added otherwise the process will cease and all that will be left once again is water. But this acid was supposed to be the catalyst and therefore impervious to the effects of the electric current! What happened to it?

As the process of electrolysis proceeds, oxygen gas and hydrogen gas are indeed released, the negatively charged hydrogen ions migrating towards the positive electrode and the positively charged oxygen ions towards the negative electrode. Are these released gases actually derived from the water, however, or do they originate from the added acid? Sulphuric acid is formed of 2 hydrogen atoms, 1 sulphur atom and 4 oxygen atoms. If these gases are in fact produced through the dissociation of the acid rather than the water, then the whole process of electrolysis as presently taught is a widespread fraud as Viktor claimed in his 1932 article "Electrolysis"[8].

The Secret Doctrine also advances thought-provoking comment on what might be the state of being of the various elements of acid and water when combined as a mixture in electrolysis.

The question whether Hydrogen and Oxygen cease to exist when they combine to form water, is still a moot one, some arguing that since they are found again when water is decomposed, they must be there all the while; others contending that as they actually turn into something totally different they must cease to exist as themselves for the time being; but neither side is able to form the faintest conception of the real condition of a thing, which has become something else and yet has not ceased to be itself.[9]

It appears then that water retains its identity when in the electrolyte (the mixture of water and acid), and once the electrolytic process has been completed, then all that remains is again water.

A further life-giving property of water is its high specific heat and thermal conductivity (which were studied in chapter 6), namely the ability and the rate at which it absorbs and releases heat. This means that a large input or extraction of heat energy is required to bring about a change in density and temperature. The lowest point of the curve of the specific heat values for water, however, is +37.5°C or 99.5°F (fig. 8.1). It is remarkable that the lowest specific heat of this 'inorganic' substance – water – lies but 0.5°C (0.9°F) above the normal +37°C (98.6°F) human blood temperature – at which the greatest amount of heat or cold is required to change the water's temperature. This property of water to resist rapid thermal change enables us, with blood composed of up to 90% water, together with many other animals and creatures, to survive a relatively large range and fluctuation of temperatures and still maintain our own internal bodily temperature. Pure accident so we are told, or is it by clever, symbiotic design?! If the blood in our bodies had a lower specific heat, it would mean that it would heat up much more rapidly to the point where we would either start to decompose or freeze if exposure was to extreme cold.

However, in our mechanistic world we are used to thinking about temperature in gross terms (automobile engines operate at temperatures of 1,000°C (1,832°F) or so and many industrial processes employ extremely high temperatures. Despite the fact that we begin to feel unwell if our temperature rises by as little as 0.5°C (0.9°F), we fail to see that non-mechanical, organic life and health are based on very subtle differences in temperature. When our body temperature is +37°C (98.6°F) we do not have a 'temperature' as such. We are healthy and, recalling Viktor's view, are in an 'indifferent' or 'temperature-less' state. Just as good water is the preserver of our proper bodily temperature, our anomaly point of greatest health and energy, so too does it preserve this planet as a habitat for our continuing existence. Water in all its forms and qualities is thus the mediator of all life and deserving of the highest focus of our esteem.

Water and its vital interaction with the forest was Viktor's principal preoccupation, viewing water as the 'Blood of Mother-Earth', which in contrast to Carl Riess' theories mentioned earlier, was born in the womb of the high forest. This will be examined more fully later. Our mechanistic, materialistic and extremely superficial way of looking at things, however, prevents us from considering water to be anything other than inorganic, i.e. supposedly without life, but which, while apparently having no life itself, can nevertheless miraculously create life in all its forms.

Life is movement and is epitomised by water in a constant state of motion and transformation, both externally and internally. Flowing as water, sap and blood, this life molecule is the creator of the myriad life-forms on this planet. How then could it ever be construed as life-less as in the chemist's clinical view of water, defined as the inorganic substance H_2O?

This cryptic symbol is a gross misrepresentation. Were water merely the sterile, distilled H_2O as presently described by science, it would be poisonous to all living things. H_2O or 'juvenile water' is sterile, distilled water and devoid of any so-called 'impurities'. It has no developed character and qualities. As a young, immature, growing entity, it grasps like a baby at everything within reach. It absorbs the characteristics and properties of whatever it comes into contact with or has attracted to itself in order to grow to maturity. This 'everything' – the 'impurities' – takes the form of trace elements, minerals, salts and even smells! Were we to drink pure H_2O constantly, it would quickly leach out all our store of minerals and trace elements, debilitating and ultimately killing us. Like a growing child, juvenile water takes and does not give. Only when mature, i.e. when suitably enriched with raw materials, is it in a position to give, to dispense itself freely and

Water Type	Description	Drinking Quality
Fresh Water has many principal qualities, which can be differentiated according to drinking quality.		
Distilled water	Purest water, contains no other elements.	*bad*
Meteoric (rainwater)	Contains some atmospheric gases.	*poor*
Juvenile (immature water)	Contains few minerals or trace elements.	*poor*
Surface water (dams, reservoirs, rivers)	Contains some minerals and salts accumulated by contact with the soil.	*adequate*
Groundwater	Contains a greater quantity of minerals.	*good*
Seepage-spring water	As for groundwater.	*good*
True spring water	High in dissolved carbons and minerals	*best*
Artesian water	Deep-lying water which may be fresh or saline and can contain a variety of dissolved elements and gases	*variable*

Fig. 8.4

willingly, thus enabling the rest of life to develop.

8.4 Qualities of Water

But what is this marvellous, colourless, tasteless and odourless substance, which quenches our thirst like no other fluid? Did we but truly understand the essential nature of water – a living liquid – we would not treat it so churlishly, but would care for it as if our lives depended on it, which undoubtedly they do.

Apart from the actual treatment of water investigated in chapter 15, certain types of water are more suitable for drinking than others, the following being a general classification to be read in conjunction with fig. 8.4.

DISTILLED WATER
This is what is considered physically and chemically to be the purest form of water. Having no characteristics other then total purity, it has a pre-programmed will to unite with or acquire, to extract or attract to itself all the substances it needs to become mature itself, and therefore absorbs and grasps at everything within reach. Such water is really quite dangerous if drunk continuously long-term. When distilled water (*aqua destillata*) is drunk it acts as a purgative, stripping the body of trace minerals and elements. On occasion it has been used for its short-term therapeutic effect, such as in the so-called 'Kneipp cure', where it acts to purge the body of excessive deposits of various materials.

METEORIC WATER – RAINWATER
While the purest naturally available water, noxious atmospheric pollutants aside, meteoric water or rainwater is also unsuitable for drinking in the long term. It is marginally better than distilled water and slightly richer in minerals, due to the absorption of atmospheric gases and dust particles. As a living organism it is still in adolescence, still immature, and needs to undergo certain ripening processes in order to be able to be absorbed by the body and to be of benefit to it. When drunk as melted snow-water, it also gives rise to certain deficiencies and if no other water is available on occasion can result in goitre, the enlargement of the thyroid gland.

JUVENILE WATER
Juvenile water, again, is immature water, but it is water coming from the ground. It has not matured properly on its passage through the ground. It emerges, perhaps in the form of geysers, etc., from quite a long way down. It has not yet resolved itself into a mature structure and is therefore still of 2-star quality. It contains a few minerals, some trace elements and only small quantities of dissolved carbons, but again as drinking water it is not very high grade.

SURFACE WATER
Surface water – dams, reservoirs, etc. – contains some minerals and salts accumulated by contact with the soil and also from the atmosphere but, generally speaking it is not a very good quality water, partly because of atmospheric exposure to heavy oxygenation and to heat exposure from the Sun. The Sun's heat removes a great deal of the character and energy of water.

GROUNDWATER
Groundwater is already much better, often expressing itself as a seepage-spring, which is water emanating from lower levels and which seeps out at the surface after passage along the top of an impervious stratum. It has a larger quota of dissolved carbons, which are the most important ingredient in high quality water, apart from other trace salts.

TRUE SPRING WATER
True springwater, and we shall explore the differences between a seepage spring and a true spring later on, is very high in dissolved carbons and minerals, and of the highest possible quality. Its high state of health and vitality is affirmed by its shimmering, vibrant bluish colour, which is not evident in inferior waters. Such water is ideal for drinking, if it can be obtained. Unfortunately there are now

very few true, high-quality springs left, due to the destruction of the environment.

Apart from the above waters, there are artesian waters obtained from bores, which are of unpredictable quality. At times they may be saline and at others, brackish, or fresh. One can never be sure that bore-water will necessarily be of drinking quality. Well-water would probably lie between ground-water and seepage-spring water, but most probably can be likened and classified as groundwater. Once again it depends on how deep the well is and what stratum of water is tapped.

But what are we actually given to drink? This subject of vital interest to us all, which so intimately affects our life, health and well-being, will be discussed in a later chapter, because we must now turn our attention to the temperature gradient which, after the anomaly point of +4°C, is the next most important factor in the understanding of water and its proper, natural handling.

8.5 *The Temperature Gradient*

Apart from other factors (some cannot be defined quantitatively), encompassing such aspects as turbidity (opaqueness), impurity, and *quality*, *the most crucial factor affecting the health and energy of water is temperature*, the various aspects of which will be addressed in greater detail later, but first of all a general overview is in order.

Conceived in the cool, dark cradle of the virgin forest, water ripens and matures as it slowly mounts from the depths. On its upward way it gathers to itself trace elements and minerals. Only when it is ripe, and not before, will it emerge from the bowels of the Earth as a spring. As a true spring, in contrast to a seepage spring, this has a water temperature of about +4°C (39.2°F). Here in the cool, diffused light of the forest it begins its long, life-giving cycle as a sparkling, lively, translucent stream, bubbling, gurgling, whirling and gyrating as it wends its way valleywards. In its natural, self-cooling, spiralling, convoluting motion, water is able to maintain its vital inner energies, health and purity. In this way it acts as the conveyor of all the necessary minerals, trace elements and other subtle energies to the surrounding environment.

Naturally flowing water seeks to flow in darkness or in the diffused light of the forest, thus avoiding the damaging direct light of the Sun. Under these conditions, even when cascading down in torrents, a stream will only rarely overflow its banks. Due to its correct natural motion, the faster it flows, the greater its carrying capacity and scouring ability and the more it deepens its bed. This is due to the formation of in-winding, longitudinal, clockwise–anti-clockwise alternating spiral vortices down the central axis of the current, which constantly cool and re-cool the water, maintaining it at a healthy temperature and leading to a faster, more laminar, spiral flow.

To protect itself from harmful effects of excess heat, water shields itself from the Sun with over-hanging vegetation, for with increasing heat and light it begins to lose its vitality and health, its capacity to enliven and animate the environment through which it passes. Ultimately becoming a broad river, the water becomes more turbid, the content of suspended small-grain sediment and silt increasing as it warms up, its flow becoming slower and more sluggish.

However, even this turbidity plays an important role, because it protects the deeper water-strata from the heating effect of the Sun. Being in a denser state, the colder bottom-strata retain the power to shift sediment of larger grain-size (pebbles, gravel, etc.) from the centre of the watercourse. In this way the danger of flooding is reduced to a minimum. The spiral, vortical motion mentioned earlier, which eventually led Viktor Schauberger to the formation of his theories concerning **'implosion'**, creates the conditions where the germination of harmful bacteria is inhibited and the water remains disease-free.

The omission of temperature in the form of the *'temperature gradient'* in all hydraulic calculation has resulted in the most devastating floods and the ruination of almost all waterways. While flow velocity, shear force (sweeping force), sediment load, turbidity, viscosity, to name a few, are taken into account in numerous formulae, the temperature gradient, which significantly affects the function of all these different factors, has so far been totally disregarded in the fields of river engineering, water supply, water resources management and the condition of water generally.

Apart from variations in its content of organic matter, minerals and salts, the so-called 'impurities', water has always been deemed a lifeless inorganic substance. Therefore, except for certain defined water-temperatures required for specific purposes, cooling, heating, etc., the temperature or variations in temperature of any given water or water-body has been considered totally immaterial to the behaviour of the water itself, since the measured range of these variations has generally been rated too small to be capable of producing any noteworthy effect. This attitude has apparently remained unchanged.

In early July 1991 I attended a symposium on river engineering at the University of New England, Armidale, Australia, for the express purpose of discovering the state of the art in hydrology with regard to water temperature. The keynote speaker was Prof. John F. Kennedy (!!), a hydraulicist of world repute, director of the Iowa Institute of Hydraulic Research and Hunter Rouse Professor of Hydraulics at the University of Iowa in the United States. As he spoke I sat ready with pencil and paper to record every mention of the word 'temperature'. By the end of the hour's very interesting address, in which Professor Kennedy expressed his great love of rivers, I had only one tick on my paper! Afterwards, wanting more precise data, I spoke with him for about 15 minutes, describing Viktor Schauberger's theories about water movement and temperature and the fact that in the 1930s they had had the full support of an equally world renowned hydrologist, Prof. Philipp Forchheimer, with whose work Professor Kennedy was acquainted. However, according to Kennedy, the influence of temperature on the dynamics of water flow was still considered negligible

and therefore never taken into account. Having had this information straight from the horse's mouth, as it were, it is therefore to be concluded that temperature, as a factor in river engineering, is still ignored. As we shall see, however, it is *precisely* the small, sometimes infinitesimal variations in temperature that are crucial to the natural, healthy movement of water and optimal flow-regimes in streams.

Viktor Schauberger defines the temperature gradient, of which there are two forms, as follows:

A positive temperature gradient exists;

a) when the temperature of the water decreases and its density increases towards the anomaly point of +4°C, or;

b) when the density and temperature increase from freezing and below towards +4°C.

c) When ground or water temperatures are cooler than air temperatures.

A negative temperature gradient exists;

d) when the movement of temperature is away from +4°C, either upwards or downwards, both of which signify a decrease in density and energy.

In fig. 8.1 (p. 109) the direction of movement of these two temperature conditions are shown as two curves delineating the variations of volume and density with temperature. Here it can be seen how, with cooling, the volume decreases and the density increases, and *vice versa* with heating. A movement of temperature towards the anomaly point of +4°C always involves a positive temperature gradient, whereas a movement in the opposite direction is indicative of a negative temperature gradient. Remember here that heat, or whatever is suspended in a given medium (air or water), always flows or is transported towards cold.

Both forms of temperature gradient are active simultaneously in Nature but, for there to be evolution instead of devolution, the positive temperature gradient must predominate. On both upward and downward paths life emerges at the intersection of these two 'temperaments' as it were, each of which has different characteristics, properties, potential and opposite directions of movement or propagation.

Whatever manifests itself as a result of the interaction of these mutually opposing essences depends on the relative proportions between them, which also determines their point of intersection. For example, if the positive temperature gradient is very powerful, then the effect of the reciprocally weaker negative temperature gradient is beneficial and promotes the outbirth into physical form of the highest quality substances. In more mathematical terms, if as seen in fig. 4.6 the total effect of two dialectic opposites equals the unity, i.e. $1 \times 1 = 1$, then if one of the aspects is reduced to a half, the value of the other is two.

Despite the changed characteristics and properties, the overall value of the unity 1 has not been changed, however, because $\frac{1}{2} \times 2$ equals 1.

Conversely, if the roles and ratios are reversed and the negative temperature gradient is very dominant, then what unfolds as material substance is of inferior worth. For evolution and growth to proceed with increasing quality, vitality and health, which form is uppermost and at what level of reciprocity their interaction takes place is of absolutely crucial importance, for this not only affects the movement of water, the movement of sap in plants and the flow of blood in our veins, but also the configuration, structure and quality of the channels, ducts and vessels surrounding and guiding them, as will be seen later.

As it flows, water acts completely differently according to whichever temperature gradient is in force. In its concentrative, cooling, energising function the +4°C-approaching, positive temperature gradient has a formative effect. It is a process whereunder living systems can be built up, since in water it draws the ionised substances together into intimate and productive contact, for here the contained oxygen becomes passive and is easily bound by the cool carbones, thereby contributing beneficially to healthy growth and development. The +4°C-deviating, negative temperature gradient, on the other hand, has a disintegrative, debilitative function, for with increasing warming the structure of a given body becomes more loosely knit with a commensurate loss in cohering energy. In this case, due to the rising temperatures, the oxygen become increasingly aggressive and reverses its role as co-creator and benefactor, turning into a destroyer and fosterer of diseases and pathogens.

In all waters, forests and other living organisms the temperature gradient is active in both positive and negative forms. In the natural processes of synthesis and decomposition each has its special role to play in Nature's great production, but each must enter upon the stage of life at its appointed time. The positive temperature gradient, however, like temperature Type A and biomagnetism (see p. 103), must play the principal role if evolution is to unfold creatively. Unfortunately with our myopic fixation on heat-producing and therefore destabilising, depletive technology, we have turned this sublime order upside down and are now reaping the ever more awesome fruits of our misguided labour.

Notes

1. "The Ox and the Chamois", by Viktor Schauberger: *TAU* magazine, No.146, p.30: Werner Zimmermann.
2. *Our Senseless Toil*, Pt.I, p.11.
3. *Our Senseless Toil*, Pt.I, p.4.
4. *The Diving Hand* by Christopher Bird: New Age Press, USA ISBN 0-87613-090-2.
5. *Water – The Mirror of Science* by K.S. Davis & J.A. Day: Heinemann Educational, London, 1964.
6. *The Secret Doctrine* by H.P. Blavatsky, (Adyar Ed., 1971), Vol.1, p.125: Theosophical Pub., Adyar, India.
7. *Wissenschaftliche Grundlagen der Homöopathie*, "Scientific Foundations of Homeopathy": Barthel & Barthel, Postfach 57, D-82069 Schaftlarn, Germany, ISBN 3-88950-025-0.
8. Quoted from Viktor Schauberger's article, "Electrolysis", *Der Wiener Tag* newspaper, No.3443, p.20, 18th December 1932.
9. *The Secret Doctrine*, by Helena Petrovna Blavatsky, (Adyar Edition 1971), Vol.2, p.266, Stanza II: Theosophical Publishing, Adyar, India.

9
THE HYDROLOGICAL CYCLE

As a precursor to the evolvement of other life-forms, water's most vital function is its ceaseless, life-giving cycle through, around and over the Earth. This is normally referred to as the *'Hydrological Cycle'* or *'Water Cycle'* and involves the movement of water from subterranean regions to the atmosphere and back again. In terms of Viktor's concepts, however, we have to differentiate between the full and the half hydrological cycles, the difference between which is presently unrecognised by science. This difference, however, is crucial to the understanding of what is presently happening worldwide climatically.

9.1 The Full Hydrological Cycle

Fig. 9.1 shows the full hydrological cycle. Here the series of upward, anti-clockwise spirals at the far left hand side depict the evaporation of water from the sea. This rises, condenses and falls as rain. Some sinks into the earth and some drains away over the ground-surface, depending on whether the ground is forested or not and what type of temperature gradient is active in a given situation. In forested areas where, under natural conditions a positive temperature gradient normally prevails, the retention of runoff is in the order of 85%, about 15% being absorbed by the vegetation and humus and about 70% going towards groundwater, aquifer and underground stream recharge.

In the full hydrological cycle the groundwater table is recharged, the water is drawn up by and through the trees, transpires via

the leaves and rises to form clouds. In this diagram the evaporation from the ocean is differentiated from the transpiration from the vegetation, the former depicted as rising spirals rotating anticlockwise, the latter as clockwise gyrating spirals. This differentiation has been made because, in my view, the energies in the transpired water from the forest are qualitatively different from those in water evaporated from the sea.

When water rises from the trees, it is rising from a living thing, rather than from a body of water, such as the ocean. This is not to suggest that such a body of water is dead, but that it is inhabited by many creatures which consume almost all that it produces, both materially and in the way of energetic emanations, CO_2, O_2, etc. Therefore in terms of transpiration from the forest, we may be concerned with an energy form derived from a more dynamic living system which carries within it the imprint of the characteristics, traits, higher vibratory matrices of its mineral and trace-element content and the resonances of its living plant source. These additional qualities and energies are largely of immaterial nature and best explained in terms of homeopathic theory, in which the finer the dilution of a substance, the greater its efficacy as a healing medium. We shall therefore digress for a moment to acquaint ourselves with them.

The publication of an article entitled "Human Basophil Degranulation Triggered by Very Dilute Antiserum Against IgE" on the 30th June 1988[1], startled the scientific world, because the discovery it described

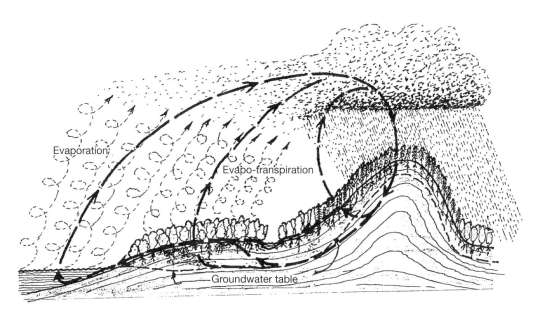

Fig. 9.1 **The full hydrological cycle**

The "FULL CYCLE" of water, the full hydrological cycle, is characterised by the following phases:

- Evaporation from oceans and evapo-transpiration from vegetation;
- Rising water-vapour;
- Cooling and condensing:
- Formation of clouds;
- Precipitation as rain;
- Infiltrates the ground under **positive temperature gradient**;
- Recharge of groundwater and aquifers;
- Maintenance and regulation of height of groundwater table;
- Formation of +4°C centre-stratum in groundwater;
- Creation of underground retention basins;
- Passage through the +4°C centre-layer of the groundwater;
- Purification at this temperature;
- Further sinking into the subterranean aquifers due to its own weight;
- Transition to a vaporous state due to the influence of the Earth's hot interior;
- Rising again towards the ground-surface with the simultaneous uptake of nutrients;
- Cooling of the water and deposition of nutrients;
- Draining away over the ground-surface;
- Evaporating and forming clouds;
- Falling again as rain, and so on.

could not be explained by the ordinary laws of physics. The article was the result of meticulous research began in 1983 by Professor Jacques Benveniste of the French National Institute for Health and Medical Research laboratory (INSERM) at the University of Paris-Sud, carried out at the instigation of Bernard Poitevin, a homeopathic researcher, this new avenue of scientific enquiry was aimed at testing the biological effects of homeopathic dilutions, and by extension, the efficacy of homeopathic medicines and the validity of homeopathic concepts.

The main ingredients of the experiment are basophils (a jelly-like white blood cell and anti-immunoglobin E – or aIgE), and a staining dye, toluene blue, whose application enables the otherwise invisible basophils to become visible. The effect of exposure of the cells thus stained to the antibody IgE, which Michel Schiff refers to as a "biological 'paint stripper'" or 'eraser'[2] is to render them partially or wholly invisible. This permitted the researchers to determine the extent to which a reaction had taken place in the basophils exposed to the antibody solution. According to Professor Benveniste, the reaction occurs even when the antibody dilutions amount to 1 part in 10^{120} parts of distilled water, that is to say, a dilution in the proportion of 1:1 + 119 zeros. To give an idea of the vast magnitude of the above figure, it is estimated by astronomers that the number of stars in the Universe amount to about 10 to the power of 20, i.e. 1 + 19 zeros or 1,000,000,000,000,000,000.

In these experiments one drop of what is described homeopathically as the 'mother-tincture' (in this case aIgE) is added to 99 drops of distilled water. This mixture is then shaken up and down or 'succussed' for about 30 seconds. 1 drop of this new mixture is then added to a further 99 drops of distilled water. This process was repeated 120 times. However, when the basophils exposed to this extraordinarily dilute antibody were observed, the reaction, i.e. the change in their visibility, could still be detected in a very large number of them.

Statistically, according to classic physics and chemistry, after 23 dilutions in which 100 trillion-billion molecules of distilled water were added to every molecule of the antibody IgE, there should have been no molecule of the antibody left. This relates to the so-called avogadro constant, $6.022\,52 \times 10^{23}$, formulated by the Italian physicist Count Amadeo Avogadro di Quaregna (1776–1856), which determines the number of atoms or molecules in 1 mole of substance, 1 mole being the amount of matter containing the same number of elementary particles as there are atoms in 0.012kg of Carbon-12. This number is in the ratio of 1:1+23 zeros, so in consideration of the above dilution in the ratio of 1:1+119 zeros, it meant that there were effectively no material residues of the original substance left in the liquid.

Another experiment showed that, after the mother-tincture had been diluted 37 times, it was more than twice as effective as a solution that had been diluted thrice. It has been mooted by theoretical physicist Lynn Trainor of the University of Toronto, who carried out parallel experiments, that these reactions may be the result of a 'physical' memory left in the water[3].

What caused this effect? Why did the cells still react with such an over-astronomically dilute solution? Is it memory as Lynn Trainor suggests? In a certain sense memory could be construed as a phenomenon of resonance, of things once heard as it were, the immaterial, energetic imprint of the image and qualities of the original preparation. Be that as it may, in my view it is for this reason that the transpirational material from the forest is endowed with a higher quality energetically than the water coming from the sea.

Just for the record, however, this discovery by Jacques Benveniste, like those of Stephan Riess and Viktor Schauberger before him, was evidently viewed as an unpardonable assault on the doctrines of established academe which tends to stray far from the principles of scientific integrity and impartiality enunciated by Sir William Grove in chapter 1. As a result Benveniste became both target and victim of much opprobrium from orthodox science and medicine. Indeed, in October 1993 it was reported that he was to be evicted as head of the immunopharmacology unit at INSERM. Moreover the research unit itself, U-200, was also supposed to be closed down by the end of the year, Benveniste claiming that he was the victim of "ideological repression"[4].

Other forces have meanwhile been at work, however, for due to the subsequent verification of his findings at other independent institutions and the establishment of their apparent irrefutability, Benveniste has been accorded certain international recognition and 'notoriety' in the interim. Fearing that it would suffer the same scorn it had heaped on Benveniste, INSERM have continued to pay his and his secretary's salaries, although it has withheld all funding for further research and refused any allocation for other day-to-day expenses and the employment of laboratory staff, for which Beneviste himself must pay. On a happier note however, while INSERM continues to maintain its obdurate stance, other more enlightened individuals have deemed Benveniste's research on water to be so important that an organisation 'Science Innovative' was formed with the specific purpose of providing him with moral support and financing his currently on-going research.[5]

Returning now to the description of the full hydrological cycle, the water first evaporates from the oceans and the forest. The rising water vapour cools with altitude, condenses, forms clouds, aggregates into larger droplets and precipitates as rain. Precipitation occurs when two systems combine, which in their separated condition float within the ambient energy-field, be it of liquid or aeriform nature, thus creating a mass in excess of the volume of air or liquid they displace.

With full forest cover the ground temperature is cooler than the incident rainwater which infiltrates the ground under the influence of a positive temperature gradient, i.e. the temperature decreases from the air through the ground towards the +4°C anomaly point of water in the central stratum of the groundwater body. Falling on the cooler ground, the warmer rainwater is readily absorbed, the groundwater is recharged and aquifers and subterranean waterways are developed. Rainwater can only infiltrate under a positive temperature gradient. A corollary of this is that the maintenance and the height of the groundwater table is wholly dependent amongst other things on the amount of infiltration and the presence of a positive temperature gradient.

Recalling that the temperature of absolute zero is −273.15°C and that the temperature spectrum in which we live lies roughly between −10°C and +40°C, any general change in a downward direction would have the direst consequences not only for our continuing existence on this planet, but for all other life-forms as well. It is therefore of vital importance to our survival that this bandwidth of temperatures, largely determined and regulated by the amount of water vapour in the atmosphere, should remain unaltered. Moreover, any activity of ours which reduces the naturally occurring water vapour content of the atmosphere should be prevented because it will inevitably lower the World's overall temperature. This is because there will no longer be sufficient water to retain the prescribed amount of heat.

Although all the evidence is there in the way of deserts, it seems that mankind has never learnt that to take away the trees is to take away the water. It is the forest cover that is responsible for fine-tuning the content of water vapour in the atmosphere and for the creation of fresh water itself. Through the continuous removal of forest, we will gradually approach the condition where what we might term the 'base quantity' of water provided by the oceans, which raises the atmospheric water level to a certain degree, is no longer tempered by the additional transpiration from the forest. It is this which augments the overall amount of water vapour both quantitatively and qualitatively, and at the same time raises the ambient temperatures sufficiently to enable us to exist.

Unfortunately this alarming disturbance of the natural cycles is already far advanced. The increasingly chaotic weather patterns we presently experience are merely the legitimate consequence of an ever more disorderly and fragmented distribution of water vapour. In some areas there is an excessive concentration, resulting in an over-accumulation of heat, a sharp rise in temperature, massive downpours and flooding, while in others there is virtually no water vapour at all, producing both severe drought conditions and premature, local cooling. The combined effect of both these processes is to provoke increasingly frequent and violent storms as these two extremes of temperature clash together in the process of restoring Nature's equilibrium.

9.2 *The Half Hydrological Cycle*

In contrast, the half hydrological cycle is the condition that presently prevails almost worldwide. The half hydrological cycle shown in fig. 9.2 has the same basic format as the full cycle, but in this instance the trees shown in fig. 9.1 have been removed from the land surface; note that the heavy broken line, representing the sub-surface movement of groundwater is missing. The type of evaporation changes, since it is no longer sourced from living things, but from barren ground, and may well be the repository of destructive rather than creative energetic imprints.

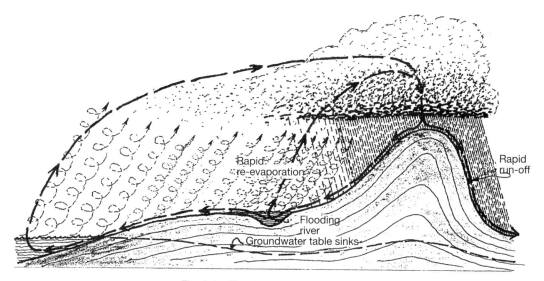

Fig. 9.2   **The half hydrological cycle**

The "HALF CYCLE", in contrast, has the following features:

- Evaporation from ocean;
- Rising water-vapour;
- Cooling and condensing:
- Formation of clouds;
- Precipitation as rain;
- **No infiltration** of rainwater due to **negative temperature gradient;**
- Rapid run-off over the ground surface;
- **No** groundwater recharge;
- Sinking water table;
- Cessation of natural supply of nutrients to vegetation;
- Under certain conditions, major flooding can occur;
- Excessively fast re-evaporation;
- Over-saturation of atmosphere with water-vapour;
- Rapid reprecipitation as storm-rain.

One flood therefore produces the next, or no rain falls at all and drought conditions prevail.

Once the forest has been removed, the exposed ground heats up rapidly, all the more so if dry, and to much higher temperatures. A negative temperature gradient now prevails, because the ground temperature in general is hotter than the incident rain; in other words the temperature increases from the clouds into the ground. If the rainfall is excessive, then flooding inevitably occurs. We have all seen how cold water sizzles and skitters rapidly sideways when it falls on a hot-plate. A hot, dry ground-surface, produces the same effect, making it impossible for the the rainwater to infiltrate and in many hot countries denuded of vegetation, dry valleys and creeks are suddenly engulfed by a wall of water as terrifying flash-floods sweep away everything in their path.

With no longer any trees to absorb it, the surface water runs off immediately, spreading over wide areas, thereby increasing the rate of evaporation locally. This overloads the atmosphere with water vapour and flooding is either soon repeated or precipitation occurs elsewhere, sometimes far away from the original source of the water vapour, and devastating drought ensues regionally. One flood therefore begets the next, or precipitates drought conditions.

Over the last few years we have all become aware of the increasingly disastrous flooding worldwide, a process that under the present conditions is self-perpetuating. In December 1993, for example, the record flooding of the Rhine caused inundations not seen since 1743. This was repeated in even more devastating measure in January 1995. Until a sufficient number of trees are replanted; not just a billion, but several hundred billions, we will be subjected to the unrelenting, merciless cycle of drought, flood, drought, flood, particularly in equatorial and warm temperate zones. There is only one solution and that is to reafforest this planet on a massive scale – now!

A further horrific consequence of the half cycle is that there is no groundwater recharge, the groundwater table sinks and the supply of nutrients to the vegetation from below ceases. This is what Viktor Schauberger called a 'biological short-circuit', for apart from the rapid transfer of substanceless water to the atmosphere, under a half hydrological cycle the nutrients present in the upper zones of the groundwater table, which are normally raised up by the trees to a level accessible to other lesser plants, are left below and sink with the sinking groundwater. It subsides to levels far beyond the reach of even deep-rooted trees, taking all soil moisture and trace-elements down with it. No water, no life and the desert reigns supreme. The groundwater is virtually lost forever, vanished into the bowels of the Earth from whence it originally came.

Not only is water lost in the depths, but it also begins to be lost at great heights. The initially greater intensity of thunderstorms and storm activity following the onset of the half-cycle, raises the water vapour to levels far higher than normal, even to as much as 40–80 kilometres. Here it reaches altitudes where it is exposed to much stronger ultra-violet and high-energy gamma-radiation, which dissociate the water-molecule, separating the oxygen from the hydrogen. Due to its lesser specific weight the hydrogen then rises, while the oxygen sinks. Worst of all, all that was once water has effectively been removed altogether. It has gone, and gone for good.

This initiates a process, in which the atmosphere is first forced to get warmer due to the overcharge of water vapour, but then, as the water rises higher, it is dissociated and disappears, and the atmosphere cools, because the amount of heat-retaining water vapour has diminished. What follows is a new ice age. All this was elaborated in detail in Viktor Schauberger's writings some 60 years ago.

Clearly, the hitherto unrecognised difference between the half and full hydrological cycles is extremely important. Only when this has become known and generally understood by the public at large and sufficient economic and political pressure applied, can appropriate remedial action be taken to counter the inevitable outcome. It is in our urgent interest to restore the full hydrological cycle as quickly as possible, for the full cycle means life and continuing existence, whereas the other signifies death and extinction.

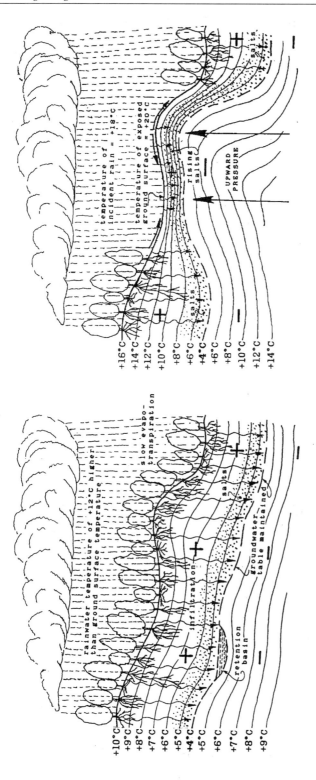

Fig. 9.3   **Positive temperature-gradient**

Ground cooler – rainwater warmer: Incident rainwater with a temperature higher than the receiving ground-stratum can infiltrate readily into the ground. Recharge of the groundwater and the formation of subterranean retention basins occurs. The supply of nutrients and moisture to the vegetation is regular. The salts (shown as dots) remain just above the groundwater table.

Fig. 9.4   **Positive and negative temperature-gradients**

Under conditions where both types of temperature-gradient are active (positive under the forest, negative under the exposed ground), infiltration mainly occurs in the forested area, where the salts also remain well below the ground-surface. Where the ground has been exposed to the sun's heat, the watertable is temporarily forced upwards by the geothermal pressure from below, bringing up the dissolved salts with it. With less than normal rainwater infiltration in this area, the salts remain near the ground-surface. Groundwater recharge is variable and problems of salination are incipient.

9.3 Temperature Gradients and Nutrient Supply

We shall now examine the temperature gradients in the ground and their effects in connection with figs. 9.3, 9.4 & 9.5, because the solution, transport and deposition of nutrients are all functions of the temperature gradient. Positive and negative temperature gradients produce opposite effects. The direction of the temperature gradient indicates the direction of movement. The direction of energy or nutrient transfer is always from heat to cold.

Viktor Schauberger's important principle on this subject states that under the exclusion of light and air the precipitation of salts and minerals occurs with cooling, whereas with exposure to light and air precipitation takes place with heating. In both cases the highest quality matter is precipitated last. In the former case all the various nutrients and salts are deposited well below the ground surface as the water cools to +4°C. In the latter case, however, due to heat-evaporation and little penetration, the lowest quality nutrients are precipitated at the surface, which not only has dire consequences for soil fertility, but also for the proper formation of trees, as we shall see later.

To recapitulate, a positive temperature gradient occurs when the incident rainwater is warmer than the receiving soil. This naturally implies that the soil is protected from the heating effect of the Sun by trees and other vegetation and, if the whole surface of the Earth is forested, then the groundwater table hugs the configuration of the ground-surface. As shown in fig. 9.3 the water infiltrates down to the lower strata, the groundwater body and aquifers are recharged, subterranean retention basins are created and the salts (shown as a dotted mass) remain at a level where they cannot contaminate the upper strata and are not damaging to those plants unable to metabolise them. Should a part of the forest be felled and the ground surface exposed to the direct light of the Sun, as in fig. 9.4, the temperature of ground in that area rises.

With this in mind it is essential that if any felling is to occur, then the trees should never be cut at the top of a hill. This creates a bald patch exposed to the Sun's heat and effectively reduces the capacity of the groundwater to rise as high as it might otherwise do were the trees left untouched. If the temperature of the incident rainwater is, say, +18°C and the temperature of the receiving ground surface +20°C, the rain will not penetrate, but will flow off laterally to areas where it can, always presuming that a healthy balance between open space and forest has been maintained. In such a case problems of salinity will be kept to a minimum, since the overall level of the groundwater table is not unduly affected.

It does rise, however, under the areas where the trees have been removed, due to the geothermally induced upward pressure from below and the reduction in the quantity of overburdening groundwater lying above the +4°C centre-stratum. In other words the counteracting downward pressure has been diminished. (This effect is discussed in more detail in chapter 10.) As this water rises so too are the salts elevated, though in this case not into the root-zone of the vegetation. However, if all the trees are removed (fig. 9.5), then there is no rainwater penetration at all, the groundwater table initially rises, bringing up all the salts with it, only eventually to sink or disappear altogether, because under these conditions no recharge is possible. This is how oversalination of the soil occurs, and the only way the problem can be remedied is to recreate a positive temperature gradient through reafforestation.

In the beginning such trees will have to be pioneer, salt-loving trees and other primitive plants, such species being the only ones that can survive under such conditions. Later, as the soil climate improves and its salt content diminishes, other species of tree can replace them since, over a period of time and due to the cooling of the ground by the shading of the pioneer trees, the rainwater enters the ground, taking the salts with it. Eventually the pioneer trees die off, because the evolved soil conditions are now no longer suitable, and the dynamic balance of Nature is restored.

Irrigation only exacerbates the problem, because during the night the ground temperatures cool somewhat, allowing the irrigation water to percolate a certain distance into the upper, now salt-containing strata. There it collects the salts and, with the increase in

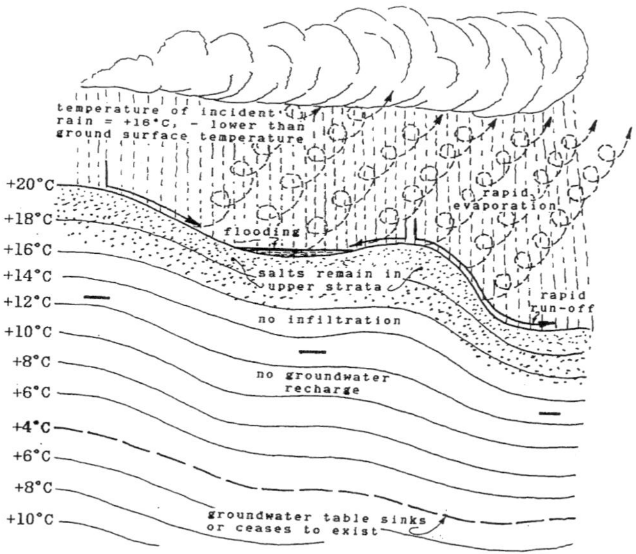

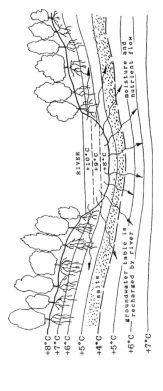

Fig. 9.6 Positive temperature gradient

When the temperature of the river water is warmer than the adjacent ground temperatures, a **positive temperature gradient** exists. The direction of the transfer of energy and nutritive material is from the river to the soil. According to their relative temperatures and depths, the adjacent ground strata are infused with fresh moisture and the surrounding vegetation is revitalised with additional nutrients. Under these conditions the groundwater table is also recharged.

Fig. 9.5 Negative temperature gradient

Ground warmer – rainwater cooler: With the overall clearing of the forest, the ground is everywhere exposed to the harsh light of the Sun. The ground heats up and any rainfall will always be colder than the ground-surface. No infiltration of rainwater occurs and hence no groundwater recharge. The groundwater table, if it exists at all, lies very deep below the ground-surface. Any infiltration of water (mostly only possible with cooler night temperatures) only serves to bring additional salts to the surface on the following day, exacerbating problems of salination.

temperature during the day, the atmosphere rises as it becomes specifically lighter, drawing up the infiltrated irrigation water plus its acquired salts, which through exposure to light and heat are deposited, and through evaporation are left lying in the uppermost soil level. The problem of salination varies according to latitude, altitude and season, since these also affect the ambient ground temperatures, the intensity of the Sun's radia-

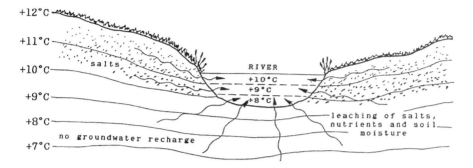

Fig. 9.7   **Negative Temperature Gradient**

If the ground temperatures are hotter than the river water, then a negative temperature gradient from river to ground exists and the transport of nutrients and salts takes place from the ground strata to the river. The ground strata are leached of their various minerals and trace elements, leading to a nett loss of biochemical material. Increasing soil infertility and river salinity results. The groundwater table also sinks for lack of resupply.

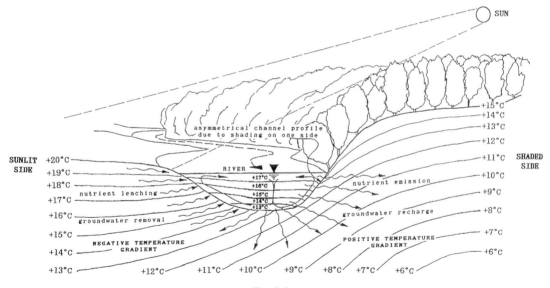

Fig. 9.8

The orientation of a river relative to the general position and height of the Sun also affects the nutrient supply. In stretches of rivers where the flow is either east->west or west->east, the side nearest the sun tends to be shaded more frequently. The water on this side is therefore cooler and on the opposite side, warmer. This produces an asymmetrical channel profile as the result of an asymmetrical temperature distribution. Should the side nearest the Sun be suitably forested, then the ground temperatures on this side are also cooler and a positive temperature gradient exists in the direction river->ground, permitting the absoprtion of moisture, trace elements and nutrients from the river. If the ground-surface on the opposite side of the river has been cleared, the ground temperatures there will be hotter, a positive temperature gradient then prevails in the direction ground->river, leading to the absorption of soil-moisture and nutrients by the river. One side of the river therefore tends to be more fertile than the other.

tion and the length of the periods of the ground's exposure to heat.

There are other conditions which also pertain to nutrient flow and, while slightly out of place here, since rivers and stream management will be discussed more fully in later chapters, it nevertheless seems more appropriate to address them while we are on the subject. Through the corrasion and abrasion of their sediment, all healthy rivers and streams are metabolisers and transporters of nutritive material, and as such are major contributors to the supply of nutrients to the surrounding vegetation. However they can only impart nutrients where the conditions are conducive to a nutrient transfer, i.e. where a positive temperature gradient between water and ground prevails.

Fig. 9.6 shows a river flowing through an entirely forested area. As an illustration the river water has a temperature range of between +10°C and +8°C from surface to riverbed. In contrast the ground temperatures under the forest are cooler, ranging from +8°C at the surface to +4°C at the level of the groundwater centre-stratum. The river water is therefore warmer than the surrounding soil, a positive temperature gradient exists and the transfer of nutrients, energy and moisture takes place from warmer to cooler regions, namely from the river in the direction of the ground. The fertility of the soil is enhanced and the groundwater table recharged.

Conversely, if the opposite condition of a negative temperature gradient prevails as shown in fig. 9.7, then the flow of energy, moisture and nutrients proceeds from the warmer ground strata towards the cooler

river. Here the river actually extracts from the ground the nutrients which have themselves been raised to the upper strata due to the processes mentioned earlier and illustrated in fig. 9.5 above. This results in an increasing leaching of the minerals, trace-elements and nutrients from the surrounding soil, leading to a nutrient deficit and eventual infertility. For the same reasons no groundwater recharge results. A corollary of this phenomenon is that the longer a river flows through irrigated, sunlit farmlands, the more it becomes contaminated with salts, artificial fertilisers, pesticides, etc. making it increasingly unusable as a source of water in the lower reaches.

In fig. 9.8 both negative and positive temperature gradients are active simultaneously. Here the variation in river water temperature, again for the purposes of discussion, is from +17°C at the water surface to +13°C at the bottom. The ground under the forested area on one side of the river has lower temperatures than the river water, whereas the cleared, treeless land on the opposite side gives rise to higher ground temperatures. In this instance the river acts to convey nutrients from the warmer left bank to the cooler right bank following the dictates of the prevailing temperature gradient which, from examination of the various ground temperatures, on the left hand side is negative and the right hand side positive. The cooling effect of the forest also affects the shape of the channel profile and is mirrored in the greater depth of water on that side, since cooler water flows faster and in a more laminar fashion, removing sediment and thereby deepening the bed at that point.

Notes

1. British scientific journal *Nature*, 30th June 1988.
2. *The Memory of Water – Homeopathy and the Battle of Ideas in the New Science* by Michel Schiff, Thorsons, an imprint of Harper Collins, 1995, ISBN 0-7225-3262-8.
3. Information from Brauer Biotherapies, 1 Para Road, P.O.Box 234, Tanunda 5352, So. Australia.
4. *Nexus New Times* magazine, Vol.2, No.17, Dec.1993–Jan.1994, quoting from *New Scientist* 23rd October 1993.
5. Christopher Bird has kindly supplied information from Mme Annie Asada, director for develop-
ment at 'Science Innovative', and from Jack Dupré, a close associate of Dr. Marie Nonclercq, pharmacist and author of a book on Antoine Béchamp; (Louis Pasteur, Béchamp's contemporary, was responsible for suppressing his significant findings). 'Science Innovative' was set up by Mme. Evelyne Besso who is also its President. S.I.'s headquarters are presently situated at 30 Ave. D'Elyau, Paris 75116 (tel: 01.4656.6650). Its aim is to foster enquiry and interest into the essential nature of water, and to support Jacques Benveniste's continuing research.

10

THE FORMATION OF SPRINGS

There, where water splits in twain,
Life is ere set free, unfolding its domain,
And in emerging from its source,
Water's blessed with vital, living force.
There flock beasts, athirst for flowers,
'Midst thrusting boughs and leafy bowers.

"God, Nature and Cosmos" by
J.W. von Goethe

10.1 Seepage and True Springs

Generally speaking, springs are understood as the emergence of groundwater that has encountered an impervious stratum. This type of spring is actually a seepage spring (fig. 10.1), but not a true spring. Under the correct conditions, namely under a positive temperature gradient – warmer rain, cooler ground, cooler substrata, etc – a seepage spring forms as water infiltrates, accumulates underground, meets an impervious layer and under the effect of gravity, drains away down the gradient to its point of egress. The temperature of seepage springs generally approximates the temperature of the ground-strata through which the water passes, which may be in the order of +6°C to +9°C. It contains a certain amount of dissolved salts and trace elements, but is not very rich in them. On the other hand, a true spring, and this is where the difference lies, is a spring which has a temperature of around +4°C. It evolves under completely different conditions and processes.

Fig. 10.2 depicts a cross-section through a mountain and shows the various ground temperatures at different levels. These may not represent the true temperatures, but are indicated here as examples. Since there is a positive temperature gradient from the ground-surface inwards, it means that rainwater can always infiltrate. Recalling that this is immature water, it greedily absorbs all the elements it can. Undesirable elements, salts, etc, lying in the upper strata are therefore dissolved by the percolating rainwater and carried down into the depths, where they are eventually precipitated as the water cools to +4°C. In this densest state at the centre of the groundwater body, the +4°C centre-stratum, the water no longer has any room for them. They are expelled from it and left in a zone above the now fresh groundwater table, where they are accessed by various deep-rooted species of trees, whose job it is to metabolise and transform them and to raise them up to the higher levels, making them available to other shallower-rooted forms of vegetation.

We might recall what Viktor Schauberger formulated on this theme, that under the exclusion of light and air the precipitation of salts and minerals occurs with cooling, whereas with exposure to light and air precipitation takes place with heating.

As the rainwater enters the ground, it exerts increasing pressure on the +4°C centre-stratum of the groundwater body. Due to this overburdening pressure from above, the lowermost strata of the groundwater body are themselves forced downwards into regions where the ground temperatures begin to rise owing to geothermal activity. As a result, the water in these strata begins to expand, creating a counter-pressure to the pressure from above.

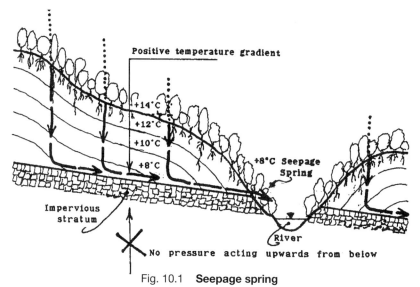

Fig. 10.1 **Seepage spring**

Seepage springs occur when water infiltrating into the ground (positive temperature gradient) encounters an impervious stratum. Due to gravity it seeps down the inclined plane of this stratum and emerges where this meets the outer ground surface. The rate of outflow is principally determined by the amount of infiltrated rainwater and its temperature roughly conforms to that of the surrounding strata. They are not often very cold. Establishment of a true groundwater table does not arise.

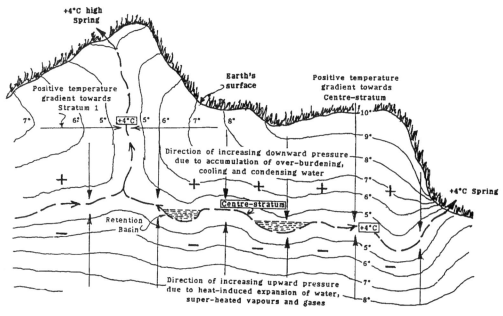

Fig. 10.2 **True spring and high altitude springs**

True springs come into being because of pressure acting from above and below on the +4°C centre-stratum of the groundwater, which at this temperature is incompressible. This centre-stratum is squeezed between the weight of the over-burdening water-strata above and the water-strata lying below it, which try to expand due to increasing heat from the Earth's interior. Finding no other avenue of escape from this immense pressure, the +4°C centre-stratum is therefore forced to move either laterally or vertically, ultimately emerging as springs. This is why springs are often to be found near the tops of mountains, where no sufficient catchment for a seepage spring exists. True springs normally exhibit temperatures closely approximating +4°C. This combination of opposing pressures is also responsible for regulating the height of the groundwater table.

The +4°C centre-stratum, which is incompressible at this temperature, is therefore increasingly squeezed between these two opposing pressures, namely the overburden of infiltrating water from above and the expanding, sometimes super-heated water from below. Its only possible avenue of escape is either laterally or vertically, or a combination of both.

On many mountains in Austria, for example, there are springs which emerge at between 100 and 200 metres below the summit. These mountain peaks are commonly composed of solid rock and, were such springs to be attributed to seepage only, there is not sufficient catchment area to provide for their continuous, year-round discharge. The temperature of these springs always lies between +4°C and +5°C; very cold water indeed. From this it can be inferred with some certainty that true springwater arises and moves within the central core of the groundwater body.

As the springwater rises, while rich in carbones, particularly in the form of carbonic acid, it is very largely deficient in dissolved oxygen, for during the course of the water's initial sinking, various organisms and tree roots have removed whatever dissolved oxygen was available in the infiltrating rainwater. By and large such water is therefore oxygen-deficient and, if this deficiency is extreme and the water is drunk directly at the place where it gushes out of the ground, its emanation of carbon-dioxide vapours are breathed in at the same time. Mountain folk in Austria call these vapours the 'waterworm'; they are also known as choke-damp and are on occasion to be found in mines, the effect of which is to do precisely what its name suggests, and if no air containing oxygen is soon available then death follows. Since the water from these so-called 'poisoned springs' has no oxygen, it actively extracts this from the tissues in the area of the trachea, esophagus and stomach, while the undiluted carbon-dioxide vapour immediately begins to attack the lungs for the same reason.

This affliction was also known as the 'vanishing lung disease,' or in plain English, 'galloping consumption'. Those who are unfortunate enough to drink much of this water are likely to die within a few days to the accompaniment of excruciating stabbing pains in the chest. However, once the water has emerged and has flowed even ten metres, due to its convoluting, splashing, flowing motion it has already made up for the lack of oxygen through its absorption from the atmosphere and the proper carbone-oxygen balance has again been restored.

The absorption of oxygen, however, has the effect of increasing the volume of the water. At a spring in Montenegro, which flowed down a smooth, unfissured face of rock, Viktor Schauberger made careful measurements of the volume of flow directly at the mouth and metre by metre below it. He discovered that it increased significantly. There being no possibility of any additional inflows due to the unbroken formation of the rock, the only possible answer was that this resulted from the absorption of oxygen.

10.2 *The Rising of Springwater*

In *Our Senseless Toil* Viktor briefly describes a 24-hour experiment designed to show the dynamics of true springs, the diurnal fluctuation in the height of the groundwater table and the flow of sap in trees. As we said earlier, there is no condition of equilibrium in Nature. The experimental arrangement shown in fig. 10.3, consists of a U-shaped tube with open connections on one arm to two capillary tubes and on the other to four capillary tubes. A certain quantity of pure quartz sand sufficient to close the internal diameter is placed in the bottom of the U-tube and saturated with salt water. The effect of this saltwater and sand is to separate and prevent direct communication between the contents of the two rising arms of the U-tube. These are then filled with fresh, high-grade springwater, containing little or no oxygen, which has not been exposed to the Sun, or other light or any atmospheric influence. The U-tube is then placed in an insulated vessel, such as a bucket, containing some ice at the bottom, and the whole filled with good, clean loam. The ice at the bottom is necessary to create an artificial zone of +4°C at the base of the U-tube and a positive temperature gradient from the outer surface of the loam inwards.

The whole arrangement is then placed outside under the Sun's heating influence. Once the lowest water has reached its ice-induced anomaly point of +4°C, where it attains its highest density and weight, and the higher-lying water begins to heat up, losing its 'temperatureless' state, the water slowly rises up the arm to which the bundle of four capillary tubes is attached and overflows due to its greater communication with atmospheric influences; the water in the other arm remaining at rest.

While I have not found more explicit details of this experiment in the material in my possession, I think this upward movement is most probably due to two factors:

1) the conversion with warming of the carbonic acid content into carbon dioxide bubbles, which rise, pushing individual packets of water ahead of them (see description of rising sap in chapter 18), and
2) the suctional effect of rising atmospheric gases, which become specifically lighter with exposure to the Sun's heat.

At day's end this water column subsides with cooling, and overnight is in a state of rest, its contained carbones now replete with absorbed oxygen and other atmospheric gases. During the night, however, the carbone-rich water in the arm under the bundle of two capillaries becomes active. This may be due partially to its largely unsatisfied appetite for oxygen, whose supply has been limited by the fewer number of capillary tubes; also to the combined pressures of the night-cooled, therefore specifically heavier, atmospheric gases entering the now evacuated bundle of 4 capillaries; and to the marginally specifically heavier weight of the condensed gas-enriched, recently subsided water. Both of these exert pressure on the salt-water in the base of the U-tube, causing it to shift laterally. This in turn exerts an uplift pressure on the unoxygenated water in the opposite arm, causing the water to rise up the bundle of two capillaries.

This emulates the continuous temperature-, pressure- and suction-related pulsation, which is the hallmark of all natural fluid movement –

water, blood and sap. These capillary tubes are very fine, i.e. their internal diameter is minute, in this case about 0.4mm internal diameter. In terms of plant anatomy, the bundle of 4 capillaries represents the xylem tubelets. These generally have a larger cross-sectional area than the phloem tubelets, which are represented by the bundle of 2 capillaries.

What is not explained in Viktor's description is whether both arms of the U-tube are positioned parallel to the Sun's rays, or at right-angles, the 2-capillary bundle lying behind the 4-capillary bundle. Not explained either is whether both capillary bundles are to be protected from light and heat. However, as this experiment is designed in part to demonstrate the ebb and flow of sap which occurs beneath the bark, it is desirable that the capillary tubes should be adequately shielded and insulated.

If the bundle of four capillary tubes is removed, then water emerges from the top of the U-tube leg, demonstrating the formation of natural springs. On the diagram, it can be seen that the two water levels on each side of the U-tube are not in communication, but remain independent of each other, representing another phenomenon in Nature inexplicable according to current theory.

This decrease in atmospheric density close to the ground during the day is also responsible for the slight diurnal fluctuation in the height of the groundwater table. Being specifically lighter, the atmosphere exerts less pressure and the groundwater rises in consequence. The weight of the atmosphere is thus a contributing factor to the height of the groundwater table and to the rate of flow of springs, which are known to deliver more water during the night than during the day.

Another experiment showing the action of true springs and one much simpler to carry out is described in *Etidorpha* (Aphrodite spelt backwards), a book published by John Uri Lloyd in 1896. The book gives an account of the experiences of William Morgan, who was mysteriously abducted on the 12th of August 1826, which he related when he appeared to Llwellyn Drury some 30 years previous to the book's publication[1]. The book gives a number of interesting insights into many natural phenomena including water and its movement.

**The constant pulsation in the capillary tube.
There is no condition of equilibrium in nature.**

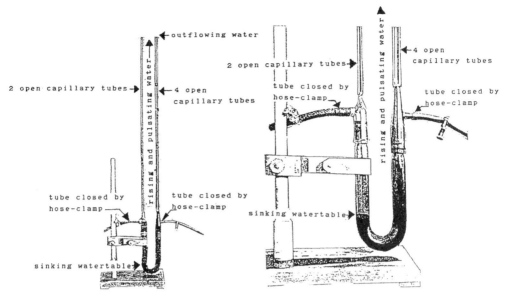

**The principle of rising sap in the tree
and circulating blood in the body**

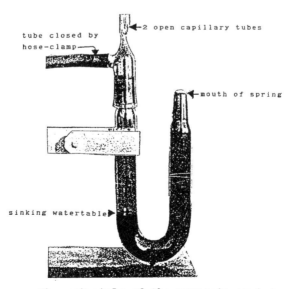

The principle of the mountain spring

Fig. 10.3

This experiment consists of the interaction between salt and fresh water as a result of their different specific gravities. Water is the basis for all specific gravities and has the value of $1g/cm^3$. Saltwater or seawater with a 4% salt content has a higher specific gravity of about $1.025g/cm^3$, depending on its temperature, thus making it 2.5% heavier than fresh water.

Fig. 10.4 depicts the experimental arrangement assembled by the author. It consists of two 4-litre glass bottles, one of which has had the bottom removed. This is turned upside down and fixed with a water-tight seal to the lower. Mixture between the two types of water is restricted by the placement of a cork where the two bottles are joined together. In the centre of the cork there is a section of glass tube with a diameter marginally larger than the hooked capillary tube. Before insertion of the capillary tube the lower bottle is filled with fresh water. The capillary tube with an internal diameter of 0.4mm is then introduced, the bottom of the hooked section being about 15mm above the surface of the saltwater in the upper bottle when this is filled with saltwater. It is suggested that a strong saline solution be used to produce the best effects, since we are here concerned with a natural process at a very small scale. Almost immediately after filling with saltwater, the fresh water can be seen to rise up the capillary and, passing over the top of the hook, it begins to form droplets. These may not fall immediately, and initially the capillary may need to be tapped once or twice. After this the fresh water continues to drop due to the effect of the heavier weight of the saltwater in the upper vessel until such time as the two waters have mixed. Dropping then ceases.

This clearly demonstrates another aspect related to the formation of true springs and mountain springs. While we have seen above that the +4°C centre-stratum of the groundwater body is compressed between two opposing pressures, the pressure resulting from the weight of the infiltrating rainwater is further enhanced by the solution of salts and other elements as it descends. This gives the water additional mass, which in turn exerts a higher pressure on the centre-stratum than if the percolating water were merely fresh water.

There are, however, two additional factors at work in the movement of springwater. These are physical in nature and not mechanical, although, as we have seen above, the mechanical forces of pressure are active as well. From chapter 5 we learned that in Viktor Schauberger's view the Earth is a female entity and that all the energies and elements she secretes within her body, principally the carbones, are also of feminine nature. The Sun and oxygen on the other hand are male and fertilising.

The first factor therefore relates to the chemical composition of the springwater itself. As result of the processes mentioned above, the +4°C centre-stratum water is virtually totally

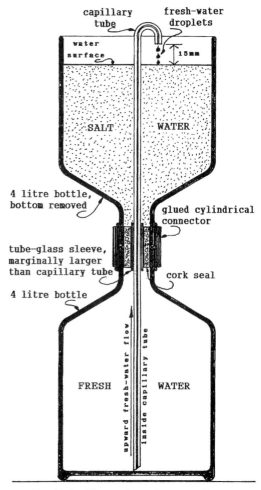

Fig. 10.4   **Mountain spring experiment**

deficient in oxygen, but very high in carbonic acid and other carbones obtained by its passage through coal-bearing and other mineral strata. From this arises a powerful mutual attraction as the female fructigenic ethericities (non-physical energies) seek to unite with those of oxygen, the seminal or fertilising substance. The uprising of springwater is therefore enhanced by this hunger, as it were, because in the process an energetic vacuity is created in the carbone-rich water which wants to be filled, giving the centre-stratum the impulse to move to wherever the oxygen is waiting.

The second factor concerns the type of motion itself. The uprising of the springwater is greatly assisted by the actual way in which the nascent springwater moves and by the particular shape of the rising underground passages through which it flows. The best example of this sinuous configuration can be seen in glaciers, where meltwater plunges down crevasses in the ice. Due to the motion of the falling water, these are sculptured into twisting, convoluting shapes; shapes, however, that are created by the water itself, reflecting the way in which water likes to move naturally. By turning these crevasses upside down so to speak, we then get some idea of the shape of the shafts in which springwater comes to the surface.

The form of movement these shafts induce is that of the cycloid-spiral-space-curve which, as mentioned in earlier chapters is responsible for the Earth's floating motion in space and is associated with the forces of levitation. Because of its incompressibility at +4°C, it is therefore the combined effect of these two additional factors of oxygen-hunger and the generation of levitational energies that permits springwater to overcome the forces of gravity and gush forth all year round and often in large quantities from the tops of mountains where, incidentally, they are also exposed to reduced atmospheric pressure.

Although they lack oxygen, both mountain springs and true springs generally emerge into the light of day from dark clefts and shaded niches so as to avoid the direct light of the Sun, exposure to which may cause the spring to dry up. A case of this was when, one day on a high plateau in the mountains with his foresters, Viktor Schauberger passed by a ramshackle dome-like stone construction from which water, apparently from a spring, was flowing. Since it was very dilapidated and might have presented a danger to his employers when hunting, he ordered it to be demolished. Whereupon he was told that if this was done the spring would vanish.

Always of an inquiring turn of mind, Viktor said that it should still be dismantled, but very carefully with the place of each stone marked in case it had to be rebuilt. On another excursion about a week later, he noticed that the flow of water had ceased. The spring was dry. As sources of good water on this high plateau were infrequent and therefore important during time of hunting, he hurriedly summoned his foresters and game wardens and had the cupola carefully reconstructed as before. A few days later the spring began to flow again.

What happens to the water after it has emerged from the spring and how it flows on its gushing, gyrating, whorling path down into the valley will be mainly addressed in chapter 13. The way water moves naturally is of extreme importance for its inner health and vitality. According to Viktor Schauberger, so subtle are the factors here concerned that even the first two curves the water makes after leaving the spring can have an effect up to 10 kilometres downstream. Therefore if we wish to ensure the maintenance of these qualities in our rivers and the water we drink, then careful attention must be paid to what follows in subsequent chapters.

10.3 Energy from the Deep Ocean

This heading may appear slightly out of context here, but while the formation of true springs is still fresh in our minds, it would seem appropriate at this juncture to examine a method of generating unlimited amounts of virtually free energy directly from the deep ocean, since this can be achieved using the same principle. As a means of generating energy, it is not only wholly sustainable and non-polluting, but it will also render all other contemporary systems of power generation obsolete. All the highly complex machinery and mechanisms presently used for such purposes will be relegated to the scrap heap.

It will become clear from what follows that nuclear power, in particular is no longer any kind of economic option. It never was in the first place, except perhaps in the short-term. With all its vast associated costs and the ever-present and known perils of radiation leakage, the inescapable, immense costs of safe storage of fissionable material after decommissioning have never really been included in the economic equation. These costs have always been hushed up, because they will have to be borne by many generations to come.

Plutonium, one of the principle end-products of nuclear fission, has a half-life of 25,000 years. That is to say that after 25,000 years its level of radioactivity has been reduced to a half, but all the while during storage its lethal energies are gnawing away at their containers. After another 25,000 years the radioactivity will have been reduced to a quarter, and so on. 2,000 years is almost beyond human comprehension, let alone 25,000. Once the public at large has become aware of this other source of cheap, unlimited and totally environmentally friendly power, the nuclear lobby will be seen to be mouthing empty phrases in defence of its life-annihilating industry.

The principle upon which this new form of energy production is based is here set out clearly for all to see. This has been done to ensure that no individual and no large corporation will ever be able to obtain a patent on it, which would enable them either to suppress it or to create a monopoly for themselves to the great detriment of the rest of humanity, which has often been the case in the past. Once a principle has been published it is no longer patentable and becomes the property of the general public and therefore freely available to all people. This principle and the processes associated with it are so simple that as Viktor Schauberger said:

Our energy technologists would abandon contemporary methods of generating electricity did they but know that this can be obtained directly from the deep sea by means of the simplest apparatus. These devices and instruments, which would lift the world off its hinges, however, would be rapidly superseded and find their way into museums, because mankind has no need to go to such lengths to obtain light, heat and other forms of energy in any desired quantity almost without effort or expense.[2]

It is a known fact that when deep-sea or abyssal fishes are brought up to the surface they burst open. This is generally attributed to the different construction of their skeletons, which are far less robust than those of their counterparts in surface waters around the coasts. It has long been assumed and explained from a purely mechanical point of view, that the rupture of their bodies is caused by the enormous reduction in pressure during their ascent to the surface, which they are unable to withstand. This is a serious, though understandable misinterpretation of the true causes, however, whose origins lie in the physical differences between surface and abyssal waters.

Dwelling as they do in waters with minimal oxygen content, the carbone-oxygen balance in the bodily tissues and the blood of these creatures is weighted very much in the carbone's favour. Moreover, such seawater as they do contain is equally deficient in oxygen. Therefore, like the growth of carbone-rich springwater exposed to atmospheric oxygen, the carbones in the bodies of these fish have a similar affinity and hunger for oxygen, whose absorption, as they are raised from the deep, causes their tissues to explode.

As was explained in the formation of true springs, the $+4°C$ water in the centre-stratum of the groundwater table is largely deficient in male, fertilising oxygen due to the latter's consumption by living organisms, tree roots and so on, but does contain a high concentration of female, fructigenic carbones. Incompressible at $+4°C$ and subject to intense pressures from above and below, this oxygen-starved water, hungry for male essences, is partially squeezed and partially lifted to the highest mountain peaks.

In fig. 10.5 it can be seen that the same physical conditions inhere at great depths in the sea, the only difference here being that the oxygen has been consumed by millions of fish and other aquatic life-forms. According to Viktor Schauberger, here the $+4°C$ saltwater centre-stratum may often be fresh due to the

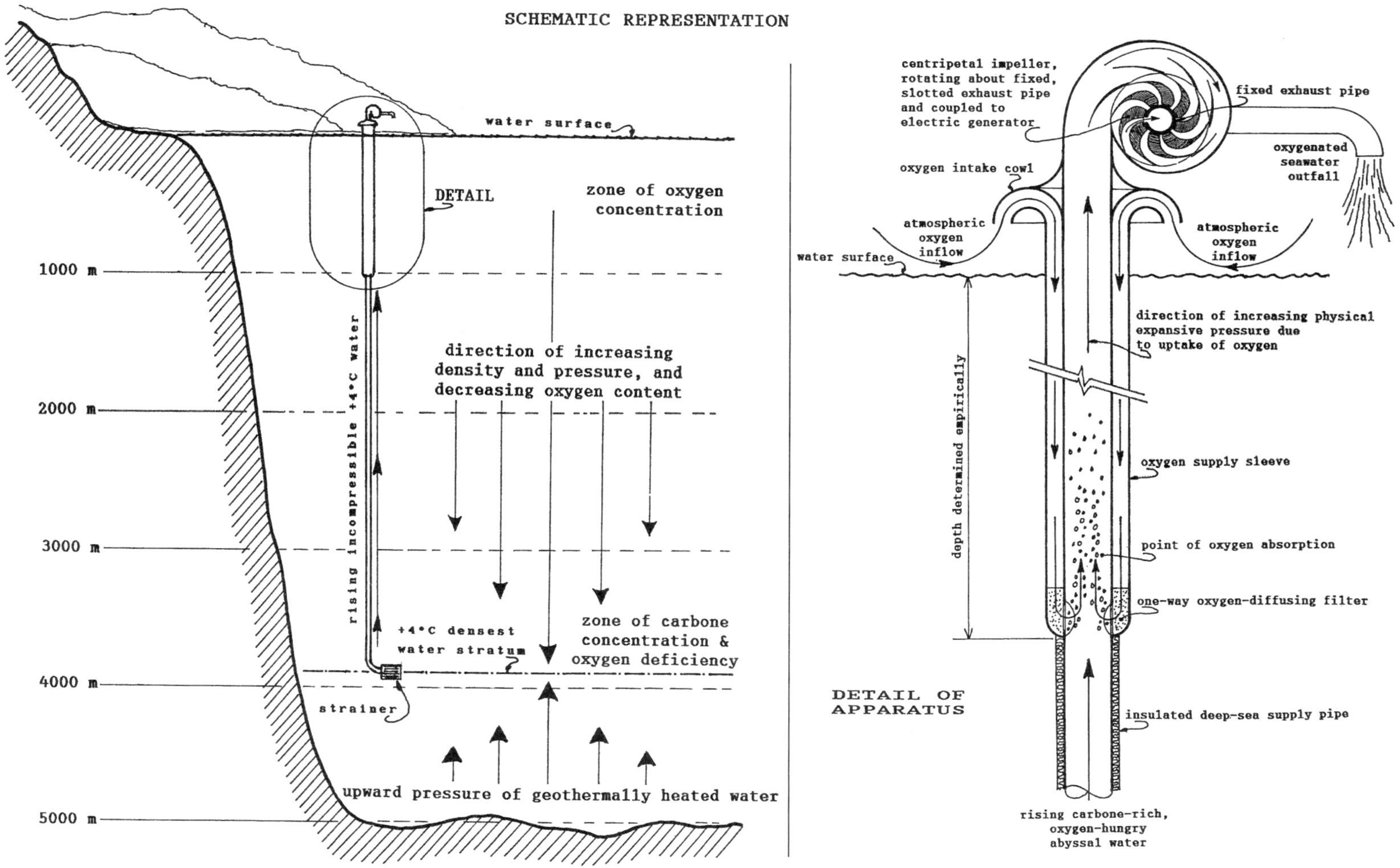

Fig. 10.5 Free energy from the deep ocean

expulsion of salts with cooling under the exclusion of light, heat and air. Moreover, due to its enormous density, it is not possible for such abyssal water to absorb any gases through processes of diffusion or convection. But most importantly, and this is the crucial factor, there is no avenue of escape, no naturally formed rising shafts for the egress of the highly compressed +4°C water.

Therefore by lowering a suitably designed length of pipe to the appropriate depth, this oxygen hungry water is provided with a means of rising to the surface. The water will rise of its own accord as it does in mountain springs. Its levitational, vortical movement will initially be induced by a dual-function strainer, whose tangentially arranged inflow provides the impulse for the creation of a vortex while at the same time preventing the entry of aquatic creatures. The rising pipe itself will be a smaller version of the double-spiral pipe equipped with vortex-inducing vanes, which is described in chapter 14 on water supply.

At a certain depth to be determined empirically as shown in the larger detail in fig. 10.5, atmospheric oxygen, delivered through a larger pipe forming an outer jacket, is diffused into the oxygen-deficient water by means of a one-way filter consisting of a substance whose physical composition permits the passage of the smaller oxygen molecule, but not that of the larger water molecule. In contact with this diffusive filter, the rising water rapidly absorbs the oxygen, warms slightly and begins to expand, to increase its volume in the same way as occurred with the spring at Montenegro.

According to Viktor Schauberger this expansion can be significantly enhanced with the addition of a few drops of a highly complex carbone, such as oil. It is this powerfully expansive phenomenon which can be very simply exploited and converted to the mechanical energy required to drive electric generators. This should not be done with conventional centrifugal impellers, however, because they destroy both the structure and the quality of the water. Rather, centripetal impellers should be used of a design similar to that shown in large scale detail in fig. 10.5, which in this case was taken from Viktor Schauberger's patent for an air turbine[3] and which improves the quality of the medium used to drive it.

While the basic principle is assured, there are some precautionary measures that should be taken initially to safeguard the investment costs and to ensure the proper functioning of the arrangement. Despite what has been stated above, since this system of power generation has so far never been attempted, it may be necessary to use a conventional pump to initiate flow and also to install a series of non-return valves to ensure that any developing expansion is directed upwards and not downwards against the uprising water. While the system may pulsate of its own accord, varying in flow between night and day, this is not a problem, since pulsation is the vibrant essence of life.

The actual investment costs of this new system would be almost nothing compared to the massive expense presently required for nuclear reprocessing plants and power stations. Furthermore, apart from the actual energy produced, the only end-product of this process is ecologically harmless oxygenated seawater which, after all is what is everywhere present in the upper strata of the oceans. All that needs to be done therefore is to make a beginning, for with this method humanity will be provided with unlimited electricity until yet another higher form of energy can be produced.

Notes

1. *Etidorpha*, now published by Health Research, Box 70, Mokelumne Hill, CA 95245, USA.

2. *Our Senseless Toil*, Part II, p.10.

3. Austrian Patent No.145141, 10 April 1936.

11

FLOATING STONES AND THE STATIONARY TROUT

11.1 *Floating Stones*

As a living, natural organism, water is formed and functions according to Nature's laws and geometry, and exhibits none of the elements of the straight line, circle and point, the basis of modern mechanical and technological constructs. Reflecting Nature's principal constant, namely that of continuous change and transformation, the vortex epitomises this form of open, fluid and flexible motion. Through his study of the vortices occurring naturally in flowing water and in the air in the form of cyclones and tornadoes, Viktor Schauberger developed his theories of Implosion. It was through the research and development of these theories that he was able to produce drinking water of mountain-spring quality and generate considerable energies in and with water and air.

What is the natural movement of water and what is the function of the vortex? In relation to all that has been discussed previously in terms of forms, shapes and so on, it can be seen that the expression or manifestation of natural energies is always in curves and vortices, but never in a straight linear fashion. In healthy, naturally flowing water these curvilinear movements are principally expressed as longitudinal vortices running parallel to the direction of flow, though minor transverse eddies do form in the area adjacent to the river banks.

Due to the centripetal action of these longitudinal vortices, in which material in the form of water is drawn inwards, the densest water is always to be found at the centre. Since water cannot actually become denser unless it is cooled, then *ipso facto* it is the central core that contains the coldest and densest water. The maintenance of low temperatures is a prerequisite for the continuing health and vitality of all waterways.

When fresh, lively water gushes forth from a shaded spring in the high forest, it cascades down the side of the mountain, often with torrential flows, but never overflows its banks. In the course of its descent it twists and turns, first to the right and then to the left as it whorls about one rock after another. Upon these rocks and on those lying on the bed of this crystal clear, cold water, undisturbed by human hand, the tips of the mosses growing there behave very peculiarly according to our conventional minds.

In his various writings Viktor Schauberger often stated that two energy streams are active simultaneously in healthily flowing water, but in opposite directions. As discussed previously there are always two processes associated with any form of natural energetic motion, which are always in a state of semi-opposition and at the same time are complementary. On the one hand, there is the gravitational movement of water from the spring down to the sea and, on the other, its levitational counterpart flowing from the sea right up to the source; in other words, a counter movement of energy. Not being aware that at least two forms of opposing, but complementary energy are active in all natural phenomena, nor having seen this phenomenon for ourselves, we would imagine that the moss-tips would bend downstream due to the pressure of the fast-flowing current.

Astonishingly, the opposite is the case as was observed on many occasions by Viktor Schauberger, who regarded it as a reliable indicator of the state of health of a given stream, because both the downstream gravitational flow of matter and the upstream, levitational flow of energy were in the proper state of balance. Contrary to expectation, and despite the fact that at +4°C this water is at its most dense, the moss-tips actually point upstream against the current. This is quite inexplicable according to current hydraulic doctrine, which only treats water mechanically as an inert substance with no perception of its other physical or energetic characteristics.

However, if through deforestation this stream is exposed to the direct light of the Sun, then the situation soon changes markedly. The water becomes warmer, specifically less dense and, lo and behold, the moss-tips point downstream! They do so because the water's intrinsic energies have been depleted by the heat and the counterflow of bio-magnetic energy from the mouth of the stream up to its source has been weakened. The moss-tips therefore act like the needle on a dial faithfully recording the health condition of the stream in which they reside. This phenomenon is now almost impossible to find, because very few mountain streams have escaped the marauding hand of humankind.

But this was by no means Viktor's only encounter with the bio-magnetic energies inherent in healthy water. As a young forest warden in a large area of private forest in the early 1900s, Viktor Schauberger was constantly on the move about the forest in his care. During these years, when hunting was common practice, on one occasion while off-duty he went after a particularly magnificent chamois buck that he knew to frequent a certain area of the forest. It was a very bright, full moonlit night in the middle of winter. Having found the buck, he followed it to the edge of a very deep ravine, where he lost track of it. Keeping very still he waited for some indication of its whereabouts. Noticing a slight fall of snow on the edge of the ravine, he espied the buck standing behind a small bush and, despite the danger of it falling into the ravine if shot, his hunting spirit got the upper hand and he fired at it.

His worst expectations were realised and the buck plunged into the ravine, hitting the bottom far below with a dull thud. Anxious to recover the much-prized horns and beard, he cast about for some way down. Losing his footing, he slid down the path of an avalanche and landed on a heap of snow at the bottom. Delighted to discover that the horns and beard had not been damaged, he removed them, afterwards going over to a pool below a waterfall, which was surrounded by ice to wash his hands.

Due to the crystal clarity of the water and the bright light of the full Moon, as he was looking down into it he became aware of a movement several metres below. Too heavy to float and colloquially called 'sinkers', a number of green logs were engaged in a strange dance. The butt of one log would suddenly rise up, move across another and then return to its former position. Then another would do the same. Totally enthralled, Viktor could not take his eyes off this uncanny phenomenon for a second. Spending several hours, wholly oblivious to the cold and with horns and beard forgotten, he stared down into the water.

More weird and wonderful happenings unfolded as some of the stones too began this rhythmical gavotte. Suddenly, one of them began to gyrate slowly along the bottom and, much to his astonishment, it gradually rose to the surface and stayed there, surrounded by a halo of ice. Thirteen more stones followed shortly thereafter. Despite his amazement at this spectacle, he still had enough presence of mind to notice that all the stones that rose to the surface were egg-shaped, having been rolled around in the bowl at the bottom of the waterfall for some considerable time. Those stones with rough and ragged edges were left lying on the bottom.

In reflecting upon this many years later, Viktor came to realise that it was the combined effect of the cold, which enhanced the bio-magnetic levitational energies, and the metalliferous composition of the stones themselves that was responsible for this remarkable occurrence. Here the term metalliferous essentially refers to silica, the name for silicon dioxide (SiO_2) which is abundant in the Earth's crust as quartz, rock crystal, flint, in granite, sandstone etc, and silicates which are oxides of various metals such as magnesium, calcium and aluminium. As will be shown later, these metalliferous stones reinforce the energies in flowing water.

The fact that the stones actually stayed on the surface is due to another phenomenon. Even though its temperature may be well below the freezing point of 0°C, the water flowing in such streams in winter does not freeze as long as it is moving. When this very cold water of say −3°C or −5°C falls to the bottom of the pool below a waterfall, it creates a certain vortical movement. At the same time, its motion having been decelerated in the process, it has a tendency to crystallise and does so on all surfaces of the floating stones, bringing them up to the surface. Here more ice forms and holds the stones in suspension.

As a result of this encounter with the floating stones, Viktor Schauberger began to realise that there were other forms which could enhance the movement of water, the egg being one of the most important, since eggs or egg-shaped bodies would appear to have a certain connection with vortical motion. A simple experiment gives an idea of what is here involved.

So as to make the experiment as fair as possible and to be able to compare the action of an egg-shaped body with that of another, a sphere − for example, a ping-pong ball − is filled with saline solution weighing slightly more than the specific weight of the contents of the egg, preferably a bantam's egg with similar surface area, in order to offset the lighter specific weight of the plastic shell *vis-a-vis* that of the heavier egg-shell. As the water in the cylindrical measuring jar (fig. 11.1) is stirred with a rod, the ping-pong ball just wobbles about at the bottom. It exhibits no quick tendency to rise, but will eventually do so if the stirring is vigorous enough. However, when an egg, which has a natural tendency to spin on its longitudinal axis, is used instead, it rises very quickly and will stay at the top of the jar for as long as the stirring action is maintained, which once the egg has been

raised can be considerably slowed. It could therefore be mooted that a sphere, which is not a natural form, is not particularly attuned to vortical motion.

11.2 The Stationary Trout

As a result of the successful operation of the several log-flumes Viktor Schauberger built in the late 1920s (to be described later), whose function was incomprehensible to hydraulic experts and could not be explained

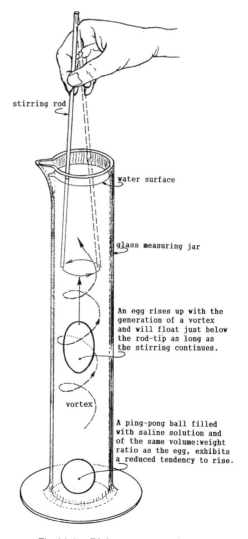

stirring rod

water surface

glass measuring jar

An egg rises up with the generation of a vortex and will float just below the rod-tip as long as the stirring continues.

vortex

A ping-pong ball filled with saline solution and of the same volume:weight ratio as the egg, exhibits a reduced tendency to rise.

Fig 11.1 **Rising egg experiment**

by conventional concepts, the then Austrian government became very interested in his theories and their practical implementation, since they might be of benefit to the country as a whole. It was therefore decided to commission Prof. Philipp Forchheimer, one of the world's foremost but recently retired hydrologists, to observe Viktor Schauberger's activities and report on them. He was to try to understand the processes, which appeared to function flawlessly, but for which there were no accepted theories.

At first Viktor Schauberger was rather irritated at having this man trotting around after him, looking over his shoulders as it were. Forchheimer, however, was always very discreet, never asking trivial questions and eventually they became firm friends, Forchheimer ultimately enabling the publication of Viktor's treatise on water in the Austrian hydrological journal "Die Wasserwirtschaft".

During their period together, and because of Forchheimer's sincere interest, Viktor was always trying to find practical examples to teach him about the substance of water, its intrinsic nature and the peculiar phenomena under which the energies in water evolve. One day he arranged a demonstration for Forchheimer and, taking him up to a certain part of the forest, they came upon a fast-flowing mountain stream which Viktor knew to contain trout. Right in the middle of this rushing cold water at the point where the flow was fastest, Schauberger pointed to the motionless stance of a so-called 'stationary trout'. The trout was standing totally still or very nearly so, apparently managing to maintain its station effortlessly with just an occasional flick of its fins.

Just holding a stick over it, or even the shadow of the stick, was enough to make the trout dart upstream. The direction of escape was never downstream, but it always accelerated upstream. Very odd, because one would normally consider movement downstream to be the fastest avenue of escape, since movement would be with the current. But not so, the movement was always upstream against the current. Once things had settled down and danger had passed, the trout would return to its former station. Viktor asked

Forchheimer to explain why the trout fled upstream instead of downstream and how it was able to do this. Unable to answer, Viktor then responded mischievously, *"Well, Professor, it is because it never had any academic training! Were you in this gushing stream, you would be swept away!"*

The process by which the trout stays motionless in flowing water is as follows: The trout always seeks out that part of the water-body, that part of the current flow where the water is densest and coldest, and the longitudinal vortex most intense. Here a factor discovered by Viktor Schauberger plays a very important role, namely that **the forward velocity of every particle of water is associated with a specific temperature**. If it exceeds this critical velocity then turbulence results. Because of its bodily form, as each filament of water passes around the trout it accelerates and in doing so exceeds the above critical velocity relative to specific temperature.

In other words, due to being deflected by the mass of the trout's body and depending on its proximity to the same, in varying degrees, each water-filament is caused to move too fast (fig. 11.2). In consequence a series of vortices are created along the trout's flanks which have a component of motion in a direction opposite to the current. The combined action of these counter movements in direct contact with the hindparts of the trout's body provides the counterthrust against the downward flow of water. A zone of negative pressure or negative thrust is created within the length of the trout's body. This negative pressure counteracts the positive pressure of the water flow and the trout rests within the zone of neutral pressure its body has created.

If the trout wants to accelerate upstream, it starts to work its gills. The flapping of the gills intensifies the vortices along its flanks, which makes the ensuing upstream thrust greater than the downward pressure. The faster it flaps its gills, the faster it moves against the current, and when its gills are going at 'full bore', so to speak, it moves upstream like a streak of lightning. The increased expulsion of oxygen-deficient, CO_2-rich and therefore carbone-rich water from the faster-functioning gills also has an energising effect. The free dissolved oxygen in the stream water is almost instantaneously absorbed by the expelled oxygen-hungry carbones causing the expansion of the water adjacent to the trout's body so that, in consort with the vortical effects and the levitational energies, the trout is squeezed forwards like a bar of slippery soap.

Considering the trout's behaviour, it is known there are some days when the fish are 'biting', as anglers say. On other days, they seem to ignore the hook altogether. The reason for this is because the water temperature is perfect, the food supply is perfect and the trout just likes to sit there and wait for all its food to float directly into its jaws. All that is necessary to alter this serene situation is a very slight change in external temperature, which also affects the temperature of the water. The water then begins to become more turbulent.

As a result of the increased turbulence, the trout's food, which normally flows down the cold central axis of the current directly into the trout's mouth, is diverted from its normal path and migrates towards the sides of the stream or river. The trout becomes agitated and casts about, hunting for its food, no doubt grumbling to itself, 'Where is my food? It's disgraceful! I actually have to work to get it!' Finally, in desperation, it jumps about, recklessly biting at anything which in any way resembles its food, because it has by this time become extremely hungry and careless, falling easy prey to the angler's hook. So before a thunderstorm or when the weather suddenly becomes warm, the fish are more likely to bite than when the weather is fairly even. Fish also tend to rise to bait in the evening because, by the end of the day, the water has warmed to a certain degree and the flow has thus become slightly more turbulent, partially disrupting the normal food supply.

On this day Viktor Schauberger had also arranged that his foresters build a fire and place a large cauldron containing 100 litres of water over it to heat up. All this occurred about 150 metres upstream from where the stationary trout was resting. Once the water

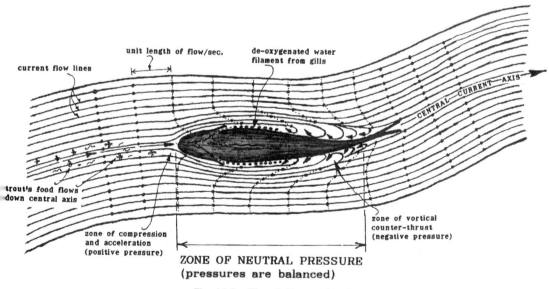

Fig. 11.2   **The stationary trout**

The trout normally swims in the middle of the central current vortex, where the water is densest and coldest. Due to the volume of its body, the individual current filaments are displaced and compressed. This causes their acceleration and eventually their critical velocities are exceeded, which results in the formation of vortices (counter-currents) along the rear part of the body. These vortices act counter to the direction of the current and provide the counter-thrust required by the trout to remain stationary in this fast flowing water. If it needs to accelerate upstream, then it flaps its gills, creating a further vortex train along its flanks, thus increasing the counter-thrust upstream. The more rapid the gill-movements, the faster the trout moves upwards against the current.

was hot enough, Viktor Schauberger gave the signal to pour it into the stream, while he and Forchheimer continued to observe the trout's behaviour very closely. As soon as the hot water hit the stream, the trout started to flail its tail, moving backwards all the while as it struggled to maintain its station. Something drastic had happened to the water and its pattern of energy, which normally aided the trout in the maintenance of its position. The upward flow of levitational energy had been totally disrupted by the introduction of the hot water 150m above. The trout was no longer able to stay where it was in the fast flow without effort, as was the case before.

Missing was the energy that the trout also exploits to progress upstream and to make its famous leaps, which it must do periodically in order to reach the spawning grounds, which are always to be found in the zone of high-quality water near the spring. When the hot water was introduced, this counter-movement of energy was cut. The energy was suddenly dissipated and became chaotic. All structure in terms of the natural thermal stratification of the water was lost and the regularity of the longitudinal vortex with its cold core, essential for the trout motionless stance, had been destroyed. All its valiant efforts to maintain station were in vain and it was swept downstream. Over a certain period of time the counter-flow of energy was slowly restored through the continuing descent of cold water and eventually the trout was able to return to its former position.

On another occasion, Viktor pointed out a stone in the middle of a stream and asked Forchheimer whether he thought the water would be hotter or colder after flowing past it. The Professor scratched his head and thinking to himself, "Hmm, friction; friction produces heat", answered "Hotter!" Schauberger then suggested he measure it to confirm his opinion, stating, however, that he thought Forchheimer's answer was incorrect. Equipped with his accurate thermometers and first furling up his trousers, the Professor entered the water. Viktor's son, Walter, who at the time was about 16 years old, was requested to hold onto the spindly professor's belt, lest he lose his footing on the slippery stones and be swept

away by the torrent. Forchheimer carefully measured the water temperature both above and below the stone and was very surprised to find there was a difference of about $^2/_{10}$ths of a degree Celsius – **colder** on the downstream side of the stone. After a number of measurements were made later on, Forchheimer found that the cooling at these points varied from 0.1°C to 0.4°C.

When moving naturally, water develops a series of vortices and eddies which brake its otherwise unimpeded forward movement and at the same time cool it. The steadiness of flow in naturally flowing river systems is closely associated with this vortical motion, which is due to the turbulence arising through the exceeding of the critical velocity relative to water temperature as mentioned previously. Such water will never accelerate continuously and rush headlong down a given gradient but, depending on its temperature and the type of temperature gradient in force, it will fairly quickly develop vortices and thereby slow its rate of forward flow, for the simple reason that these vortices represent the application of an automatic brake by creating a counter movement in an upstream direction, a phenomenon that will be explained in the following chapter.

11.3 Fishes from Eggs

Another interesting aspect about the trout is that the form of its body arises from the combination of three egg-shapes, two elongated in the form of seeds or grain and the other in the form of an egg (fig. 11.3), all of which can be precisely calculated with the hyperbolic mathematical system devised by Walter Schauberger. We are therefore concerned with a complex egg-form. As was demonstrated in the measuring jar, the egg-shape does seem to have a certain affinity for vortical motion and it is very possible that the resistance of this form to forward motion, or any kind of pressure, is much less than it would be in the case of a cylindrical or an elliptical system.

Here we need briefly to address Walter Schauberger's Pythagoras-Kepler System and its associated mathematics, which are devel-

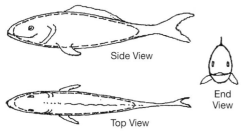

Fig. 11.3 **Three eggs make a fish**

The form of most fishes consists of three interacting egg-shapes. Because an egg-shape is of constantly changing, non-euclidean curvature, it is conducive to a reduction in friction and the generation of counter-thrusting vortices, which, if intensified sufficiently, result in accelerated forward movement.

oped from the Pythagorean concepts of harmonics derived from the Monochord, a single resonating string, and the planetary motion and harmonies of Johannes Kepler. Through the whole-numbered division of the length of its string, i.e. by 2, 3, 4, 5, etc., certain musically harmonic intervals can be obtained from the Monochord which, in their numerical ratios of string length to pitch, can be interpreted as reciprocities.

These are the same reciprocities from which the rectangular hyperbola mentioned in previous chapters is constructed according to Walter Schauberger's simple equation $\frac{1}{n} \times n = 1$. Here $\frac{1}{n}$ represents the radius or stringlength, and n the height above the baseline or the pitch of the vibrating string. If $n = 1$, then $\frac{1}{1} \times 1 = 1$, actually 1^2 since multiplying the radius by the height produces a square with sides of unit length (see fig. 11.4) whereas, musically speaking, stringlength 1 produces pitch 1. If $n = 2$ on the other hand, then $\frac{1}{2}$(radius) $\times 2$ (height) also equals 1, in this case a rectangle of $\frac{1}{2}$-unit width and 2-unit height and equal in area to the square mentioned above or, in terms of tone, string length $\frac{1}{2}$ produces the first octave or double the original pitch. If $n = 3$, then $\frac{1}{3} \times 3$ also make a rectangle with the overall area of 1. In other words by multiplying both reciprocal terms together, the answer is always 1. What could be simpler mathematically!

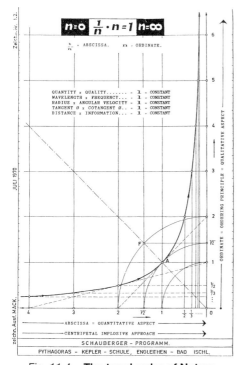

Fig. 11.4 **The tonal order of Nature constitution of the Universe**

Fig. 11.5 **Hyperbolic cone**

Fig. 11.6 **Truncated cone**

Applied to the concepts of Kepler, who was the first person to determine that the orbits of the planets were eccentric about the Sun, this same equation opens up a plethora of interesting insights in its three-dimensional form, namely as the hyperbolic cone shown in fig. 11.5. When he first put pen to paper, Kepler initially described the planetary orbits

as oval, i.e. egg-shaped (*ovum*=egg), but because he was unable to define them mathematically, he was eventually forced to adopt the simpler ellipse, which for most of the planetary orbits is a fairly close approximation. Whereas an elliptical orbit has two foci – the Sun occupying one, the other being empty – and a symmetry about both axes, an egg-orbit has but one focus – the unequivocal and only possible location for the Sun – and is symmetrical about the longitudinal axis only.

In comparison with the thoroughly symmetrical ellipse, the constantly changing curvature of the egg-orbit far better reflects the varying strength of the Sun's gravitational attraction as the planet moves around it. Moreover the egg's dissimilar curvature at opposite ends likewise far better reflects the varying speed and the resultant path followed by the planet as it accelerates towards the Sun, until it reaches its maximum orbital velocity at perihelion (position closest to the Sun; blunt end of the egg). Having passed this point the planet then decelerates, attaining its minimum velocity at aphelion (position furthest from the Sun; sharp end of the egg). Both terms, perihelion and aphelion, are of Kepler's coinage.

By taking a section through this solid cone at a steeply inclined plane, the resultant flat

Fig. 11.7 **Different shapes produced at varying levels of a hyperbolic cone**

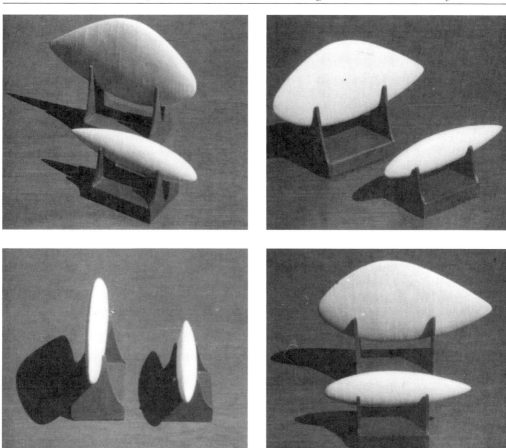

Fig. 11.8   **The making of a fish**
Computer Generated Fish Shapes.

surface is grain-shaped as in fig. 11.6. If the section is tangential to the surface of the hyperbolic cone, then the resultant profile is sharply pointed at one end. On the other hand a section taken at a flatter angle produces the egg-shape shown in fig. 11.7. Even shallower angles will produce the planetary orbits that Kepler originally described with the term oval.

Using an appropriate computer program to combine data from two tangential sections of different widths, but the same length, very fish-like forms can be created which are depicted in fig. 11.8. Here the four images of the two fishes produced by the author are shown. This well demonstrates the possibilities for the natural, non-Euclidean design of various apparatuses and devices afforded by the mathematics of the Pythagoras-Kepler System, with which any desired egg-shape, from extreme to mean, can be accurately calculated.

12

THE LOG FLUME

In the previous chapters we began to learn more about the behaviour of water and in order to get even more into the swim of things, as it were, we shall now take a look at Viktor Schauberger's first major project, whose successful function was founded on his growing knowledge of water and its essential nature. This was the log-flume at Steyrling which began operations in the latter part of 1923.

Owing to his great inherited love of the forest and, as an apprentice forester, during the period from 1903 to 1914, Viktor Schauberger quickly acquired a great deal of knowledge about the forest, demonstrating an expertise far beyond those of his peers and rapidly rising from the rank of forester to forest warden, the highest position for those with no academic training in forestry. His progress as a forester was interrupted by conscription into the army to fight in the First World War, during which he was wounded. At the end of the war at the age of 33 he continued his career and, in a relatively short time, he developed a certain reputation which led to his employment in 1920 on a hunting and forest reserve owned by the German Prince Adolf zu Schaumburg-Lippe, whose family seat was at Bückeburg in Lower Saxony. As a forest warden Viktor's position was that of overseer of this very extensive domain at Brunnenthal in Steyrling, Upper Austria.

During the period immediately after the war the economic situation in the vanquished countries of Austria and Germany was particularly difficult. Despite this, some of the well-

to-do still believed that they could continue life as before and returned to frequent the tables at Monte Carlo. Prince Adolph and his new young wife, Princess Ellen (née Bischoff-Korthaus), were no exception. The only problem was that she lost heavily, which presented the Prince with the recurring problem of trying to recoup what she had lost. The only means available to him to avoid bankruptcy was to sell the timber still untouched in the large tracts of virgin forest on their Brunnenthal estate, some of which were in very remote areas and access to them very difficult. How therefore could it be got out?

Before and during his early employ with Prince Adolph, Viktor Schauberger had been working on the design of a log-flume for the safe transport of timber, using his own knowledge of the natural movement of water and what had been passed down to him from his ancestors' long association with log-rafting. He was very concerned about the damage to the forest and streams associated with the normal system for recovery from otherwise inaccessible sites, for in those days the usual method of recovery was to fell the trees and throw the green logs into the nearest available stream at high-water in the hope that some of them would arrive at the sawmill in a usable condition. This system was extremely wasteful, much valuable timber never arrived and many logs were so splintered by the rough passage that they were useless for anything other than firewood (fig. 12.1).

On several occasions Viktor presented his designs to the Estate Administration, only to have them haughtily rejected and ridiculed, because the way the flume was supposed to function was totally contrary to proven hydraulic theory and therefore would never work. After all, everyone with any good academic education knew that, in accordance with Archimedes' Principle, logs heavier than water – 'sinkers' – could not be transported in water but merely sank to the bottom.

Much sobered by the spectre of eventual bankruptcy and having heard rumour of Viktor Schauberger's unusual log-flume design, the young Princess approached him to find out what savings could be achieved over the normal costs of timber transportation which amounted to 12 schillings per solid cubic metre, because the substantial losses mentioned above always had to be taken into account. Viktor answered that the costs could be reduced to 1 schilling/m³, including the amortisation of construction costs, because every log would arrive in good condition. The Princess jumped at the idea.

Despite the fact that Viktor had no academic qualifications, she offered him three times his normal salary if he agreed to build it and begged her husband to agree to its construction. He concurred, saying that, while it was very unconventional, if all went well it would solve their financial problems, due to the large returns anticipated. His agreement, however, was subject to two conditions: 1. the flume was to be built at Viktor's own expense and in the event of its non-function he was also to pay for its demolition; 2. the flume had to deliver a minimum of 1,000m³ of solid timber daily.

Viktor was delighted to take up the challenge and immediately began preparation for the construction of his first log-flume. It was not long before word was out, eventually attracting the attention of the Estate Administration and the Institute of Hydraulics at the University of Vienna, who were outraged that a young upstart forester should be awarded such a lucrative contract when they should have been called upon for their expertise. The whole thing was totally out of order and quite preposterous!

Instead of the usual rectangular or trapezoid concrete channel, Schauberger's log-flume was to be constructed of timber, the cross-section of the log-flume was egg-shaped, or rather half egg-shaped (figs. 12.2 & 12.3 – actually a later log-flume at Neuberg 1928), and it was to function in total contravention of the established principles of conventional hydraulics. When they were ready to start, the carpenters and labourers asked Viktor Schauberger where it was to be built. He told them to study the shape of the river and the valley and to follow these as closely as possible, because water never likes to move in a straight line, but always curves in its natural meandering motion and Nature's examples should always be followed. Therefore, as eventually built, it followed the contours of the valley (figs. 12.4, 12.5 & 12.6).

The day before it was due to be commissioned, Viktor decided to make a preliminary test of the flume's performance. An average-sized green beech log was ushered into the mouth of the flume and to his horror it stranded on the bottom after a few metres and would not budge. This was a catastrophe and something had to be done at once if the next day's opening was to be successful. Sending his workers away to give himself space to think, Viktor sat on a rock to ponder the situation. As he sat down he felt something scrabbling underneath his leather breeches and sprang up to find a very alive snake. Grabbing it quickly, he flung it into the holding basin, which supplied the flume with water and where the logs were to be assembled before being entrained into the flume. As he watched it swim to the other side, wondering how it was able to swim so fast, he suddenly became aware of its peculiar sinuous movement. Nature had again come to his aid.

The snake's movement was that of a spiral-space curve and like the shape of the Kudu horn (shown in fig. 12.7). Summoning his workers, he ordered the holding basin to be drained and the offending log removed. He then gave them instructions on how to attach thin wooden slats to the curved sides of the flume walls, which would act like the rifling in gun-barrels and cause the water to rotate anti-clockwise at left hand bends and clockwise at right hand bends (fig. 12.8). Working all through the night with the promise of double wages, the work was finished by early next morning ready for commissioning at the Grand Opening.

This momentous event was to be attended by the Prince and Princess, the Chief Forestry Commissioner and a number of hydraulic specialists and experts. Nothing would have prevented the latter from attending since their dearest wish was to have the opportunity publicly to heap scorn on Schauberger and to witness his humiliation.

The first item on the agenda was the refilling of the 18 metre deep holding basin. It was of novel design and the inspecting experts considered its construction far too flimsy and the wall too thin to withstand the pressures of being filled. Viktor assured them that it was strong enough and, ignoring their strident protests for his safety, strode down to the middle of the wall directly opposite where the water would enter, at the same time calling back to the assembled company that, if he was wrong, then at least the world would be rid of another fool. If they had

thought him eccentric before, the experts were convinced that he had become mentally unhinged when his only response to their calls to return was to fire his shotgun into the air.

This was the prearranged signal to open the sluicegates at a higher weir. Having done this, he then stood looking down over the wall as a 6 metre high wall of muddy water full of flotsam and jetsam boiled and surged into the basin from the other side. In spite of the thrusting power of this roiling maelstrom, the wall held and the basin gradually filled.

From subsequent static calculation it was determined that it had been built 12 times more strongly than it need have been. The experts were dumbfounded and asked how he came to build it in this particular form. He answered very archly that he had obtained the shape from a common chicken's egg! What he had known, but the experts had not, was that when the first inflow of water entered the basin it would swirl across the bottom and around the sides (fig. 12.9). All the flows would then meet at the centre where he was standing and recoil in the opposite direction, thus creating an opposing

Fig. 12.1   **Wasteful, conventional method of transporting logs**

Fig. 12.2   **Building of Neuberg log flume**

Fig. 12.3   **Egg-shaped form of log flume**

Fig. 12.4   **Schauberger's log flume followed the contours of the valley**

Fig. 12.5 & 6   **The carefully engineered log flume**

surge of water, which would counteract the momentum of the oncoming water and relieve the wall of destructive pressure.

All this having been achieved with much astonishment and no doubt a certain secret chagrin in some quarters, it was now time to test the flume itself. When everything was ready the flume sluice-gates were opened and the logs guided into the mouth of this half-egg-shaped channel. One very large beech log managed to get itself included with the first few logs and, half way into the flume it suddenly jammed and the water began to back up behind it. While all watched with bated breath, all at once with a loud gurgling sound it was sucked forwards and departed round the first bend. Many other logs followed, passing easily down the flume, being kept away from the sides at the bends by the longitudinal vortices induced by the rifling slats as shown in fig. 12.8.

Against all official expectations, on its very first day of operation it proved its worth and actually delivered 1,600 cubic metres of timber to the mill and Viktor Schauberger was paid. Delighted with the success, but unable to raise him to the position of 'Forstmeister' (Forest Superintendent) due to the vehement opposition of forestry officialdom, the Prince awarded Viktor the title of 'Wildmeister', or 'Master of the Wilderness' for his efforts. Later on, however, Viktor Schauberger had cause to rue the day he had built it, because the greed of the Prince and Princess was insatiable and, instead of the sustainable, economic extraction of timber he had foreseen, the whole area was clear-felled. After

expressing his disgust to the royal couple, he tendered his resignation and was summarily dismissed without pay.

The way in which the log flume operated, however, is as follows: Water for the flume was initially collected in a deep holding basin fed by an adjacent stream. In this storage reservoir the water gradually stratified according to temperature and density, the colder water lying at the bottom (fig. 12.10a). Water of different temperatures was then drawn off from various levels in the reservoir, in particular low-temperature +4°C water, and introduced into the flume.

Now it is a known fact that waters of different temperatures do not mix immediately and, indeed, on many occasions, not for quite a long period. On the basis of the Archimedean principle of the specifically denser carrying the specifically lighter, through the generation of the longitudinal vortices mentioned earlier, the only place for the denser water was in the middle, the increasingly less specifically dense layers or skeins of water being at the outside. Because the temperature of the water at the central core of the longitudinal vortex was colder, its flow was faster and more laminar; an increase in water temperature, on the other hand, increases the incidence of turbulence.

Although no actual details of vortex-inducing elements exist for flumes constructed later, apart from the rifling slats, it is most probable that, when water was initially introduced into the flume from the holding basin, it was introduced into the system

Fig. 12.7 **Kudu horn**

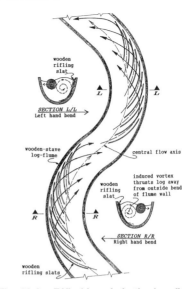

Fig. 12.8 **Rifled bends in the log-flume**

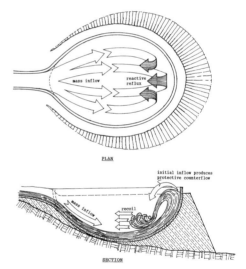

Fig. 12.9 **Egg-shaped holding basin**

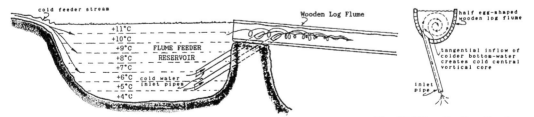

Fig. 12.10a **Thermal stratification in holding basin**

Fig. 12.10b **Section thro' flume**

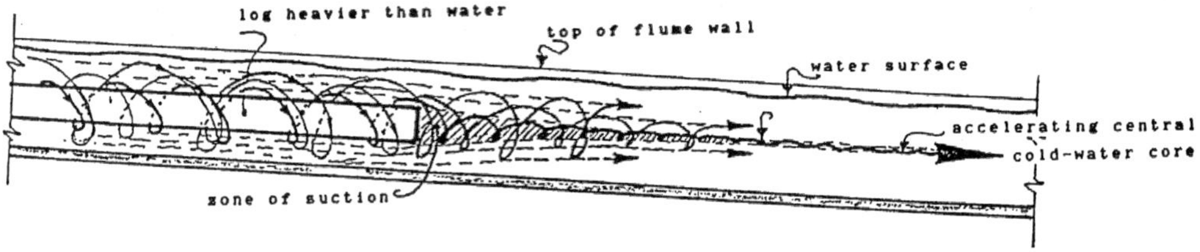

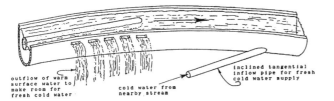

Fig. 12.11   **The transport of logs heavier than water**

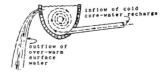

Fig. 12.12a   **Detail of warm/cold water exchange**

Fig. 12.12b   **Section thro'
flume**

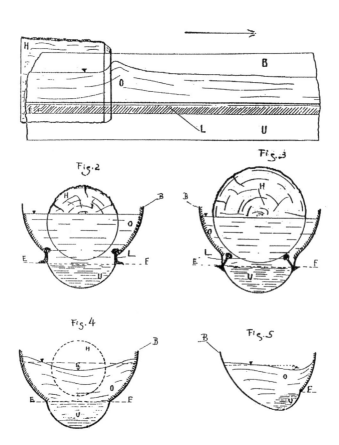

Fig. 12.13   **Illustrations from Schauberger's patent application**

tangentially (fig. 12.10b). As this central core of water moved away faster than the outer layers, it created an area of suction in front of the logs, particularly the 'sinkers', and drew these logs along with it (fig. 12.11). The logs themselves did not touch the sides and neither the timber nor the flume was ever damaged.

Periodically, in order to retain the water's energy, some water was drained off and replaced by fresh, colder 'energy-water' from affluent streams or adjacent springs. Viktor Schauberger knew that, once the water had been warmed to a certain degree, it lost its transporting ability, its carrying power and its energy to move the material. It therefore had to be re-energised with colder water. The warmer water was therefore skimmed off and colder water introduced, probably tangentially again, (as depicted in figs. 12.12a & 12b). This maintained the stratified vortical movement of the whole water-body.

The extent to which these flumes were operated at night is not recorded. However, in the early morning, when the overall temperature of the water was between +9°C and +10°C a block of wood took 29 minutes to cover the distance of 2km at the Neuberg flume at Steiermark. At midday, when the water temperature was between +13°C and +15°C the same block of wood took 40 minutes to travel the same distance under otherwise equal conditions. There can be little doubt that Viktor was aware that the carrying capacity and flow velocity of water varied according to the time of day and season, because his forebears always rafted timber during the cold nights of the full Moon in winter, when the water was at its very densest.

Always inventive and wanting to test his theories further, using the same principle, Viktor Schauberger developed a log-flume capable of carrying even larger logs, which was provided with skid-rails to take the additional weight of the heavier timber. Here there was a difference in the roughness of the channel wall surfaces. In the upper part, above the rails, the walls were rougher and below them smoother, allowing a faster flow underneath, so if a log had a tendency to jam, it was sucked along by the faster flow of cold water underneath. Fig. 12.13 illustrates the patented arrangement of this flume[1].

All in all Viktor Schauberger built seventeen such flumes in various parts of Bohemia, Czechoslovakia, Hungary, Bulgaria and Romania, all of which functioned perfectly and remained in working order for about 20 years. The timber they were made of would not rot due to the water's artificially induced, but nevertheless natural, form of motion. How this comes about will be elaborated in chapter 15 concerning water supply.

Note

1. Austrian Patent No.122144, 10 April 1931.

13

THE DYNAMICS OF FLOW

13.1 Temperature Gradients during Flow

The temperature gradient in moving water plays a very decisive role both in its movement and in the configuration of its flow. This vital factor seems to have been completely lost to conventional river management, both historically and still to this day. Indeed the standard methods of regulating and rectifying the channel, taking into account, as they do, just a mechanical point of view, only wreak damage to the waterway and attract increasing damage and maintenance costs in their wake.

Standard river engineering practice always attempts to regulate a river through the agency of the riverbank or other artificial flow-confining structures, never by reorganising the flow of the water's intrinsic energies, to which Viktor Schauberger offers the following trenchant critique:

To regulate a waterway by means of the riverbank itself is verily to fight cause with effect. ...It cannot and should not be the task of the river engineer to correct Nature by violating her. Rather, in all watercourses requiring regulation his job should be to investigate Nature's processes as far as this is possible, and to emulate the examples that Nature provides in the way of healthy streams. ...Every violation, however, rebounds on the perpetrator. ...As water flows down a natural gradient, it does so according to a sublime inner law, whose power our hydraulic experts are quite unable to comprehend. ...The more the engineer endeavours to channel water, of whose spirit and nature he is today still ignorant, by the shortest and straightest route to the sea, the more the flow of water weighs into the bends, the longer its path and the worse the water will become.[1]

In the light of this, unless the physical factor of temperature and the more immaterial magnitudes of the water's inherent energies are taken into consideration, no river engineering project will ever be wholly successful and in many cases will be downright harm-

ful, for it is precisely upon these very subtle differences in temperature that the orderly drainage of water depends. The variations in the temperature of the water-body as a whole and in its various parts are so subtle, lying perhaps within a range of 0.1°C to 2.0°C, that contemporary hydraulic engineers have never paid the slightest heed to them. Indeed, they generally regard the temperature of the water as irrelevant either to the form of the flow or to its energy.

These small, but crucial, differences in water temperature were therefore never included in any hydraulic calculation. Nothing appears to have changed, as I discovered in my brief discussion with Professor John F. Kennedy described in chapter 8. This omission has had disastrous consequences not only for those living next to rivers conventionally regulated, but also for the general climate and for the quality of the water itself.

Viktor Schauberger, on the other hand, considered these factors to be all-important and absolutely essential to all natural water resources management. He stated categori-

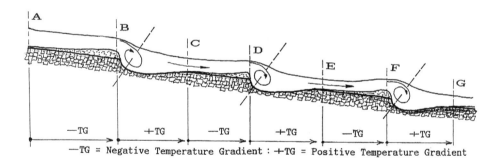

−TG = Negative Temperature Gradient : +TG = Positive Temperature Gradient

Fig. 13.1   **Alternate deposition and screwing**

1. Flow from A to B occurs under a negative temperature gradient by which the water is increasingly warmed and begins to deposit its suspended sediment.
2. Maximum deposition takes place at B, also the position of least carrying power.
3. The accumulation of sediment here causes water to back up, resulting in an overfall with a transverse horizontally aligned vortex immediately downstream from B.
4. Just after B, D or F these vortices not only cool the water, but also scour into the riverbed material, forming potholes.
5. As a result of this cooling vortexial action the temperature gradient from B to C becomes positive and the sediment is transported and not deposited. Deposition gradually occurs as the negative temperature gradient beginning at C becomes more intense.
6. This results in a similar situation at D to that occuring at B.
7. Correction of this unwelcome phenomenon can be achieved by bringing about the extension of this alternation over longer distances through the incorporation of the appropriate internal flow control structures.

cally that no regulation could ever be successful unless they were taken into account, since it is dependent upon the water temperature and the temperature gradient predominantly active along its course whether a river will either remove, transport or deposit its sediment.

Under natural conditions when water descends a gradient, its flow is affected by a naturally occurring sequence of positive and negative temperature gradients because, in the course of flow, the water rhythmically heats up and cools down. How much it heats up, however, depends on the degree of friction with the riverbed, the external temperature and the extent to which the water is directly exposed to the Sun. It only requires a very minute change in temperature for water to pick up, transport or deposit its sediment and it is the type and duration of the temperature gradient prevailing that determines what happens and for how long. A negative temperature gradient causes the deposition of sediment, whereas a positive temperature gradient ensures its removal. This whole process can become very aggravated, however, if the temperature gradients alternate too suddenly or abruptly.

In fig. 13.1, for example, from *A* to *B* the temperature gradient is negative. From *A* to *B* the water gradually heats up and in the process is unable to retain the sediment in suspension and drops it progressively as the water becomes warmer. At *B*, the zone of maximum deposition, the accumulated material creates an overfall which, in turn, creates a horizontal barrel vortex immediately downstream. This vortex, however, cools the water and therefore from *B* to *C* the temperature gradient becomes positive. The sediment is once more picked up and transported. Upon reaching *C*, the effect of the positive temperature gradient gives way to its negative counterpart and the suspended matter is again dropped, reaching a maximum at *D*.

This pulsation or alternation can be likened to breathing; a positive temperature gradient representing the inward breath, the absorbing, material-collecting movement, the negative temperature gradient representing the outward breath, where the energetically transformed matter is exhaled from the system and deposited.

So it becomes clear that, in order to regulate a river naturally, and satisfactorily, it is essential to take the temperature gradients

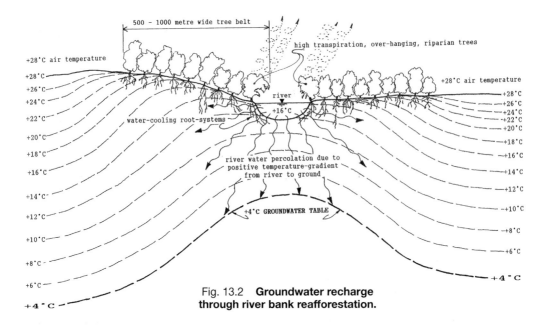

Fig. 13.2 **Groundwater recharge through river bank reafforestation.**

and their alternating sequence into consideration. In order to reduce the danger of flooding to a minimum it is therefore clear that the longer the duration of a positive temperature gradient can be preserved, the less likely a river is to flood, since only minor sediment deposition will occur.

The duration of the positive temperature gradient can be extended or it can be recreated where necessary in four principal ways:

1. By shading the river through the replanting of trees.
2. By the construction of appropriately designed dams in which the temperature of the discharge can be suited to the prevailing air temperatures and the water temperatures of the downstream flow regime.
3. By installing flow-deflecting guides which direct the flow of water at the bends towards the centre of the river and simultaneously cause the creation of cooling longitudinal vortices.
4. By the implanting of 'energy-bodies' in the river bed, which re-energise the water by inducing the formation of longitudinal vortices.

On point no. 1: This is particularly important at the riverbends, where the friction and therefore the warming tendencies are greatest. Here species of timber which have a high evaporation rate should be planted. In the process of evaporation the sap in the tree is cooled and, because the roots develop underneath the river bed this cooling effect is also extended to the riverbed and thus to the water as well. The tree therefore acts like a refrigerator.

The key factors here in terms of land and water resources management are, firstly, never remove forest from the banks of a river. Indeed a belt of trees of at least 500 to 1000 metres wide should be maintained along all rivers banks for the health of the river. Rivers flowing through cleared, barren countryside should be reafforested (as shown in fig. 13.2) in order to re-establish healthy flow conditions, restore the nutrient supply and recharge the groundwater table in its vicinity.

On point no. 2: As presently constructed, the majority of dams and most water storage

facilities either release cold bed-water from the bottom-sluices or warm surface water over the top of the dam wall by means of the spillway. This is done without considering the temperature of the water released or its possible effect on the downstream flow regime and on many occasions has disastrous consequences. The discharge of warm water, for example, into a stretch of river where the temperature gradient is only slightly positive, will effectively remove it altogether, resulting in the automatic and almost simultaneous deposition of silt and sediment. The result will be flooding.

The discharge of cold bed-water only, on the other hand, may over-cool the lower reaches, causing excessive scouring and the transport of very heavy sediment loads, which the lower flow regime is unable to handle due to a number of factors. These

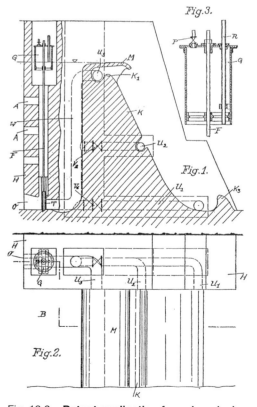

Fig. 13.3   **Patent application for a dam design**

may involve the slope of the bed-gradient and thereby the speed of flow, the width of the channel – wide, shallow channels dropping sediment more quickly, the temperature gradients operative lower down, etc. Each type of discharge eventually produces the same results – silting up followed by flooding.

The control of the downstream flow for the purposes of extending the period of a positive temperature gradient can be achieved through the construction of appropriately designed dams. Fig. 13.3 depicts a patented design for a dam by Viktor Schauberger, which shows various outlet-sluices at different heights on the dam-wall. The aim of this arrangement is to remove large and therefore disruptive temperature differences and to bring the external air temperature and the temperature of the riverwater into a closer approximation. Controlled by a floating caisson, which in turn is operated by the ambient external temperature, these sluice-gates take water from different levels of the dam, each level having a different water temperature. The higher the external temperature, the higher the relative temperature of the water released, although this is always cooler than any water overflowing via the spillway.

To ensure the best possible mixing of the variously tempered waters, a vortex is created at the foot of the wall by the upwardly curving element shown at *K3*. In this way the temperature of the discharge can be attuned as far as possible to that of the downstream flow regime, thereby reducing large and harmful fluctuations in the temperature of the water itself and avoiding any premature inversions of the positive temperature gradients.

A further advantage to this novel approach is that the stability of the dam wall itself can also be greatly enhanced if the above design is used. In the period immediately after the construction of a new dam has been completed, relatively high temperatures are frequently generated inside the wall by the curing heat of the concrete. A positive temperature gradient is created between the warmer structure and the cooler reservoir water, under the influence of which the water present in the wall moves towards the water in the reservoir. As it moves through the wall it dissolves and dislodges particles of the structure. In the process, cavities in the material are formed, thereby weakening the wall. When rain falls on the outer surface of the wall, it too is drawn in by the positive temperature gradient. As juvenile water it attacks the substances of the wall, enlarging the cavities as it transports further material towards the reservoir. Now fissured, the dam wall is open to frost attack in winter and, little by little, the wall is rendered increasingly unstable.

With this design, however, measures can be taken to remove this danger completely. By over-trickling the exterior of the wall with small quantities of cold, +4°C bed-water, thereby cooling it and protecting it from the effects of external temperature (e.g. the Sun), a positive temperature gradient can be established from the reservoir in the direction of the outer surface of the wall. Under its influence the suspended matter in the reservoir water is drawn into the wall through all the small fissures and capillaries in the wall-structure. It should be borne in mind that by excluding light, heat and air the deposition of salts and other elements increases as the temperature decreases towards +4°C. In this way the cavities are gradually filled until the dam wall is totally sealed. Ultimately the wall will even resist the penetration of water, becomes impervious and as a structure is thoroughly consolidated.

Viktor Schauberger built fourteen of these dams. Their efficacy was confirmed in a paper given by Professor Forchheimer on April 15th, 1930, in which he stated:

Finally it may be said that Herr Schauberger has already built a number of dams which have proved successful. Some of his structures I myself have inspected, and I can affirm that these new concepts of Schauberger's have completely fulfilled the purpose for which they were designed.[2]

On point no. 3: Being aware of the harmful effects of heat and the dissipation of a river's inherent energies through faulty regulation, on the 31st of January 1927 Viktor Schauberger applied for a patent for a flow-deflecting guide-vane with which to re-establish a

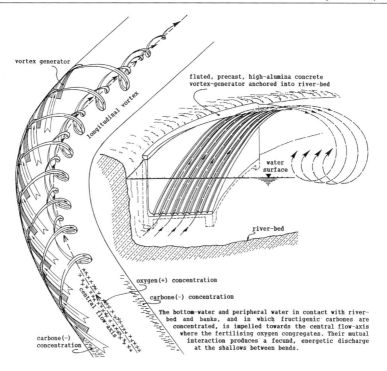

vortex generator

longitudinal vortex

fluted, precast, high-alumina concrete
vortex-generator anchored into river-bed

water
surface

river-bed

central flow-axis

oxygen(+) concentration

carbone(-) concentration

The bottom-water and peripheral water in contact with river-
bed and banks, and in which fructigenic carbones are
concentrated, is impelled towards the central flow-axis
where the fertilising oxygen congregates. Their mutual
interaction produces a fecund, energetic discharge
at the shallows between bends.

carbone(-)
concentration

Fig. 13.4   **Longitudinal vortex-generator**

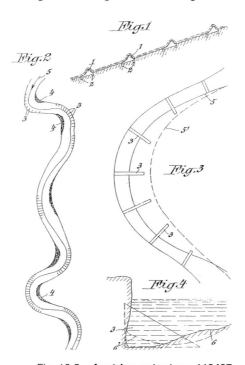

Fig.1

Fig.2

Fig.3

Fig.4

Fig. 13.5   **Austrian patent no. 113487**

river's natural longitudinal vortices. Viewed along the direction of flow, these induce anti-clockwise rotating vortices at left hand bends and clockwise vortices at right hand bends.

The flow-guide shown in fig. 13.4 does not correspond precisely to the one depicted as figs. 1 and 4 on the patent diagram (fig. 13.5 – Austrian Patent No.113487) which, as in other instances, seems almost deliberately to have misrepresented Viktor's ideas. In this particular case the actual text is at variance with the diagram. Having been shown other diagrams drawn by Viktor personally, the one shown here in fig. 13.4 is in my view more representative of what is actually entailed.

The actual shape of the flow-guide is more or less triangular in plan, the apex pointing downstream as shown. It consists of a curved precast concrete flow-form, the curved surface of which is fluted with grooves running parallel to the direction of flow in order to prevent any lateral slip. The wider, upstream end of the triangle is horizontal and flush with the riverbed, so as to scoop up the onflowing water and curl it over centripetally into a vortex in the centre of the channel. At the same time the suspended and dissolved carbones, which generally congregate along the banks and the bed, are lifted towards the dissolved oxygen which in all healthy streams normally resides in the central flow axis.

These fructigenic carbones react to centripetence. In other words they become very active if moved centripetally and in this condition are able to bind the fertilising oxygen, which becomes passive with the cooling centripetence of the central vortical flow, but highly active with warming centrifugence. Whatever the condition of the channel, therefore, and whatever the state of activity of these two elements, with the use of this device not only are the vital longitudinal vortices recreated, but the most productive interaction between the two opposing substances is also assured. Here they interact not only to increase the energies in the water, but also to augment its carbonic acid content which, as discussed previously, is one of the principal constituents of good water. Moreover they

create conditions conducive to the propagation of bacteria and micro-organisms beneficial to the environment through which the water passes. All this will be discussed in greater detail in the section on water supply.

On point no. 4: Where use of the above flow-guides is inappropriate – in the straighter stretches of a channel for instance – and where the removal of sediment is desirable, so-called 'energy-bodies' can be installed which have a similar effect on the flow of water. Though these have not been described in detail in the documents in the author's possession, from various hints it would appear that they consist of egg-shaped elements with neutral buoyancy, which are anchored to the river bed or its banks. In order to maintain their neutral buoyancy these flow-energisers or vortex-generators are provided with small holes fore and aft so that their inner density always equals that of the outer water. As in the case of the stationary trout, the effect of these egg-bodies is to create longitudinal vortices as the water swirls around them (fig. 13.6). The actual shape itself is naturally open to experiment and more grain-like forms may perform better.

Another method of introducing vortices is the emplacement of large stones or boulders in the centre of the channel. If these stones are metalliferous, then their effect is even greater, since they contain metals and minerals with different atomic valencies (+ and – charges). In chapter 11 the chemical composition of such stones was elaborated and found generally to be compounds of silicon (Si), molecular oxygen (O_2) (SiO_2 = silica) and metal oxides (silicates). The base element here, silicon, is classed as a semiconductor. In wide use today in electronics, silicon releases or retains electrons according to temperature here being relative to absolute zero (–273.15°C) where no electron emission occurs at all. The higher the temperature therefore, the greater the number of electrons released, i.e. in varying measure an electric current is caused to flow. At a state of zero electron emission at absolute zero, silicon might also be classified as a dielectric, a substance that resists the transfer of an electric charge (see chapter 6, 6.1). From a dialectic

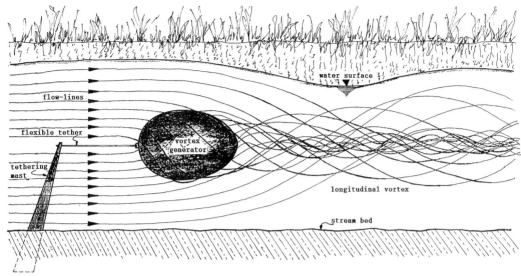

Fig. 13.6   **An egg-shaped "energy-body" for the regeneration of longitudinal vortices in streams**

viewpoint, which takes both sides of a given phenomenon into account, its semi-conductor function at higher temperatures could be equally interpreted as semi-dielectric. Through combination with other substances, silicon would thus give rise to the creation of materials with diverse dielectric properties and if two such substances with different degrees of permittivity are brought into contact, then a current flows from the lower to the higher. In view of pure water's high dissolving power and high dielectric value of 81, a current flow inaugurated by the presence of water could thus be of significant magnitude.

Here then are two possibilities for the generation and increase of energy in water. But as has been mentioned earlier with regard to falling rain droplets (chapter 6, 6.3), whenever an electric charge or field is caused to rotate, which would be inevitable in flowing water, then a magnetic or biomagnetic field is also generated reciprocally. The effect of these vitalising interactions with other elements, further increases the life-evolving production of fructigens, dynagens and qualigens and thereby the greater health of the water. In other cases these elements may also act as catalysts for other functions. In addition emplacement of such stones would

produce a similar effect to the one investigated by Professor Forchheimer on the excursion with Viktor Schauberger discussed in the previous chapter. On one occasion Viktor Schauberger admits to making use of 'energy-bodies', when he secretly installed them in a sediment-choked stream during the night. By morning it had all been carried away, the channel bed deepened considerably and the natural flow of water restored. All of this to the amazement of the engineers in charge of the stream's regulation, whose gross mismanagement coupled with the equally serious misdemeanours of the forestry department had brought about the constriction of the channel in the first place.

Before addressing the depletive and degenerative effects of modern river-engineering practices and hydro-electric power generation, however, we shall first examine the natural movement of water. As will have become apparent from all previous chapters, such movement is sinuous, convoluting and vortical.

13.2 *The Formation of Vortices*

Apart from the general function of temperature gradients described above, in order to explain the various aspects of temperature-

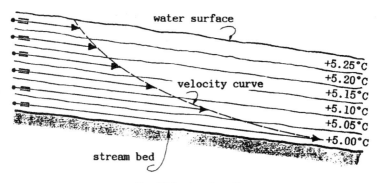

Fig. 13.7   **Laminar flow**

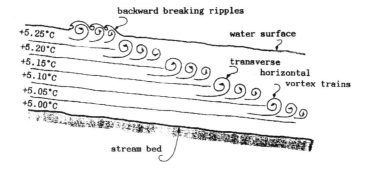

Fig. 13.8   **Longitudinal turbulance vortices**

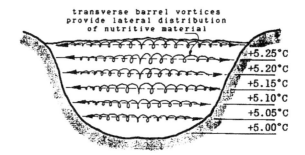

Fig. 13.9   **Transverse vortices**

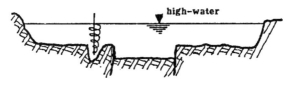

Fig. 13.10

related flow as clearly as possible, each one will be dealt with individually, although by and large in any river or stream all of them are interactive in diverse combinations. As already stated in the previous chapter, every particle of water is directly connected to a particular velocity relative to its specific weight and temperature, a phenomenon described in great detail by Viktor Schauberger in his 1930–31 treatise "Temperature and the Movement of Water"[3].

To give some idea of what is here involved, a series of superimposed water-strata with their respective temperatures are shown schematically in fig. 13.7, the coldest layer flowing over the stream bed. Here the velocity curve shows the different distances travelled by the respective water-strata in the same period of time, as denoted by the length of the arrows. Relative to the upper layer, the lowest can be seen to flow far more rapidly due to its greater density and coolness.

At the interface between these various layers, even though the temperature differences may be minimal, there is nevertheless a difference in their relative, temperature-related velocities, the lower layer sliding forwards slightly faster than its immediate upper neighbour. This slip creates a sort of vacuity at the 'end', as it were, of the higher-lying layer, into which the lower layer rises. In the process vortices are formed at right-angles to the current, which rotate on a horizontal plane from the bottom upwards as shown in fig. 13.8. These mix the water, but at the same time cool it, because the water temperatures within the centre of these vortices are identifiably cooler than those without, the uppermost vortex train manifesting itself as the familiar backward-breaking ripples seen on rivers at the surface. This type of vortex also distributes the lighter weight sediment and the nutrient material carried by the river from the centre towards the sides (fig. 13.9).

The movement of water can also be further categorised into laminar and turbulent flows, the simplest form of laminar flow being the one shown in fig. 13.7. Turbulence, however, can take the form of longitudinal or transverse vortices. As far as the latter are concerned there are two principal types; the first operates horizontally at right-angles to the direction of flow as shown in figs. 13.8 & 13.9; the second, potentially the more harmful, also acts at right-angles to the current, but on a vertical plane and, if too powerful, will gouge deep pot-holes or trenches in the river bed, seriously dislocating the natural flow (fig. 13.10).

Longitudinal vortices, as the name suggests, are aligned parallel to the flow-axis of the channel. While these may constitute turbulence according to the meaning of the word, longitudinal vortices have an extremely beneficial function, as will be shown later, and represent the structuring of those energies required to dislodge and transport sediment, and without which all

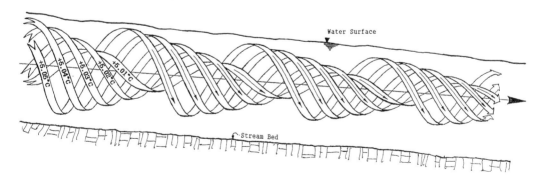

Fig. 13.11   **The Longitudinal Vortex**
A longitudinal vortex showing laminar flow about the central axis. The coldest water-filaments are always closest to the central axis of flow. Thermal stratification occurs even with minimal differences in water temperature. The central core water is subjected to the least turbulence and acclerates ahead, drawing the rest of the water-body in its wake.

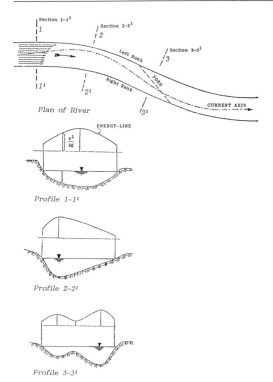

Plan of River

ENERGY-LINE

Profile 1–1¹

Profile 2–2¹

Profile 3–3¹

Fig. 13.12

channels will eventually silt up. At the same time they are those vessels which create and enhance the counterflow of levitational energy, the immaterial psyche of a waterway.

Although there are not many left, a naturally flowing river, undisturbed by modern river engineering, only rarely if ever overflows its banks. In their cool, faster flow down the flow-axis, longitudinal vortices clear the channel bed of sediment as well as deepen it, varying this capacity to suit the volume of the discharge. These vortices are also thermally stratified in a laminar fashion. As an example, in fig. 13.11 the central core-water of such a vortex has a temperature of +5.01°C, very dense and cold, and it moves faster than the more outlying water layers, which become progressively less dense as they warm towards the outside.

According to the Archimedean principle of the denser carrying the lighter, here the densest core-water carries the specifically lighter water, because in this inwinding, centripetal, vortical movement the densest water has to

flow down the very centre. It was this phenomenon which was responsible for the transport of the 'sinkers' mentioned in chapter 12.

Apart from cooling the river water, the other principal function of both transverse and longitudinal vortices in naturally flowing rivers and streams is to apply the automatic brake to the descending water. Without this naturally applied brake, the heavy masses of water would over-accelerate, rupture the river banks and cause immense havoc. It is this aspect that forms the nub of Viktor Schauberger's initial treatise, "Turbulence"[4], deposited under seal by Professor Exner at the Austrian Academy of Science in 1930.

13.3 The Formation of Bends

As the reflection of a primary energy path, the serpentine, meandering pattern of bends in a river is a manifestation of the physical secondary effect. Apart from large, immovable obstacles such as mountains and cliff faces for example, the course of a river or stream always follows the path in which the energies in a given situation like to move. In some instances it is difficult to say whether the topographical features of a landscape produced the form of the river or whether the river gave rise to the landscape through which it flows (viz. the Grand Canyon of Colorado), so intimately connected are the two. Since rivers are the mirrors of an unseen flow of energy, however, we need to examine how these bends are formed.

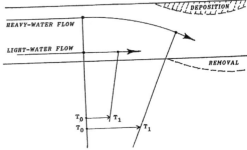

Fig. 13.13   **Cooler, faster water overtakes slower**

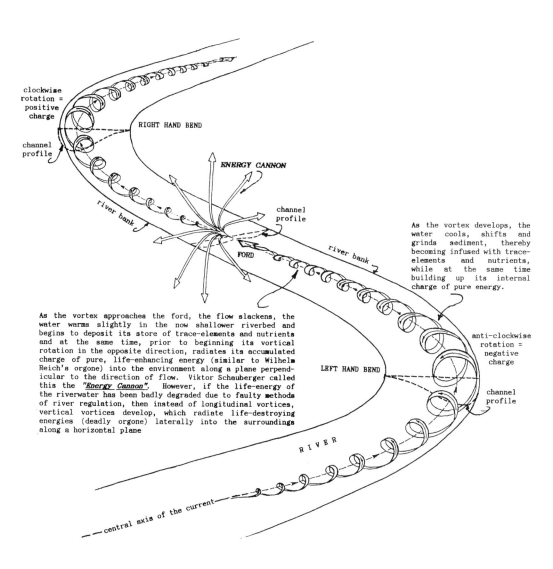

clockwise
rotation =
positive
charge

RIGHT HAND BEND

channel
profile

ENERGY CANNON

river bank

channel
profile

FORD

river bank

As the vortex develops, the
water cools, shifts and
grinds sediment, thereby
becoming infused with trace-
elements and nutrients,
while at the same time
building up its internal
charge of pure energy.

As the vortex approaches the ford, the flow slackens, the
water warms slightly in the now shallower riverbed and
begins to deposit its store of trace-elements and nutrients
and at the same time, prior to beginning its vortical
rotation in the opposite direction, radiates its accumulated
charge of pure, life-enhancing energy (similar to Wilhelm
Reich's orgone) into the environment along a plane perpendicular to the direction of flow. Viktor Schauberger called
this the *"Energy Cannon"*. However, if the life-energy of
the riverwater has been badly degraded due to faulty methods
of river regulation, then instead of longitudinal vortices,
vertical vortices develop, which radiate life-destroying
energies (deadly orgone) laterally into the surroundings
along a horizontal plane

LEFT HAND BEND

anti-clockwise
rotation =
negative
charge

channel
profile

RIVER

central axis of the current

Fig. 13.14   **The *"Energy Cannon"* of Viktor Schauberger**

The processes in the flow of water leading to the formation of bends is shown in fig. 13.12 in plan and section. Assuming that the river is initially shaded on both banks, the profile of the channel at section $1-1^1$ is symmetrical, as shown in the corresponding profile $1-1^1$. The curved line at the top of the diagram reflects the velocity of flow at each vertical and shows that the velocity of flow increases from the banks, reaching a maximum at the centre of the channel.

Proceeding now to section $2-2^1$ and profile $2-2^1$, where the flow of water on the right bank has been exposed to the Sun's heat, the water so exposed heats up, becomes more turbulent and begins to flow more slowly relative to the main body of water. The cooler, faster moving water flowing along the left-hand bank then overtakes the slower moving water and curls towards the right around it (fig. 13.13), due to the increasing turbulence and deceleration of the warmer water, eventually creating a bend. Some of the heavier sediment transported by the faster flow is thrown towards the left due to centrifugal force, while to the right the removal of sediment occurs as a result of the impacting colder water. At the same time the cross-sectional profile of the river at this point becomes asymmetrical, due to the unequal flows and temperatures, the deeper section of the channel being where the coldest water flows.

In section $3-3^1$ and profile $3-3^1$, due to the momentum of the cold water-masses, the cold water swaps sides of the channel and a bend is eventually formed in the opposite direction. If this natural, rhythmical alternation from right to left and left to right is in any way disrupted, it has dire consequences not only for the immediate surroundings, which become starved of nutrients, but also for all the life dependent on the river downstream. Indeed when regulating the course of a river naturally it is very important to ensure that a left hand bend, for example, does not occur where a right hand bend would complete this natural alternation.

The location of this current cross-over is where the river is shallowest and where it can most easily be forded. Since the flow-velocity tends to decelerate here, fords are also the major deposition zones for the river's suspended nutrients and minerals and where the river can transfer these to the environment. The bends on the other hand are where the rocks and stones are ground up and their pulverised substances transported in the vortical flow for later deposition. These pebbles, boulders and sediment, however, are not to be considered merely as inert matter, for in Viktor Schauberger's view they constitute the river's bread, its source of nourishment on its journey to the sea. If the temperature gradient at the ford is positively related to the ground temperatures these vital nutrients will be further absorbed into the ground and the groundwater table recharged and enriched. This is another of the many ways in which a river constantly regenerates its energies and vitality, while at the same time imparting them to the environment.

The ford is also the focus or target of what Viktor Schauberger called the 'energy-cannon' (fig. 13.14). It is where the upbuilding immaterial energies or etheiricities of the river are released into the environment which, as a form of energy are akin to the life-endowing, animalistic 'orgone' energies of Wilhelm Reich. They are freed at this location, because all the energies accumulated in the previous inwinding, anti-clockwise, longitudinal vortex have to be released before the movement turns clockwise. In other words, the point has been reached where the energy concentration of the vortex culminates in a process akin to breathing. One cannot continually breathe in and therefore the moment is reached where inhalation has to give way to exhalation, each of which is coupled with a different energy form and both of which are necessary for life to continue.

As these stones are ground together, which can only occur if the water is sufficiently cold, dense and dynamic, small particles of the minerals they contain are released into the water and partially or wholly dissolved, replacing those previously lost through transfer to the surroundings. Not only are these trace elements and minerals released, but pure ionising energy as well through the generation of

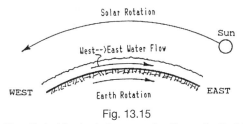

Fig. 13.15

The effect of flowing in the same direction as the Earth's rotation accelerates the water's relative movement and reduces the period of exposure to the heat of the Sun. The water remains cooler, increasing its carrying power and its capacity to transport nutrients. Both riverbanks normally remain fertile.

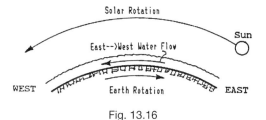

Fig. 13.16

The effect of flowing counter to the direction of the Earth's rotation not only slows the water's movement, but also causes the water to be exposed to the heat of the Sun for a longer period, heating it up. This reduces its carrying power and its capacity to transport nutrients. Both riverbanks can eventually become barren.

the triboluminescence mentioned in chapter 8. When two crystalline stones of similar composition are rubbed hard together or struck against one another, a golden flash of light is produced inside them. According to Viktor Schauberger the same effect occurs when two pieces of high-grade timbers of similar chemical composition are rubbed together.

In my experiments with this phenomenon, the generation of the sparks does not appear to cause an electrical disturbance, since a radio placed immediately adjacent to the sparking stones does not crackle in time with the production of the spark. In fact it does not crackle at all. There appears to be no interference whatsoever. We are therefore here concerned with some form of oxidation, a combustion process. That this sparking can also occur under water has never been imagined or investigated scientifically. It does take place under water, however, and is therefore a process of cold oxidation, an oxidation not necessarily associated with the generation of heat.

A further point of interest in this regard is the origin of the fabled 'Gold of the Nibelungs', the 'Rhinegold' that supposedly lay on the bottom of the Rhine in days of yore and which gleamed during the hours of darkness. This legend is also to be ascribed to the phenomenon of triboluminescence. About 200–250 years ago, the water of the Rhine was doubtless pure, clear and translucent enough for people to observe what appeared to be the flashing of gold on the river-bed. Today, however, along with many other rivers, the Rhine is a thick, turbid, grey-green muddy brew, its life-force having been extinguished by modern mechanistic methods of river engineering.

The vitalising energies generated in natural flows are principally the result of cooling coalescing vortical movement along the longitudinal axis of flow, which brings the dispersed suspensions of finely ground material into intimate contact in the densely packed cold core-water, a liquid intermixture Viktor referred to as an 'emulsion'. Both the extreme densation and the rapid rate of rotation at the vortex core induce higher states of ionisation, which in turn enable new combinations and recombinations of the various elements, thereby enhancing the generation of electromagnetic energies (viz. function of metalliferous rocks and triboluminescence). Since longitudinal vortices are associated with natural self-cooling flows, the energies they release are *cold-sourced* through processes Viktor called 'cold fermentation' and their effect is therefore beneficial. This is because the immaterial emanations of these emulsions containing oxygen – also a component of silicates, which becomes passive with centripetal cooling and easily bound by the carbones, are essentially formative in function. These environmentally vitalising energies are discharged on a plane perpendicular to the axis of the vortex as shown in fig. 13.14 and can be likened in character to the bio-magnetic discharge above the water-jet described in chapter 6, ftn. 7 and fig. 6.11.

With transverse vortices, however, and vertically aligned transverse vortices in particular (fig. 13.10) which form because the water has become over-warmed by over-exposure

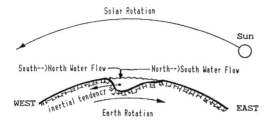

Fig. 13.17

The effect of the Earth's rotation on North–South and South–North flowing rivers induces an asymmetrical channel profile due to the inertial resistance of the water. Being specifically heaviest, the colder bottom water has the greatest inertial resistance and is forced to the western side of the current. The colder water with greater carrying power and sweeping force therefore flows along the western bank, deepening the bed on this side and carrying the greater proportion of nutrients, whereas the warmer, specifically lighter water, reduced in carrying power and sweeping force and thus deficient in nutrients, flows along the eastern bank. As a result the western bank is generally more fertile than the eastern bank.

to the Sun or through unnatural regulation, the energies emitted are *heat-sourced* and debilitating. This is largely the result of the heat induced aggresiveness of the oxygen and the lower quality emulsions this produces. Here we are concerned with warm fermentation, which gives rise to the propagation of pathogenic bacteria. Moreover, because the axis of this vortex is vertical, lethal horizontally propagated radiation is broadcast, harmful to the surroundings. This functions in a manner similar to Wilhelm Reich's "deadly orgone radiation" (DOR), whose insidious effect is to upset the metabolism of all organic life. In character it is akin to the red discharge described in the water-jet experiment above. These injurious emissions chaoticise or create 'holes' as it were, in the procreative matrix of female fructigenic ethericities which also propagate horizontally (chapter 5, fig. 5.2), severely inhibiting their germinating function.

While the differences in water temperature responsible for either of the above phenomena are minimal, it is also important to remember that life and death are merely a question temperature variations that our modern scientific world considers wholly insignificant.

13.4 The Geostrophic Effect on Flow

A further important factor associated with the movement and vitality of rivers is known as the 'geostrophic effect', which is related to the Earth's rotation and its influence on the movement of the water. It goes without saying that the temperature gradient is also influenced.

Fig. 13.15 shows a section through the Earth and its curvature. The Sun, seen from the southern hemisphere, is shown rising on the right and moving across the sky towards the left. At the same time the Earth is rotating towards the Sun to the right. In a river with a west->east flow direction, the water therefore flows towards the Sun. Any individual 'packet' of water, as it were, in such a river is exposed to the Sun for a shorter period than if the flow was in the opposite direc-

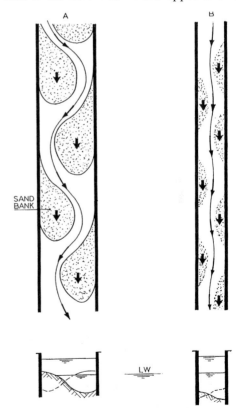

Fig. 13.18 Propagation of sand banks in straight channels

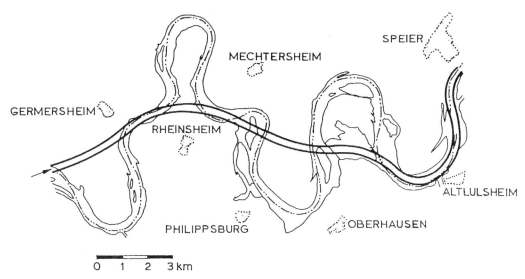

Fig. 13.19   **Channel regulation on the Rhine upstream of Mannheim (19th Century)**

tion. Since it is moving towards the Sun, this water-packet is therefore exposed to less heat.

At the same time; the flow of water is also faster than the Earth's rotation, due to the gradient down which it flows, so that the absolute velocity of flow relative to a stationary observer looking down from the South Pole is more rapid than if the movement were in the opposite direction. Such rivers tend to build up their banks evenly on both sides and the fertility of the adjacent areas is also higher, because the overall temperature of the water is cooler, the sediment transport and the associated distribution of nutrients greater.

With an east->west flow (fig. 13.16), however, a similar water-packet is exposed to the Sun for much longer not only because it is moving in the same direction as the Sun, but also as a result of the water's own inertia, which causes its forward movement to be slightly retarded by the Earth's rotation. The upshot of this is that the water becomes far

Fig. 13.21   **A canalised river**

warmer and less able to transport sediment and nutrients. In the lower reaches of such rivers the banks tend to become barren for lack of them and the river has a greater tendency to flood and to form deltas at its confluence with the sea.

The flow conditions in north->south and south->north flowing rivers is again different to the above. Their flow-patterns are governed more by their lateral inertia relative to the Earth's rotation than by the passage of the Sun across the heavens. In fig. 13.17 the section drawn through such a river exhibits an asymmetrical profile. Owing to the water's fluid inertia, the main body of water has a tendency to bank up against against the riverbank on the western side. i.e. the side opposite to the direction of the Earth's rotation.

Being the densest and heaviest, the coldest water is the most affected and therefore the main flow occurs along the western bank, where the channel is also generally deeper. Such rivers tend to be barren on the eastern

side, because, being shallower, the water on that side is hotter and the deposition of sediment therefore takes place sooner. When a positive temperature gradient is operative its effect tends to be more marked on the western bank than on the eastern and consequently the nutrient flow is greater towards the west than towards the east with a commensurate difference in relative fertility, or, as was shown in fig. 9.8, the river acts to extract nutrients from the warmer bank and deposit them on the cooler one.

If these rivers are at fairly high latitudes, however, and flow into cold or arctic seas, then as they move polewards the angle of incidence of the Sun's rays decreases, the water cools and such rivers carry their sediment far out into the seas, creating tongues and peninsulas in what is known as 'haff' formation. In the opposite case, such as the Nile, whose confluence with the sea is at much lower latitudes, in lieu of haff development, deltas form as the flow has become overheated and the water correspondingly

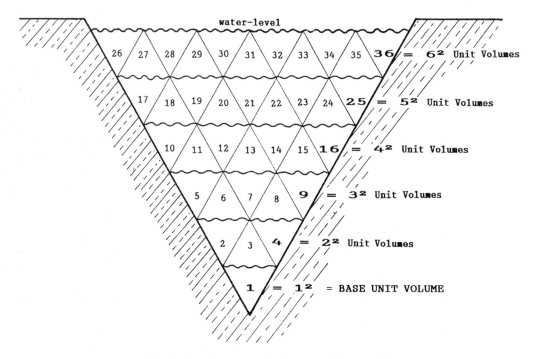

Fig. 13.22 **The rationale of trapezoid channels**
Relative to the base unit volume, the volume of water carried by the channel increases exponentially as the water-level rises

Fig. 13.20a **A natural river**

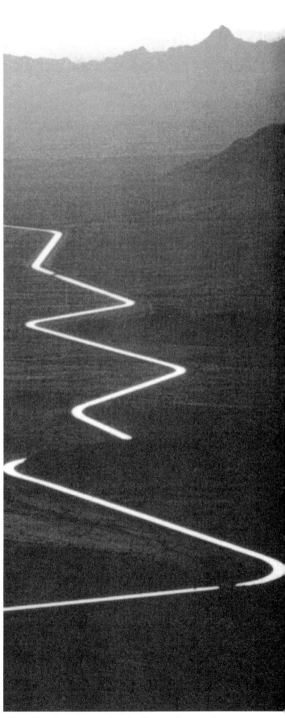

Fig. 13.20b **A mechanically engineered watercourse**

more sluggish and unable to keep its sediment in suspension.

13.5 The Effects of Conventional River Engineering

Of particular concern to Viktor Schauberger was the way in which rivers were being regulated and water handled in total ignorance of Nature's laws. Forcing water to move in concrete trapezoid canals, in cylindrical steel pipes, etc., had the same effect as enshrouding a human being in a straitjacket, which makes it aggressive (effect of over-warming on the oxygen content), takes away its character, its freedom and robs it of all its energy. Under such conditions water can no longer remain benign and disease-free, but becomes violent and disease-promoting.

In fig. 13.18 taken from a textbook on hydraulics[5], it can be seen that even in a straight channel, in this terrible 'straight'-jacket in which the water is confined, it still strives to dance, to waltz and, instead of flowing straight through this rigid canal, in which the flow should be straight and laminar according to hydraulic theory, the water still attempts to adopt its natural energetic flow-pattern in order to regain its former vitality.

To give the reader an idea of what modern river regulation entails, let us examine a section of that famous river, the Rhine fig. 13.19[6], which, as documented in chapter 1, Viktor Schauberger fought very strenuously, but in vain, to save. As with all naturally flowing watercourses, the meandering pattern of flow shown here is the way in which the Rhine wanted to move. It was the way in which it was able to optimise its energy and carrying capacity, although by the time this regulation was carried out, no doubt a great deal of the surrounding countryside had been deforested, with the inevitable consequences already discussed.

This natural pattern was not acceptable to the authorities, perhaps because it occupied too much space and very probably flooded fairly often. It was decided to build a trapezoid canal of uniform cross-section for its full length. In other words, a constant was introduced into what is naturally a continually varying system, restricting the flow to a particular dimension and, of course, the river, this now almost moribund body of water, was unable to transport its sediment. As a result the bed needed constant dredging in order to maintain a safe flood depth.

The way the Rhine has been truncated with the construction of this trapezoid canal illustrates the awful deformation such regulations cause. All the wonderful serpentine bends have gone. There is nothing natural in the river bends shown here. Shown in dark outline (fig. 13.19), this 'hard-edged' trapezoid channel was laid out by river engineers in the misplaced belief that the flow of water would be improved and drainage accelerated.

The stark contrast between the configuration of naturally organic and artificially mechanical watercourses becomes even more apparent in figs. 13.20a and 13.20b[7]. In the first the variation in channel width, the radii and curvature of the river bends and the splitting of the channel can clearly be seen. These are entirely the result of the natural flow of water in this situation. It has carefully formed the bed in which it desires to move and can move with the least loss of energy. In the second, however, there is no variation in width at all. All the straight sections are very straight and all the bends have the same radius. The whole arrangement has a very sterile, unnatural and lifeless appearance and most certainly will deliver no vital, healthy water to the point of use. The design of this tree-less and shade-less irrigation canal also shows quite unequivocally that its designers were totally oblivious of the fact that water is a living substance and concerned themselves solely with the transport of a supposedly inert liquid.

The drainage channel in fig. 13.21 shows what a trapezoid profile actually is. The choice of a trapezoid shape for these canals is founded on the rationale that the amount of water they can carry rises exponentially as the volume of flow increases. In fig. 13.22 at the bottom of the 'V' the figure 1 denotes the cross-sectional area and height of the

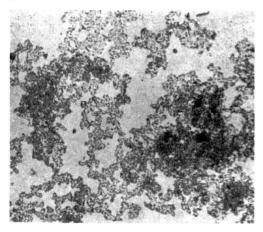

Centrifugally Killed Water
The strongly crystalline structure of heavily oxygenated water can be detected with a microscope. If warmed it becomes an incubator of dangerous bacteria.

Centripetally Vitalised Water
Magnetically charged water is characterised by an amorphous structure. its content of free oxygen is for the most part bound.

Fig. 13.23   **Viktor Schauberger's evidence from the microscope**

base unit of flow. When the height is doubled, the volume of flow is quadrupled, i.e. it is four times as much as the base unit. If the height of water is trebled, then the amount of water conducted is nine-fold, and so on, the increase in the quantity of water for each level being indicated by the larger size number at the right hand side of the 'V'. Whatever the apparent logic behind the design, such canals in no way conform to water's natural flow-pattern, since the design is based on the small scale channelling of lifeless water in hydraulic laboratories, with no consideration given to temperature.

As a result of this the Rhine was robbed of all its internal energies, of all its dynamism. A living thing robbed of its energy is also robbed to a large extent of its character. Character, however, is a very subtle and immaterial form of energy. We cannot define it on a material scale, but it is nevertheless a form of energetic expression. Water possesses character just as much as you or I.

When it is prevented from moving, or when it is no longer given the freedom to move in the way it desires, it acts in the same way as an imprisoned human being. It becomes violent, tries vigorously to remove its shackles and, once free, wreaks havoc

until its inner sense of equilibrium has once more been restored. Here the callous treatment meted out to the Rhine by the authorities could be likened to a surgeon who amputates his patient's legs the better to enable him or her to walk!

But what actually happens to the water under these circumstances? By being prevented from flowing in its naturally ordained manner, both flow and water temperature tend to become uniform. No longitudinal vortices can form and therefore no cooling and energising processes can take place. On the contrary, vertically inclined transverse swirls of water form producing the pernicious horizontal emanations mentioned earlier. A negative temperature gradient also prevails almost constantly.

The sediment is left lying on the river bed and, with no longitudinal vortical activity; the pebbles and stones are no longer ground up and the river is starved of its life-giving provisions, as is the landscape through which it passes, all the more so if the riverbank is 'hard-edged'. The water becomes warmer, insipid, its flow sluggish and evaporation increases. Instead of the sparkling crystal clarity characteristic of vitally healthy streams, the water becomes opaque and murky. With all of its energies forcefully

Fig. 13.25
The Egg and Hyperbolic Cone arrangement built in 1986 by the members of the Schaldming Group at Birnberg, Austria.

It is most probable that the intended electricity generator was that designed by Viktor Schauberger in the 1920s for which he received a Patent No. 117749 on the 10th May 1930.

The PKS-Schladming Group:
R. Harbacher, H. Zefferer,
H. Schrempf, A. Schwab,
T. Promberger, M. Dainhofer,
V. Knaus, H. Mayer,
11 January 1986

Fig. 13.24

removed, all that is left is a stale and lifeless liquid.

Becoming warmer as a result of all this gross mismanagement, its content of dissolved oxygen becomes increasingly aggressive. Lower forms of pathogenic bacteria freely evolve and propagate profusely in all areas in which the water can infiltrate. The river becomes an epicentre of all manner of diseases including cancer, imparting this condition to all forms of life forced to drink it or with which it comes in contact. Not only that but, in time of flood, the water itself becomes even more aggressive and malicious as it casts about, vainly seeking to regain its lost soul. With no automatic brake to restrain its forward movement, when the opportunity arises the water smashes into all in its path as it tries with its sheer weight and momentum to destroy the very structures that have robbed it of its psyche and to free itself of its bonds.

In the process, since it can no longer obtain its reproductive, uplifting energies in the lower reaches, which are derived from the carbones normally present in the river bank and made available through the corrosion of sediment, it attempts to compensate for this by drawing down the remnants of its levitational energies from the upper reaches, thereby exhausting these higher stretches of their live-giving function. Instead of being a carrier, mediator, accumulator and transformer of life-energies, the river has become a corpse. All of which is the appalling consequence of a mechanistically-minded science combined with a total ignorance of the true nature of water.

13.6 *Hydro-Electric Power*

This condition is further aggravated by present methods of hydro-electric power generation. Apart from the inappropriate design of dams used to store the water, discussed earlier in this chapter, the water itself is thrust down cylindrical pipes under enormous pressure. Upon leaving these it is then hurled against steel turbine blades where it is smashed to smithereens. The physical structure of the water is literally demolished and all the dissolved oxygen, and even some of the oxygen in the water molecule itself, is centrifuged out of the water.

Viktor Schauberger obtained evidence of this effect and the photographs taken through a microscope in fig. 13.23 show the marked difference in the structure of water that has been subjected to centrifugence on the one hand and centripetence on the other. The fragmented appearance of the centrifugally moved water is unmistakable. Due to the high friction and warming caused by the slicing action of the blades, the oxygen becomes extremely aggressive and highly active. Drawn to the rear side of the blades by the partial vacuum (known as cavitation) created there due to their high rotational velocity, the naked oxygen savagely attacks the bare metal, severely pitting the surface. This damage is greatly aggravated if the percentage of dissolved oxygen is fairly high, with the result that the blades become perforated, making them virtually useless.

What emerges as the end-product of this physical and energetic disintegration, while certainly a liquid, is merely the skeleton of what was once healthy water. When this fragmented and largely oxygen-deficient water is finally ejected into the river, it has a disastrous effect on the fish and other aquatic life. It has long been known that certain species of fish disappear once these power stations are commissioned, and other forms of life have great difficulty in surviving below them.

In Australia, for example, it was recently reported that the fish in a Tasmanian river appeared to have been poisoned when water was discharged from the Riess Dam by the hydro-electric authority[8]. There was no evidence of chemical poisoning, but the water produced reactions in the fish, which killed them. These were akin to the 'bends' suffered by divers as a result of the formation of nitrogen bubbles in the blood. Generally speaking, it is only the more inferior species of fish that do manage to exist.

Now thoroughly impoverished, the water has to build itself up again completely before it can be of any benefit to the environment. In order to do so it seeks out renewed supplies of oxygen and other high quality substances wherever it can find them, including living things. The first to fall victim to this onslaught are high quality aquatic organisms in which these high-grade substances are found. Fish are especially prone to attack due to the particularly intimate contact with this 'ravenous' water, as it is drawn in through their very delicate gill systems. Rather than the 'bends' as such, here we are more probably concerned with the 'galloping consumption' mentioned in chapter 10, in which the body's tissues are attacked by oxygen-hungry carbones. But fish-life is not the only victim, the soil bordering on the river is also leached of its nutrients as the water searches to recover them for itself. The result: a large drop in soil fertility and productivity.

This extraordinarily destructive power-generating process, however, is totally unnecessary, because there is another way of generating hydro-electric power which does not harm the water. Not only that, but this method, devised by Viktor Schauberger in the early 1920s and eventually patented in 1930[9], can produce 90% more electricity with a given volume of water, i.e. his invention uses 10% of the volume of water presently used to generate the same amount of power. Using water from a nearby stream Viktor installed this device to light his forest warden's house, which was too remote to be connected to any other source of supply. The design shown in fig. 13.24 is very simple, reflecting his statement that what is natural is silent, simple and cheap.

It consists of a brass or bronze nozzle, which is internally rifled in order to create a vortical flow, thereby reducing both pressure and friction as the water is centripetally drawn away from the sides. The water is therefore cooled, densified and energised as it passes through before encountering a double-spiral, or multiple-spiral, shell-like impeller attached to the shaft of a generator (not shown). Though not apparent on the diagram, the windings of these two or more entwined spirals are formed as semi-circular channels facing upwards towards the nozzle. They widen towards the base, and at the same time gradually twist outwards and backwards in the opposite direction to the direction of rotation. As the whirling water emerges from the nozzle it is entrapped by these grooves and the impeller is made to spin at high speed. The purpose of the upwardly curving tails at the ends of the spirals is to exploit the very last ounce of the water's momentum.

I happened to see an example of a possible installation using this device while staying with Walter Schauberger in Austria. In 1986 we were invited to visit a group of enthusiasts living around the township of Schladming who were interested in the practical application of Viktor Schauberger's ideas and Walter Schauberger's mathematics, intending to produce their own electricity. On the property of one of their members living on the Birnberg, they had carefully constructed the combination of egg and hyperbolic cone shown in fig. 13.25, which was sourced from a nearby brook. Water from the stream was fed into the upper part of the egg tangentially, thereby providing the initial impulse for the creation of a vortex.

At the time no generator had been installed and I was told it was being specially manufactured. At first I assumed that it would be a small conventional turbine but, knowing their keen interest in all things Schauberger, the impeller that was being built was probably the one described above. Unfortunately I have had no further contact with this group and therefore I cannot relate what was the outcome.

Successful or not, what this does show is that small groups of people working together cooperatively can provide their own sources of cheap power and can do much to re-establish their independence from centralised power and control over their lives. The problem that confronts us all, alas, is that it is the centralised electricity authorities who write the rules which ensure as far as possible that no-one can escape the net. The greater the number of people who are willing to challenge this central control over their independence, the more difficult it will become for those to continue holding such power over us.

Notes

1. From Viktor Schauberger's treatise, "Temperature and the Movement of Water" ("Temperatur und Wasserbewegung"): *Die Wasserwirtschaft*, No.20, 1930.
2. *Trees and the New Earth*, p.117, published 1953.
3. Much of this material is to be found translated into English in the book *Eco-technology*, Viktor Schauberger's own writings in three volumes, trans. & ed. by Callum Coats: Gateway Books, Bath, 1997; (Nat.Book Network, Lanham, MD, USA; Banyan Tree Book Distr., Stirling, So. Australia).
4. Parts of which are also to be found in *ibid*.
5. Figs. 5/2.14a & 5/2.14b from *Principles of River Engineering* by P.Ph.Jansen and others: Longman, Harlow, England. ISBN 0-273-01139-1.
6. *ibid*. fig. 5/2.17.
7. Photographs by Peter Essick, c/o Aurora & Quanta Productions, Main Street, Box 266, Lovell, ME 04051, USA.
8. ABC News item 27 November 1990.
9. Austrian Patent No.117749.

14
WATER SUPPLY

14.1 The Wooden Water Main

Ever active in the sphere of water, Viktor Schauberger also turned his attention to the problems of water supply and ways of overcoming them through his profound knowledge of this essence of life. From archeological excavations it has become evident that in earlier times, in the time of the Romans and Greeks, the ancient Egyptians and Babylonians, for example, water and its nature were far better understood than today. We, however, in our love affair with mechanics, have largely lost contact with the organics of Nature.

In their systems of water reticulation, as far as possible water mains were constructed of natural stone or high-grade timber. In time, however, the sources of high-quality timber for these pipes was exhausted and if no suitable stone was easily available, then other materials such as metals had to be sought. To find the right type of metal, coins of various alloys, which had been thrown into fountains for ritualistic purposes, were studied. Some dissolved altogether, while others became totally encrusted. The coins that remained clean, though perhaps slightly tarnished, were chosen as most suitable and it was noted that pure iron did not rust.

However, even here great errors were made. The Romans unfortunately stumbled upon lead, which eventually led to their undoing. While its use in the production of water conduits no doubt contributed to the increasing lead-induced madness amongst the rich upper classes like Caligula's who

could afford its use, it was actually the leaden tankards and goblets from which they drank copiously which brought about their ultimate demise. The acid in the wine reacted with the lead, dissolving some of it in the process, the cumulative effect of which caused insanity.

Originally, before the advent of the Industrial Revolution and the enormous expansion of cities and towns, the water in many cities in Europe and even in New York had long been supplied in wooden water mains, there being an ample supply of suitable timber, coopering expertise and no other technical alternative. As advances were made in technology, our civilisation then decided to use the economically more viable cast-iron water mains – subsequently to be replaced with steel – in ignorance of the fact that the longer water is transported in such mains, the worse its quality.

Nothing natural and alive can ever maintain its quality in sealed vessels, because all natural systems are open and must be able to interact with the environment. They all need to be able to breathe, and water is no exception. But because of our rather jaundiced, superficial view of life, we do not readily credit any process of Nature with any autonomy, any consciousness, self-organisational ability or intelligence. As a result we inaugurate processes that eventually bring about our own undoing.

Viktor Schauberger's research showed that in Vienna, when the existing wooden water mains were extended with cast-iron or steel pipes, internally coated with bituminous material in order to supply new suburbs, the incidence of cancer also rose commensurately as shown by the following statistics assembled by him:

In 1920, 2400 people died of cancer in Vienna; in 1926, 3700 fatal cases of cancer were recorded; in 1931, 4900 human lives fell victim to this terrible illness. In the figures quoted above the progressive spread of this disease is clearly evident.[1]

The flow in a cylindrical pipe is generally chaotic, so that the whole structure of water is gradually broken up in the process. In its passage down the pipe, the water is exposed to processes similar to electrolysis, generated through the friction of the water against the pipe-walls which gradually decompose the dissolved trace and other substances, heating up the water at the same time. It should be remembered here that very slight differences in temperature can produce effects apparently out of all proportion to the magnitude of the original causes. The water's dis-

solved oxygen content is gradually consumed as the material of the pipe gradually oxidises into rust. While rust itself is not poisonous, in association with the warmer water, its precipitation as sludge on the bottom of a steel pipe makes it an admirable medium for the breeding and propagation of pathogenic bacteria.

But rust also has other disadvantages. Since the volume it takes up is about ten times that of the base, unrusted material, its deposition decreases the effective diameter of the pipe, further constricting the flow, thereby unfavourably affecting the carrying and transportive capacity of the water. Instead of healthy, wholesome water, what emerges at the point of use is an unholy brew, a water-corpse, made even worse by all the chemical additives, such as the chlorine required to disinfect it. By drinking such chlorinated water, people become vulnerable to disease. It is no wonder therefore, and as Viktor Schauberger often said, that a bottle of good water will one day become far more expensive than a bottle of

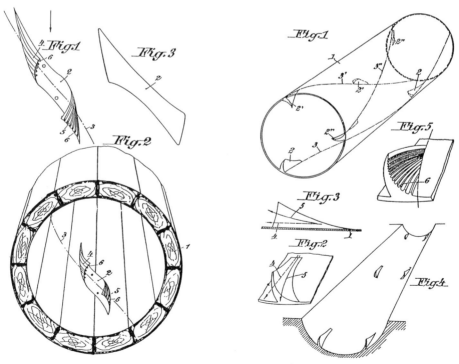

Fig. 14.1 & 2   **Illustrations from a patent application for a wooden drinking water pipe**

wine and it will be all the more highly prized because of its rarity.

In an attempt to remedy the situation and to reduce the incidence of cancer, in 1930 Viktor applied for patents for a pipe[2] made of wooden staves, like a barrel, which was designed to enhance the energy and purity of water flowing through it. This was followed about 15 months later by a further patent application[3] in 1931. As designed, the flow dynamics of this wooden pipe and the pipe itself, which breathes, are ideally suited to the containment of an alive body, i.e. water, and to the transport of drinking water, so that when the water arrives at the point of use, it has already been totally purified without the use of any artificial additives or more importantly, contaminants. Both pipes, shown in figs. 14.1 & 14.2, will be examined jointly since they perform the same function.

The two designs involve the creation of longitudinal vortices within the pipe. These are not simple vortices, however, but are double-spiral ones. That is to say, the coldest central core-water describes a single spiral motion, while the peripheral flow describes a double-spiral motion, i.e. it rotates about itself, while at the same time spiralling around the central core. This double-spiral motion is induced by three parallel systems of guide-vanes, which have the same effect as rifling, and are attached to the pipe-walls at certain specific locations.

The vanes themselves are made of silver-plated copper, partly because of the energies derived from the galvanic currents and other more subtle energies generated between the two metals of opposite gender in this copper(female)-silver(male) biometal composition, and partly because silver has bactericidal properties. In order to reduce any lateral movement of the water across their surfaces, the guide-vanes are fluted, directing the water towards the centre. These are placed at intervals along a helical path inside the pipe, as shown on fig. 14.2, and are angled and aligned to the spiral flow of water, directing it from one guide-vane to the next. The relation of their curvature to the axis of the pipe is always constant. The purpose of the guide-vanes is not only to create the necessary vortices, but also to deflect the flow away from the sides, thereby reducing the heating effects of friction to a minimum. In order to understand this complex double-spiral dynamic figs.14.3 & 14.4, which respectively show the pipe in longitudinal section and cross-section should be studied simultaneously.

As the water is deflected from a straight path by the guide-vanes, a certain amount acts in a manner akin to ball-bearings and is in contact with both the outer face of the

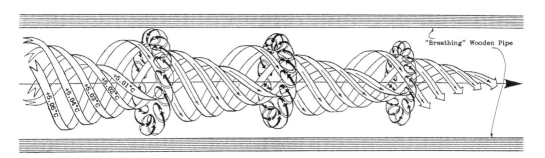

Fig. 14.3 The double-spiral longitudinal vortex
A longitudinal vortex showing the development of toroidal counter-vortices. These occur due to the interaction with the pipe-walls and have an effect similar to ball-bearings, enhancing the forward movement. Their interior rotation follows the direction of rotation and forward motion of the central vortex, whereas the direction of their exterior rotation and translatory motion are reversed. These toroidal vortices act to transfer oxygen, bacteria and other impurities to the periphery of the pipe, where, due to the accumulation of excessive oxygen, the inferior, pathogenic bacteria are destroyed and the water rendered bacteria-free.

Callum Coats, July 1992

inner core-water and the inner face of the pipe. It is a peculiar movement and difficult to describe, having components of motion in different directions. In a certain sense this outer, peripheral movement could be described as toroidal, i.e. a doughnut-shaped vortical rotation like a smoke ring. 'Helically toroidal' might be a more appropriate description, however, since this outer water also has a translatory motion in a spiral around and with the core-water.

Viewed along the longitudinal section (fig. 14.3) the inner portion of the toroid in contact with the inner core-water moves to the right in the direction of flow, whereas the direction of movement of the outer portion, which is in contact with the pipe, has a motion component in the opposite direction. This is only a figure of speech, however, in an attempt to explain the process, because upon coming in contact with the wall-surfaces, each water particle does not actually move backwards up the pipe, but pauses briefly before being caught up again in the forward flow.

Looking at the cross-section in fig. 14.4 the situation is similar, the small-scale rotation being in the opposite sense to that of the central spiral flow. The overall direction of rotation of the whole of this peripheral water as a body, however, is in the same direction as the central core as indicated by the larger triangular-headed arrows. That the movement of all the water in this type of pipe is faster than in conventional cylindrical pipes was con-

firmed by Professor Forchheimer in his expert opinion[3] on Viktor Schauberger's novel dam design discussed previously, wherein he states with regard to a proposed overflow pipe that:

...when a substantial influx of water occurs, some of it is to be discharged directly into the Eger through a fairly large diameter pipe, which branches off on the left-hand side of the reservoir at a high level. This pipe will be rifled, since it has been shown that this produces a sharp increase in the flow-velocity.

With differing water temperatures, once again the colder water is drawn down the middle and the coldest, heaviest core-water accelerates, sucking the other specifically lighter waters after it. Here centripetal and centrifugal forces are again active, and in the initial phases of flow the dissolved oxygen is squeezed out of the central core and impelled centrifugally towards the periphery, assisted by the toroidal flow. In the same way that the oxygen is removed from the centre, so too is any fine suspended matter which is then pressed against the pipe walls. The larger suspended solids, owing to their greater density and mass, continue to be transported down the central axis.

At the periphery, friction is at a maximum and due to the resultant warming, the oxygen, already stimulated by centrifugence, becomes even more aggressive and through processes of oxidation the fine suspended matter combines with the material of the walls, thereby sealing them. Because no oxygen is present in the core-water, all bacteria, noxious and beneficial alike, migrate to the periphery of the pipe, where the inferior, less complex, pathogenic bacteria are overwhelmed by a surplus of aggressive oxygen and eliminated. The higher quality microorganisms, which can support and require higher levels of oxygen to exist are however, largely unscathed. In this way the water becomes increasingly pure, disease- and germ-free.

There being no iron or steel to interact with, and the pathogens having now been removed, the remaining free dissolved oxy-

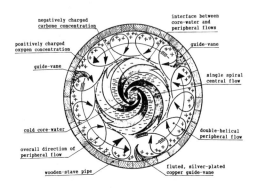

Fig. 14.4 **Flow dynamics of the double-spiral pipe**

gen in the pipe does not get totally consumed. With the cessation of oxidative activity coupled with the resultant cooling, the residual oxygen is returned by the toroidal vortices to the interface with the central core-water. Here it interacts energetically with the now oxygen-hungry carbones in the core flow under cold processes of oxidation. This principally centripetal 'original' or 'life-originating' form of motion not only produces dynagens – the immaterial energy generators – but also increases the carbonic acid content, which together raise the overall vitality, life-energy and wholesomeness of the water.

In order to function properly it is important that certain precautions are taken. To be laid properly, these wooden water mains should be embedded in sand and insulated from both light and heat. In other words, a cool controlled environment is necessary, which, if maintained, will make the wooden pipe outlast a steel one, since is is not subjected to decay. Because it is a breathing system, a certain minimal amount (like sweat) of the water reaches the outside of the pipe, where some evaporation occurs. This acts to cool the exterior of the pipe, which in turn further cools the contents. Coupled with the internal vortical flow which, as discussed before is a process involving cooling and the enhancement of the water's intrinsic life-energy, then the whole body of water gradually becomes cooler as it flows.

Due to the various oxidation processes taking place en route, certain reduction processes also occur which improve the quality of the water and any other matter transported in it, such as ore, etc., which are carried down the middle of the pipe without touching the sides. Owing to the external pressure-relieving action of the longitudinal vortices, the actual size and thickness of the pipe-wall can be fairly minimal.

14.2 The Stuttgart Investigation

Having long been ridiculed by the scientific establishment and wanting to obtain irrefutable proof of the validity of his ideas on water movement, in 1952, at his own expense, Viktor Schauberger approached the Stuttgart Technical University to have the matter settled once and for all. Here his theories on water were to be tested on a strictly scientific basis under the direction of Professor Franz Pöpel, director of the Institute of Hygiene. When first approached Pöpel refused, saying that it would be a waste of his time and in any case would produce no worthwhile results.

But, yet again, higher powers came to Viktor's aid in the unlikely form of the then Bonn Government, who had been so incensed at Viktor's vigorous attacks on their management of the Rhine that they were only too delighted to pay half the costs of the investigation, believing that it would thoroughly discredit him. Under these changed circumstances Professor Pöpel agreed to undertake the investigation using the pipes of various configurations that Viktor supplied (fig. 14.5). These were never returned to him upon completion of the project, despite the fact that these rifled and helical pipes were extremely difficult and expensive to fabricate, because their unusual shape made any of the normal casting processes almost impossible. An accurate description of these various shapes and their respective flows is rather difficult. They could be construed as 'double-rifled', 'double torsional flow' or 'spiral helical' pipes.

The experimental arrangement, the basis of the investigation shown in fig. 14.6, is such that the water enters the pipe from a levelling vessel, which supplies a constant head of water. The water then passes through whichever pipe is under test and into the outlet chamber, subsequently flowing to waste. Adjacent to the outlet, three small, calibrated vertical glass tubes are arranged. The left-hand tube measures the available head of water and is directly connected to the levelling vessel. The middle tube is connected into the system immediately at the end of the test pipe and the right-hand tube at a point just below the outlet at the top of the expanding cone. The middle and right-hand tubes measure the drop or rise in pressure. The higher the indicated water-levels, the less the loss of head and friction. By lowering the whole of

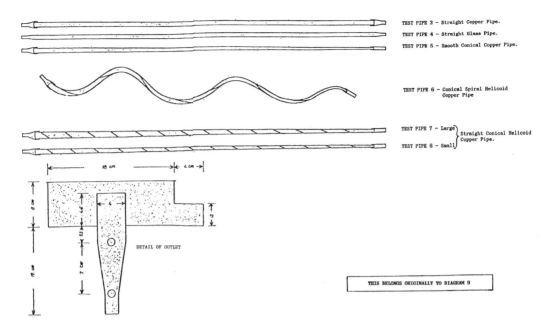

TEST PIPE 3 – Straight Copper Pipe.

TEST PIPE 4 – Straight Glass Pipe.

TEST PIPE 5 – Smooth Conical Copper Pipe.

TEST PIPE 6 – Conical Spiral Helicoid Copper Pipe

TEST PIPE 7 – Large } Straight Conical Helicoid Copper Pipe.

TEST PIPE 8 – Small }

DETAIL OF OUTLET

THIS BELONGS ORIGINALLY TO DIAGRAM 9

Fig. 14.5   **Pipes of various configurations that Schauberger supplied to Prof. Pöpel**

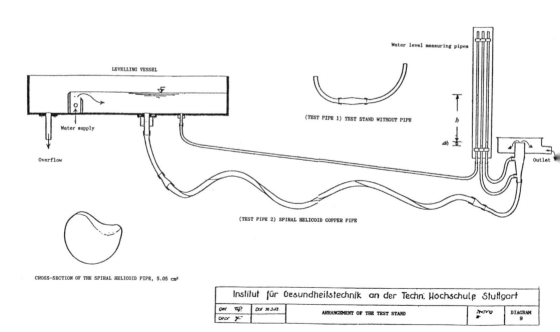

Fig. 14.6   **Prof. Pöpel's experiment with the spherical-helical copper pipe**

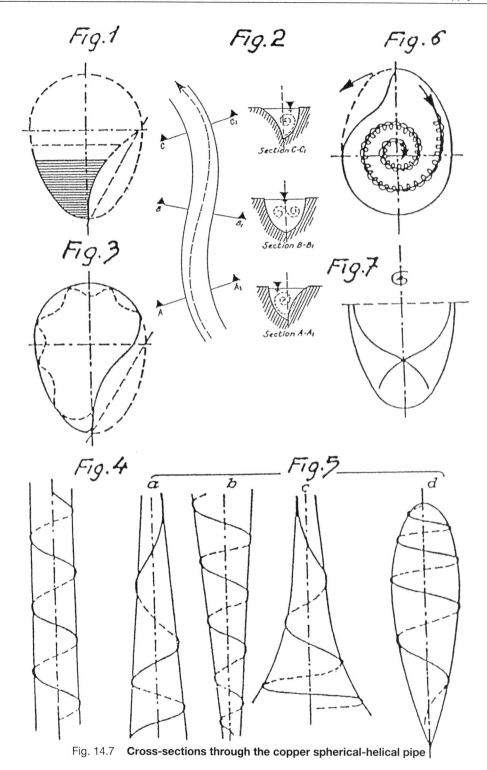

Fig.1

Fig.2

Section C-C₁

Section B-B₁

Section A-A₁

Fig.6

Fig.3

Fig.7

Fig.4

Fig.5

a b c d

Fig. 14.7 **Cross-sections through the copper spherical-helical pipe**

the right-hand side of the arrangement, the flow can be increased due to the steepening of the gradient and the effect of gravity.

The actual final presentation of the report[5] was rather biased. The most significant and revolutionary data were largely glossed over, because it would have caused an unwanted upheaval in the scientific world by overturning the hitherto scientifically sacred 'Second Law of Thermodynamics'. According to this law, without further or continuous input of energy, all (closed) systems must degenerate into a condition of total chaos or entropy. These experiments proved the contrary to be true.

The most interesting pipe (no. 2) portrayed in larger scale just below the levelling vessel in fig. 14.6 has the cross-section shown in fig. 14.7 and is similar to that taken through an antelope or Kudu horn, supporting Viktor's maxim *"Comprehend and Copy Nature!"* This was the object of two successful patents[6], which were applied for and granted in many countries, the one shown in fig. 14.7 being the more comprehensive illustration of it[7]. Strangely enough, while I was able to obtain copies of the fuller patent from Brazil, Portugal and France through friends, I was unable to trace any in Great Britain, Germany and Austria. No approach was made to the United States.

In the diagram showing the increase and decrease in friction of the pipes under test (fig. 14.8), the upward portions of the curve indicate that friction is being generated or pressure is increasing and the downward sections where these are reducing. The glass pipe (No. 4) was actually found to be the least suitable for water transfer, having a higher frictional coefficient than a similar copper pipe, in which friction begins to take effect only at higher flow volumes. Both straight glass and straight copper (No. 3) pipes exhibit a certain fluctuation in values but, in the main, friction is constantly on the increase.

Fluctuation in frictional values becomes more evident in the straight rifled pipes, but it can be seen that the spiral-helical pipe (No. 2) produces a markedly different profile to those of the other test-pipes. On two occasions, it dips below the line of zero friction at

the bottom of the graph. Instead of interpreting the downward curves on the graph as a decrease in friction or pressure, they could be viewed as those sections where suction is increasing. What is happening here is that due to the involuting flow movement caused by the configuration of the pipe-walls, the water is directed away from the walls, thus reducing the friction.

In his report, Pöpel does not refer to this phenomenon, other than to state that on two occasions friction appeared to diminish to zero. What he does not mention, which must have been apparent at the time, was that the measured frictional values also dipped below the line of zero friction; a condition that could be termed *'Negative Friction'*, a paradox of physics. This expression is not of my making, but one which Walter Schauberger averred was coined by Pöpel himself. Due to the far-reaching implications of this startling discovery for accepted hydraulic theory, Pöpel may well have been disinclined to record it in writing for fear of suffering an 'ideological repression' akin to that of Jacques Benveniste, discussed earlier.

While moving at this particular velocity relative to the form of the pipe, the flow of water was in harmony with the configuration of the pipe. When something is in harmony with something else, then there is no friction. This unexpected phenomenon invalidates the Second Law of Thermodynamics and is no doubt why Pöpel never aired it publicly, because it would mean that a system can actually generate energy spontaneously; that once started, a further input of energy is unnecessary; that energy is not a constant quantity, but that it can also be increased, since once again we are here concerned with the presence of immaterial dynagens created through 'original' motion.

In further confirmation of the periodically lower and nonexistent levels of friction in the spiral-helical pipe, the table in fig. 14.9 lists the relative frictional losses of the various pipes under test. In the case of the spiral-helical pipe it can be seen that these losses are reduced to zero on three occasions and reach a periodic minimum at flow-rates of 0.19lit/sec and 0.44lit/sec. With only one or

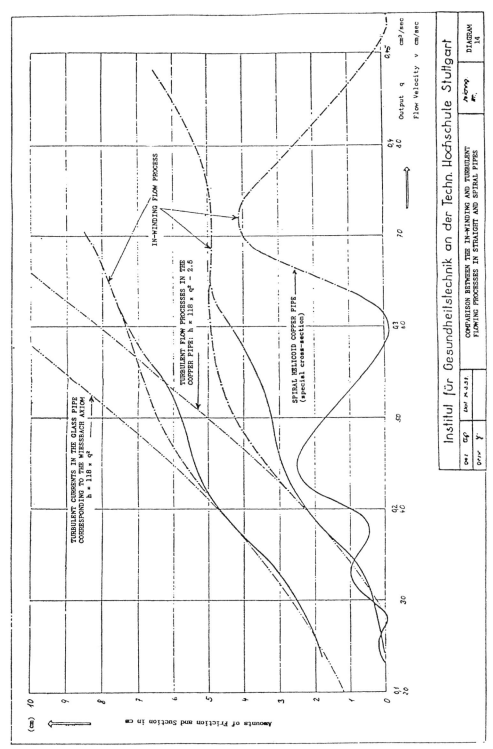

Fig. 14.8   The increase and decrease of friction in pipes

two exceptions, the frictional losses of this pipe are always far less than those of the other pipes.

14.3 The Circulation of Blood

Continuing our examination of enclosed flows we will now examine another form of flow, namely the circulation of the blood. Viktor Schauberger stated on many occasions that the heart was not a pump, for it does not pump as much as **'being pumped'**! In a similar vein, he also said that a bird does not fly, but is 'flown' and a fish 'is swum'. In view of the results of the Stuttgart investigation described above, this statement seems in part confirmed. Its function, in his view, was far more that of a regulator of the blood flow,

and although the heart does produce spurts of blood during its contraction, it was not actually a pump.

His explanation for the Stuttgart phenomenon was that the flow of water was in resonance with the double-helical form of the pipe, stating that this also applied to blood vessels too, which were the elements responsible for the blood's circulation. While the arteries and capillaries themselves have a peristaltic, pulsatory action, there are also other factors involved, which will be examined later. This pulsation was observed by Professor Kurt Bergel of Berlin (ca.1925–30) when, after a few days of incubation to allow for small blood vessels to form around the yolk-sac, he carefully opened up a bird's egg. Upon doing so he noticed that the blood vessels surrounding the yolk-sac pulsated before

Output q	Friction Losses in		Straight Glass Pipe
	Spiral Helicoid	Straight	
		Copper Pipe	
l/sec	cm	cm	cm
0,12	0,10	0,05	1,85
0,13	0,19	0,20	2,07
0,14	0,00	0,23	2,20
0,15	0,40	0,33	2,48
0,16	0,95	0,45	2,85
0,17	0,95	0,70	3,25
0,18	0,65	1,20	3,75
0,19	0,45	1,85	4,25
0,20	0,95	2,25	4,65
0,21	2,05	2,55	5,05
0,22	2,50	2,85	5,30
0,23	2,45	2,95	5,45
0,24	2,10	3,10	5,60
0,25	1,70	3,24	5,79
0,26	1,25	3,35	6,00
0,27	0,80	3,50	6,20
0,28	0,35	3,75	6,65
0,29	0,00	4,00	7,00
0,30	0,00	4,30	7,30
0,31	0,10	–	–
0,32	0,80	4,90	7,30
0,34	3,50	4,90	–
0,36	4,60	4,90	–
0,38	3,70	5,05	–
0,40	2,50	5,38	–
0,42	1,60	5,80	–
0,44	0,70	6,50	–

Fig. 14.9   **Output and friction losses of straight and spiral test pipes of glass and copper**

they cooled off, although no heart had as yet been formed.

Professor Bergel also held the same view as Viktor Schauberger, rejecting the idea that the heart was a sort of pump whose task was to impel blood to every part of the body. Bergel maintained that this was carried out by *"the millions of highly active capillaries permeating the body,"* and that *"health and disease are primarily dependent on the faultless or disturbed activity of the capillaries."*[8]

The actual movement of the blood, therefore, would appear to arise initially due to the processes of pulsation. In the light of the Stuttgart Investigation, however, it could be argued that the flow is enhanced by the configuration of the blood vessels themselves, whose shape and structure, recalling the discussion on new energies in chapter 3, represent the secondary effect of the immaterial energy flow that created them in the first place. In addition, the viscosity of the blood is known to decrease usefully or intentionally in inverse proportion to the diameter of the blood vessels, which also adds to its friction-free movement in the smallest vessels – the capillaries.

Two further contributing factors are also present. The first is the positive temperature gradient between the innermost parts of the body and the extremities which, as shown previously induces a movement from warm to cold areas. In this regard the vitalising effect of a cold shower on the blood circulation is well known (stimulation and enhancement of warm-to-cold flow), whereas a long hot bath tends to produce physical lassitude (reduction of differences between internal and external temperatures). The second is the result of the difference in the physico-chemical composition and therefore the energetic characteristics of arterial and venal blood.

This qualitative difference is partly due to the developing physical vacuity (and therefore suction) created by the progressive absorption of positively-charged oxygen carried by the arterial blood, which increases towards the extremities (skin and hair replacement, wound repair, etc.), where the absorption is greatest, and partly due to the rising desire for the reabsorption of oxygen

in the lungs by the negatively-charged, carbone-rich venal blood. Since these two types of blood carry opposite charges, the muscular contraction and closing action of the heart is therefore triggered through the periodic equalisation of positive and negative charges, which reach a maximum in the venal and arterial chambers of the heart itself, due to the large charge-carrying volume of both.

The hallmark of all life-processes is pulsation and, rather than acting as a pump, the vital function of the heart is therefore to promote a pulsation in the flow. Following from the above it can also be stated with a large degree of certainty that we breathe not because the heart 'pumps', but that the heart 'pumps' because we breathe (intake of positively charged oxygen and expulsion of negatively charged CO_2 and water).

In the case of a growing foetus, however, which does not breathe as we do (its blood being oxygenated via the placenta), the heart may actually behave like a pump, reinforcing the action of the pulsating blood vessels until the moment of birth. Since the movement of blood is conditioned in part by differences in internal and external temperature, prior to this event the normal temperature-induced component of blood flow would be rendered virtually inoperative, due to the minimal temperature variations within the insulating amniotic fluid of the womb. Therefore during pregnancy a 'pump' might well be a necessary auxiliary. Once birth has occurred, the first vital breath taken and the infant's body exposed to larger variations in temperature, then the heart assumes its proper function of pulsator and flow regulator. But if the heart actually is a pump, as presently claimed in medical circles, then what force must it apply to carry out this vital task?

A while ago I happened upon an article by Dr. Ernst O. Attinger entitled "Hydrodynamics of Blood Flow"[9] in which was described the blood circulation of a 13kg dog. The upper diagram in fig. 14.10 depicts the general organisation of the cardiovascular system, where the venal beds are shown in black, whereas the lower stepped diagram provides data concerning the various vascular beds (the different types of blood vessel) of a 13kg dog, listing the values of the viscous resistance, length of branches, volume of flow, diameter, etc, of the different categories of blood vessel. When I calculated the total length of all the branches in each segment of the 13kg dog's vascular tree, I found that the total overall length of all the blood vessels in the system amounted to 144,017,280 centimetres or 1,440.173km! On a pro rata basis, this would mean that the human body, averagely 5.5 times the size of the dog by weight, i.e. 71.5kg, would contain at least 7,920km of blood vessels! Data from other sources on the other hand places this at 60,000 miles or 96,500km[10].

In recent correspondence with Dr. Attinger about his paper, the average value of the viscous resistance to be overcome by the dog's heart in order to move the blood, amounts to 5,332 dyne sec/cm^{-5}, which is equal to a force of 0.005437kg or about 5½ grams (1 dyne=1.01972 x 10^{-6}kg), the average flow velocity in the capillaries being considerably less than 1cm/sec.

According to Walter Schauberger the output of the human heart amounts to 0.003 horsepower but, wanting further confirmation, I made enquiries at the University of Queensland and was told that it functions at about 1.5 watts. With this small amount of energy, equivalent to the average torch battery, $\frac{1}{10}$th of a litre of blood is delivered to the arterial network about 75 times a minute or 100,000 times a day. Over an average lifetime at roughly 8,000 litres per day, 175 million litres of blood pass through the heart.

Presumably this dog's heart functioned with somewhat less energy due to its smaller size. It therefore seems almost inconceivable that the relatively small heart of this 13kg dog would have sufficient power to force the blood through 1,440km of blood vessels, which in the light of the above does seem to be a Herculean task. The power of the heart, therefore, would appear phenomenal for its size and, according to Walter Schauberger's research in this area, it has been determined that the work of the human heart would be enough to raise a weight of about 40 tonnes per year to a height of 1m. I have also carried out my own calculations, and the figure I arrived at was 4,296.78 tonnes[11].

Apart from the reduction in blood viscosity with the decrease in the size of the blood vessels, if as has been suggested earlier, energy creates the vessel most conducive to its desired form of movement in a given situation, then the pulsating, almost frictionless flow of blood over these enormous distances becomes more understandable. The factor omitted in all scientific calculation in hydrodynamics, however, or any other energetic process for that matter, is the natural desire for energy to move frictionlessly in healthy, animate, organic systems.

In the light of this research, of the description of double-spiral pipes, the Stuttgart investigation and the circulation of blood, it can be see that Viktor Schauberger's theories have been thoroughly vindicated. Perhaps, therefore, their description here will provide the basis for more productive investigative research and practical application, which is most urgently needed if we are to emerge from our present ecological and environmental crisis.

Organisation and Physical Properties of the Cardiovascular System

A. Functional Anatomy

The general organization of the cardiovascular system is schematically represented in Fig. 1. It can be divided roughly into four parts:

1. **Two pumps, the left and right hearts.**
2. A distributing system, the arteries, leading from each ventricle into the periphery.
3. An exchange system, the capillaries, where metabolites diffuse across a membrane both from and into the tissue.
4. A collecting system, the veins, which transport the blood back to the pump.

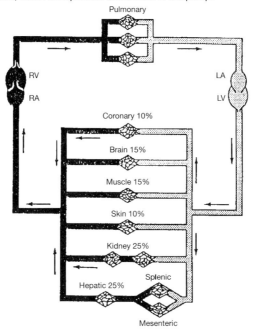

Fig. 1   Schema of the circulation. The numbers indicate the approximate percentage of the cardiac output fed into each of the six (arbitrarily selected) parallel beds. Note that there are two capillary systems in the kidney and three in the splanchnic circulation. LA, left atrium; LV, left ventricle; RA, right atrium; RV, right ventricle.

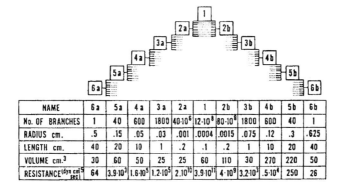

NAME	6a	5a	4a	3a	2a	1	2b	3b	4b	5b	6b
No. OF BRANCHES	1	40	600	1800	$40 \cdot 10^6$	$12 \cdot 10^8$	$80 \cdot 10^6$	1800	600	40	1
RADIUS cm.	.5	.15	.05	.03	.001	.0004	.0015	.075	.12	.3	.625
LENGTH cm.	40	20	10	1	.2	.1	.2	1	10	20	40
VOLUME cm.^{3}	30	60	50	25	25	60	110	30	270	220	50
RESISTANCE$^{(\frac{dyn \cdot cm^5}{sec})}$	64	$3.9 \cdot 10^3$	$1.6 \cdot 10^5$	$1.2 \cdot 10^5$	$2 \cdot 10^{10}$	$3.9 \cdot 10^{11}$	$4 \cdot 10^9$	$3.2 \cdot 10^3$	$.5 \cdot 10^4$	250	26

Fig. 3   Geometry of the peripheral vascular tree of a 13-kg dog. The diagram illustrates the marked changes in total cross section along the peripheral vascular bed. Blocks are numbered as follows: 1, capillaries; 2a, arterioles; 2b, venules; 3a, terminal arterial branches; 3b, terminal veins; 4a, main arterial branches; 4b, main venous branches; 5a, large arteries; 5b, large veins; 6a, aorta; 6b, venae cavae. Resistance values pertain to the total effect of one segment.

Fig. 14.10   **Hydrodynamics of blood flow (E. O. Attinger)**
Research Institute of the Presbyterian University of Pennslyvania Medical Center, Philadelphia, Pennsylvania

Notes

1. Our *Senseless Toil*, Pt.II, p.14.
2. Austrian Patent No. 136214, applied for April 23, 1930, granted January 10, 1934.
3. Austrian Patent No. 134543, applied for August 12, 1931, granted August 25th, 1933.
4. Expert opinion dated 15 Apr. 1930, by Prof. Dr. Philipp Forchheimer, life-member of the Austrian Academy of Science, Vienna.
5. "Report Concerning The Preliminary Investigation Of Helical Pipes With Various Shapes of Pipe-Wall" ("Bericht über die Voruntersuchungen mit Wendelrohren mit verschiedener Wandform"), carried out at the Inst.of Hygiene, Stuttgart Univ. of Technology, Germany, by Prof. Dr. Ing. habil Franz Pöpel. February to March 1952.
6. Austrian Patent No. 196680, applied May 30, 1951, granted March 25, 1958, exactly 6 months before Viktor Schauberger died on 25 September that year.
7. French Patent No. 1.057.576, applied May 30th, 1952, granted October 28th, 1953. Brazilian Patent No. 43,431, granted in 1953. Portuguese Patent No. 29,729, granted in 1953.
8. *Our Senseless Toil*, Pt.II, p.34.
9. "Hydrodynamics of Blood Flow", by Dr. Ernst O.Attinger, Div. Biomedical Engineering, Univ. Virginia Medical Center, Charlottesville, VA 22901, USA. (I unfortunately failed to take note of the title and publisher. This was a paper written during Dr. Attinger's tenure of a special fellowship from the National Institute of Health (5-F3-GM-14037) and details research carried out at the Research Inst, Presbyterian Univ. Pennsylvania Medical Center, Univ. of Pennsylvania, Philadelphia, USA.
10. British United Patients Assoc. (BUPA) advert., *Evening Standard*, London, 31st January 1994.

11. **HEART PERFORMANCE CALCULATIONS**

The quantity of blood moved per beat $= 0.1$ litres
$$= 100cc$$

Since blood consists of about 90% water and 1cc of water weighs 1 gram(g), assuming that the remaining blood constituents have the same specific weight as water, then the weight of blood moved by the heart per beat $= 1.09g \times 100cc$
$$= 109g$$
$$= 0.109 \text{ kg}$$

At averagely 75 beats per minute the weight of blood moved per minute $= 75 \times 0.109kg$
$$= 8.175kg$$

$\therefore$ the weight of blood moved in 1 hour $= 8.175kg \times 60$ minutes
$$= 490.5kg$$
$$= 0.4905 \text{ tonnes (t)}$$

$\therefore$ the weight of blood moved in 24 hrs $= 0.4905t \times 24$ hrs
$$= 11.772t$$

$\therefore$ the weight of blood moved in 1 year $= 11.772t \times 365$ days
$$= 4,296.78t.$$

The magnitude of a force is normally calculated in newtons. 1 newton (N) represents a force of 0.101972kg acting through a distance of 1 metre. 1 newton is also equal to an expenditure of energy of 1 joule or 1 watt per second. Therefore calculated in terms of newtons, it could be inferred that the heart expends sufficient energy annually to raise the above weight of 4,296.78 tonnes to a height of 1 metre.

As far as the energy of the heart is concerned, using the above figures, at 0.109kg per heartbeat energy required per heartbeat $= 0.109kg/N$ (N $= 0.101972$ kg)
$$= 1.06892088N$$
$$= 1.06892088 \text{ joules}$$
$$= 1.06892088 \text{ watts/second}$$

The heart would therefore appear to function at 1.07 watts/second.

15
DRINKING WATER SUPPLY

15.1 The Consequences of Chlorination and Fluoridation

Water is **the** issue most crucial to all life on Earth. Water is the life-blood of our planet, the life-giving fluid in all organisms, plants, animals and human beings alike, flowing as sap, lymph or blood; our very existence is therefore intimately connected with the quality of water available to us. It is vital for our own lives and those of our children that we should become seriously concerned not only for the health, vitality and quality of the water we drink, but also for its original source and the treatment it receives. Apart from our own consumption of it, this same water is also used to grow everything we eat. If we want to live in health and happiness, then the living entity – **water** – should be highly revered and the most sensitive care taken of it.

In the previous chapter we briefly mentioned the harmful effects of chlorination, but we need to examine the process and its ramifications more fully. Today the drinking water supplied to almost all the inhabitants of so-called civilised countries is chlorinated and sometimes even fluoridated. The purpose of this treatment is to sterilise the water, to free it of all noxious micro-organisms and pathogenic bacteria.

Present methods of water treatment and reticulation kill water, however, and bad water or wrongly treated water debilitates, degrades, degenerates and ultimately destroys those organisms constantly forced to drink it. Science, however, completely overlooks the fact that water – as life-carrier – is itself alive and needs to be kept in this condition if it is to fulfill its naturally ordained function for, as Viktor Schauberger has stated:

Science views the blood-building and character-influencing UR-ORGANISM – 'WATER' merely as a chemical compound and provides millions of people with a liquid prepared from this point of view, which is everything but healthy water.[1]

But what does modern, denaturised civilisation care, as long as it receives a suitably hygienised, clear liquid with which to shower, wash its dishes, clothes and cars? Once down the plug-hole, in company with all manner of toxic chemicals and detergents, all is comfortingly out of sight and out of mind. As proof of the efficacy of current disinfective practices and to justify their continuance, officialdom usually points out that such water-borne diseases as cholera and typhoid are virtually unknown in all countries where the water is chlorinated.

Thus reassured, the broad mass of the population blithely continues to bask in the luxury of apparently disease-free water in complete ignorance of the perils arising from its constant consumption, for what is never stated in official explanations is the cumulative effect this treatment of water has on the organisms forced to drink it. What people do not know is that, although the chlorination of drinking and household water-supplies ostensibly disinfects it and removes the threat of water-borne diseases, it does so to the detriment of the consumer.

In its function as water steriliser or disin-

In view of the fact that our body's water content amounts to 45 litres and that our daily consumption of water is about 2.4 litres, just consider the following:[2]

THE BLOOD PLASMA ————————->	(main blood component) ———————->	about 92% water
THE HUMAN FOETUS ————————>	(our growing physical vehicle)————->	about 90% water
THE BLOOD ————————————>	(life-fluid & nutrient conveyor) ————->	up to 90% water
THE HUMAN BRAIN CELLS ———->	(intellect, creativity, behaviour) ——->	are 85% water
THE KIDNEYS ———————————>	(fluid processors & purifiers) ————->	are 82% water
THE MUSCLES ——————————>	(prime movers of the body) ———->	average 75% water
THE BODY ————————————>	(our abode on Earth) ———————->	is 71% water
THE LIVER ————————————>	(metabolism regulator) ——————->	is 69% water
THE BONES ————————————>	(structural support system) ————->	are 22% water
THE BODY'S CELL-FLUIDS ——->	(basis of growth & development) ——->	are mainly water

fectant, chlorine eradicates all types of bacteria, beneficial and harmful alike, so that what arrives at the tap or faucet, while indeed free of every possible organism, is water that has been sterilised to death; in other words, a water-corpse. More importantly and more alarmingly, however, it also disinfects the blood (up to 90% water) or sap (ditto) and in doing so kills off or seriously weakens many of the immunity-enhancing micro-organisms living in the body of those organisms that continuously consume it.

This eventually impairs their immune systems to such a degree that they are no longer able to eject viruses, germs and cancer cells, to which the respective host-bodies ultimately fall victim. **We therefore actually sterilise our blood when we drink chlorinated water, thereby readying ourselves for the onset of disease.**

Of late there has been an alarming increase, not only in hitherto unknown diseases, but in all forms of sickness, cancer in particular. Even the appearance of other lethal afflictions such as AIDS would have come as no surprise to Viktor Schauberger, for apart from the other inevitable disturbances to the ecology and the environment occasioned by humanity's unthinking activities, as early as 1933 he foresaw all these unwholesome developments as the legitimate and inevitable consequence of the mistreatment and artificial pollution of water with chemical additives.

Just imagine what effect the constant drinking of dead or diseased water has on the blood and all the vital organs of the body.

What happens to the life-force essential for healthy growth?

And what are the effects of chlorination? Chlorine is not added to drinking water in vast quantities. Averagely it is administered at about 10 parts per million (ppm), (see fig. 5.1) providing always that the dispensing and metering equipment is properly maintained and monitored. Malfunction, however, can never be ruled out, with the result that over-chlorination may occur more frequently than we are led to believe. [In the 1995 drought, thousands of residents of Cornwall in south-west England got ill, when the volume of water in the supplies was insufficient to 'water down' these chemicals 'safely'.]

According to Nobel-prizewinner Prof. Otto Warburg, later confirmed by Nobel-prizewinner Prof. Gerhard Domagk, cancer cells were formed as a result of a deficiency of oxygen, which produces a reversal in the metabolism whereby the nutritive substances are fermented by the cells into lactic acid. This provides the cell with additional energy to grow more rapidly and to divide faster than other cells, eventually developing into a cancer cell proper, oxygen shortage and over-acidity being the characteristic hallmarks of cancer cells.[4]

There is a further noxious characteristic of chlorine worthy of note. Because even a small ray of light suffices to make it explode, chlorine gas has to be mixed with water in darkness. It could therefore be reasonably assumed that even on the minutest scale, explosions will occur when the capillaries immediately under the skin are exposed to sunlight, causing their partial rupture. Chlorine-dioxide

To give the reader an idea of what 10ppm entails, the cube below measures 100cm x 100cm x 100cm. The content of this cube is therefore 1,000,000cm³. The minute cube at the upper left hand corner of the cube at *(A)* is equal to 1ppm and could be likened to a cube of sugar in a metre-cube box. Relative to the total volume of drinking water the amount of chlorine added to it amounts to 10 such minute cubes as shown at *(B)*. This seems hardly worth worrying about except that, as we learnt in chapter 9 in connection with Prof. Jacques Benveniste's research into the efficacy of homeopathic medicines, the smaller the physical quantity, the greater the resultant effect.

Just to complete the description of the diagram, the 3½ rows of cubes at *(C)* represent the amount of carbon-dioxide presently in the atmosphere, which as a result of its rise from 290ppm early this century to its current 355ppm level, is producing unwelcome effects in the global climate, all of which further underscores how minimal causes produce large effects.

Used in chemical warfare chlorine is poisonous gas. It has a greenish-yellow colour and reacts with the majority of organic compounds. In the process it replaces hydrogen, one of the key elements of the water molecule and present in all carbohydrates and fats, both of which are essential to the metabolism in all organic life. One effect of this hydrogen replacement may well be the removal of the hydrogen atoms in the fatty substances surrounding and enclosing the cells, the cell-walls, which act as a dielectric membrane and conserve and separate the bioelectric charges responsible for the cells' correct function.

On the other hand, it may also create certain quantities of hydrochloric acid in the blood itself, which as a digestive juice normally resides safely confined within the walls of the stomach, and as a result adds to the overall acidity of the blood, thereby reducing the blood-pH [(see ftnt 3)] to levels below the normal level of 7. As a powerful oxidant it also accelerates the metabolic processes of oxidation, on the one hand creating additional heat and on the other consuming oxygen destined for other purposes, and if these occur above the naturally prescribed levels, in most organisms it leads to premature aging.

A volume measuring:

$$100\text{cm} \times 100\text{cm} \times 100 \text{ cm} = 1 \text{ cubic metre (m}^3\text{),}$$
$$\text{or} = 1,000,000 \text{ cm}^3$$

In relation to such a volume, therefore,

(A) 1 cc (**1 ppm**) = 1,000,000th of a m³.

(B) **10 ppm** is the amount of chlorine and/or chlorine dioxide generally used for the so-called "purification" of drinking water.

(C) **355 ppm** is the amount of carbon dioxide (CO_2) presently in the atmosphere, which, with water vapour, is a co-contributor to the "greenhouse effect". In the late 19th century, the amount of CO_2 in the atmosphere was circa **290 ppm**, considered to be the normal, natural level.

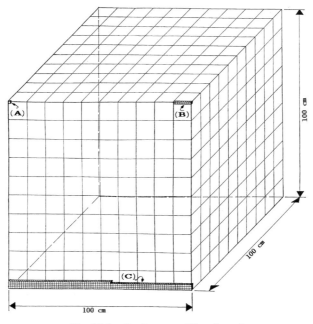

Fig. 15.1 **Parts per million (ppm)**

(ClO₂) is also used for water purification and, while it is soluble in cold water, it begins to decompose as the water warms up and at roughly +90°C it forms chloric(VII) acid which similarly explodes and oxidises strongly. In biochemistry and biology it is employed for the decomposition of organic matter for analytical purposes.

What more needs to be said, apart from the fact that all these abnormal oxidising processes cause the dislocation of the natural energy-flows in the body, which in turn raise its general temperature, thus placing it in a disease-prone condition. Disease after all is the way that Nature removes all organisms that are no longer healthy or viable in her scheme of things and which stand in the path of evolutionary progress. In confirmation of chlorine's disease-causing function, a recent study found that in water purification it *"produces by-products that cause 18% of rectal cancers and 9% of bladder cancers."*[5].

Artificial fluoridation of the water supplies is another pernicious process with equally alarming consequences for the drinker. There are two different forms of fluoride, one of which, calcium fluoride, is naturally occurring. Where present in the groundwater or wells it has been observed that the teeth of those who drink such water are much stronger and less prone to caries. The other, sodium fluoride is not found naturally and is a poisonous by-product of aluminium smelting and used in insecticides.

But what to do with this growing pile of poison without incurring huge storage costs? It could not merely be flushed into rivers or used in agriculture, because it kills livestock, wildlife, fish and crops. Indeed the offspring of the 3rd generation of rats given 1ppm of sodium fluoride in their drinking water were crippled at birth[6]. How and why sodium fluoride ever found its way into toothpaste is a mystery. Perhaps some mistaken bureaucrat thought it had the same beneficial effect as calcium fluoride and required its addition to drinking water.

Many children, however, have become innocent victims of this disastrous confusion, their bright smiles having been disfigured with seriously discoloured teeth, as well as increased brittleness of their bones. In a recent New Jersey Department of Health study fluoridation has been linked to a rare form of bone cancer known as osteosarcoma[7]. This study showed that, in contrast to non-fluoridated municipalities, the incidence of osteosarcoma was 50% higher in males under 20, an almost seven-fold increase in young males between the ages of 10 and 19 occurring in the three most affected communities.

But this is not where it all ends. Ultimately all these malpractices not only have the direst consequences for the body, but also for its more immaterial attributes and here we shall quote Viktor Schauberger once more:

A particular inner temperature produces a certain physical form which in turn generates the special kind of immaterial energy we encounter in a more or less highly developed form as character. Hence the old saying 'Mens sana in corpore sano' (a healthy mind in a healthy body). If the composition of the basic substances of the body should in any way be altered, then the metabolic basis for the further growth of the body must not only change, but its spiritual and intellectual growth and further development as well.[8]

Viktor saw the proper physical formation of the brain as being crucial to what it was able to produce in the way of concepts, ideas and behaviour, ethical and otherwise; the lower the quality of the physical structure, the more inferior the morals and ethics. In the same way that the narrowly spaced annual rings of trees produced high-quality, resonant timber, the production of good thoughts in harmony with Nature, and in consequence good character traits, was only possible with a well and healthily-grown and developed brain with close-knit windings.

Unwholesome food, poor water and the resultant slight overheating, in his view, gave rise to the formation of coarse convolutions in the brain's overall structure, creating a brain that was incapable of either functioning intuitively or of comprehending the subtleties of Nature's processes. It degenerated into an organ able only to think logically, but never biologically, never with a living logic aware of natural energetic interrelations and interdependencies. In a sense, such a brain could be likened to a poorly designed musical instrument constructed of inferior materials and thus unable to create truly harmonious sounds affecting the world harmoniously. There is plenty of evidence in support of this, for daily we are made aware of the rise in mental afflictions, depression, dyslexia, irrational and brutal behaviour, and hyperactivity to name a few, which are affecting more and more people at an increasingly younger age.

The water we drink and food we eat are by no means the sole cause, but in the light of all this precautionary evidence we should at the very least ensure that what we eat and drink is of the highest possible quality. Moreover, we should call the responsible authorities to account for their misdemeanours, even though these may have been unintentional, for it is we, particularly the poor, and not they, who finally have to pay the price in suffering and misery for their inaction. We should refuse to continue to be forced to drink water as presently prepared, for in drinking chlorinated and fluoridated water not only do we harm ourselves physically and mentally, but we also pass on a terrible genetic legacy to our children.

A thorough investigation and highly publicised public inquiry into present methods of water purification should be put in hand immediately by an independent body of competent, unintimidatable individuals. These should be selected from all branches of science and medicine, including so-called alternative practitioners, whose awareness in some areas far exceeds those of orthodox disciplines. Should its publicised findings recommend the immediate cessation of current practices in water purification, then neither the government nor the respective authorities will be able to continue to brainwash the population and will be forced by the ballot box to take action and put the necessary and urgent remedial measures in hand forthwith.

15.2 The Springwater Producing Device

During the the early 1930s Viktor Schauberger was active in writing and publication, in river engineering, power generation and forestry. However, he felt so strongly about the dangers associated with contemporary systems of water treatment and the suffering they caused, that he designed a device which both purified water, and also raised it to mountain-spring quality. In 1934 he applied for patents[9] for this apparatus, which produced pure, high-grade, spring-quality drinking water (fig. 15.2 see also box on page following). This was his first prototype for the artificial production of high quality drinking water. This crude arrangement was his first attempt to combine the necessary elements, so its construction was cumbersome compared to the elegance of later designs.

In Viktor Schauberger's understanding of the deep subterranean cycle of water (see chapter 9, fig. 9.1, "The Full Hydrological Cycle" and figure 9.1, p. 119), he considered the Earth's rapidly depleting deposits of coal and oil, which today we stupidly plunder and squander by combusting them as fuel, to be the vital sources of carbone upon which the whole natural production of carbonic acid depends and without which there is no good water and therefore no healthy growth.

Although Walter Schauberger achieved a stable solution of water and carbon-dioxide using a partial vacuum in conjunction with a hyperbolic vortex, because of the way in which carbon-dioxide is infused into water under high pressure in contemporary chemical and industrial processes, such a combination cannot be stabilised and is only theoretically possible. Under such technically contrived conditions the carbon-dioxide can only be constrained in a dissolved state under constant pressure, which is why there is an immediate evolution of bubbles and gases when bottles of soft drinks or aerated mineral water are opened. Incidentally, by inhaling these vapours the reader will get an idea of what 'chokedamp' is, and its effect. Just because we cannot produce a stable solution of carbon-dioxide, however, does not mean that Nature cannot achieve it. In her acts of creation, Nature operates differently, without pressure and heat, but in cool implosive ways. She employs attracting

In the apparatus on the next page surface water, i.e. the most available form of water, is introduced into a container *A*, where it is irradiated by a mercury-vapour lamp, which kills off many of the harmful bacteria, and where the necessary cooling process also begins. The water then flows down to the outlet *m* below a mixing vessel *C*, where, under a pressure of half an atmosphere, this largely mineral-deficient water is mixed drop by drop with the salts and other minerals necessary to build up a high quality water. From here it proceeds to a vessel *D*, where it is sprayed through perforations in a spiral pipe *n* from the outside inwards, at the same time that carbonated water is sprayed from a similar perforated tube *k*, but from the inside outwards. A mixing between the two types of water occurs, gradually blending them, and they fall through what appears to be a mesh screen (not described in the patent document), from where, now as a combined liquid, they move up through a series of tulip-shaped glass vessels *E*.

As this liquid rises, the carbon-dioxide (also known as CO_2 or carbonic acid gas) in the water accumulates at the top of each tulip, as shown in the larger detail inset, the amount progressively diminishing, the higher the tulip on the column. The greater part of the water, however, first moves upwards around the outer bowl of the tulip *q* and then downwards around the inner bowl. Upon reaching the central core, it then moves upwards again. As the water pressure gradually builds, the carbon-dioxide trapped in the upper part, is forced upwards through the small tube above the tulip and back into the main body of water.

By the time the water reaches the top of the tulip column, there is no free carbon-dioxide left. All of it has been absorbed into the water in the form of carbonic acid (H_2CO_3). Whether we are concerned with H_2CO_3 or ($H_2O + CO_2$) as discrete entities is largely dependent on temperature and pressure. Somewhere in this series of tulips, laminates of silver and gold are attached, (their actual position is not described), which create a small electrostatic charge that ionises the various particles in the water, enhancing the combination and

recombination of the various minerals and salts. From the top of the tulip-column, the water then flows into a silver-lined[10] cooling vessel *F*, containing a large auger, i.e. an archimedean screw, which slowly rotates in the opposite direction to its slope, thus encouraging the water to remain there to be cooled by the cooling coils mounted on the exterior of this well-insulated chamber.

Moving upwards from this vessel, the water then enters a large, insulated sleeve-pipe *u*, through which the pipe containing the descending saline and mineral solution passes, pre-cooling it on its way to the spray chamber *D*. From here the prepared water passes into the final chamber *I*, which is divided into two compartments. The first *G* (left-hand side) allows certain residual reactions to take place, such as the interaction between the content of carbon-dioxide and oxygen, before finally over-flowing into the second compartment *H*, when it is in a condition suitable for drinking. From here it passes to the outlet *z*, ready for consumption.

In this process carbon-dioxide is bound with the water in stable form as occurs in Nature, i.e. by processes of cooling and densation through which the carbon-dioxide is converted into carbonic acid. In its simplest representation carbonic acid is a compound of the three elements of carbone (C^e), oxygen (O) and hydrogen (H) in the form of water (H_2O) plus carbon-dioxide (C^eO_2), and is produced naturally in the coolness and darkness of the Earth. According to the legitimate interpretation of chemical formulae, the combination of these elements should produce the following result:

$$H_2O + C^eO_2 + DARK + COLD \longrightarrow H_2C^eO_3$$
$$(= \text{carbonic acid})$$

which is the very foundation and the most important ingredient of high-quality, mountain-spring water, the other form of energy that makes all life on this planet possible. Conversely

$$H_2C^eO_3 + LIGHT + HEAT \longrightarrow H_2O + C^eO_2 \uparrow$$
$$(= \text{water + carbon-dioxide})$$
[the upward arrow denotes the release of a gas]

The springwater producing device

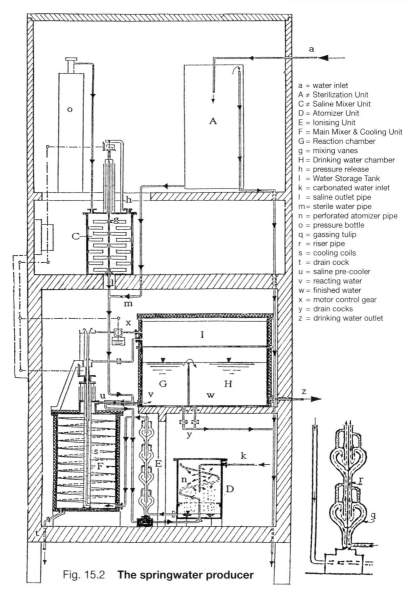

a = water inlet
A ≠ Sterilization Unit
C ≠ Saline Mixer Unit
D = Atomizer Unit
E = Ionising Unit
F = Main Mixer & Cooling Unit
G = Reaction chamber
g = mixing vanes
H = Drinking water chamber
h = pressure release
I = Water Storage Tank
k = carbonated water inlet
l = saline outlet pipe
m = sterile water pipe
n = perforated atomizer pipe
o = pressure bottle
q = gassing tulip
r = riser pipe
s = cooling coils
t = drain cock
u = saline pre-cooler
v = reacting water
w = finished water
x = motor control gear
y = drain cocks
z = drinking water outlet

Fig. 15.2   **The springwater producer**

forces of suction in lieu of life-destroying forces of pressure.

Despite its gross construction, with this apparatus Viktor Schauberger was able to produce a very high-grade spring water from any reasonably good quality, i.e. unpolluted, surface water. Pressing on with his research, in the late 1930s and early 1940s he worked on the design for another device, far more compact than the previous one. This one was egg-shaped and, while it really

belongs to this chapter on drinking water, because the principles on which it functions are similar to those of his other apparatuses, its discussion will be reserved to chapter 21 on Implosion. With it, however, he helped many people stricken with cancer. By providing them with very high-quality water he was able to achieve remission in quite a large measure. However, as is frequently the case, he came up against the established authorities, who accused him of charlatanism and lack of qualifications to treat cancer, since he was merely a forester with no medical training or background. Ultimately they forced him to quit, confiscated his machine and destroyed it. This was yet another of the many setbacks that Viktor had already suffered at the hands of the Establishment.

The proper storage of drinking water, however, is another aspect that needs to be carefully taken into consideration and will now be addressed in the following section.

15.3 *The Storage of Water*

Whether our water is produced through the process described or whether we obtain it from natural sources, we must care for the very limited supplies that are still available. This means we must treat it in the way demonstrated to us by Nature. First and foremost, water should be protected from sunlight and kept in the dark, far removed from all sources of heat, light and atmospheric influences. (How much of your drinking water comes from reservoirs open to the Sun?) Ideally it should be placed in opaque, porous containers, which both cut out all direct light and heat, and allow the water to breathe (which, in common with all other living things, it must do in order to stay alive and healthy).

The present system of bottling water in clear, transparent bottles degrades the water, because it is exposed to light and heat. When a glass of good water is left out in the Sun, little bubbles form on the glass as the carbonic acid, the principle ingredient of good water, is converted into CO_2 through increased temperature and light. Like wine, water needs to be kept in the dark in an opaque bottle sealed with a breathing cork. It is not without reason that good wine is matured in wooden casks.

In terms of what we can achieve personally, we should at all times ensure that our storage vessels, bottles, tanks, etc., are thoroughly insulated so that the contained water is maintained at the coolest temperature possible. The materials most suited to this are natural stone, timber (wooden barrels) and terracotta. Perhaps more than any other material, terracotta has been used for this purpose for millennia. Terracotta exhibits a porosity particularly well-suited to water storage, because it enables a very small percentage of the contained water to evaporate through the vessel walls.

Evaporation is always associated with cooling (vaporisation, however, with heat) and, according to Walter Schauberger, if the porosity is correct, then for every 600th part of the contents evaporated, the contents will be cooled by 1°C (1.8°F). Therefore, if such a vessel is positioned where there is a reasonable movement of air, the water will cool and approach its anomaly point, its state of highest health and 'indifference' at a temperature of +4°C (39.2°).

Another important storage factor is the actual shape of the container itself. Most of the storage containers commonly in use today are cubic or rectangular volumes of one form or another, or cylinders. While these shapes are most easily and economically produced by today's technology, they do impede natural water circulation and promote water suffocation.

Due to their rectangular shape and/or right-angled corners, stagnant zones are created which can provide a suitable environment for the propagation of pathogenic bacteria. Moreover, since the materials used are generally galvanised iron, fibre glass, concrete, steel, etc., i.e. all impervious materials, the contained water is unable to breathe and suffocates as a result. In this debilitated state or as a water-cadaver, it quickly becomes diseased and will require further disinfection.

Taking Viktor Schauberger's maxim *Comprehend and Copy Nature!* as our guide, we should therefore use the shapes that Nature herself selects to contain, guard and maintain life, i.e. eggs and their derivations. The cubes and cylinders mentioned above have no place in Nature's scheme of things. To store her vital fluids and other materials wise Nature chose eggs and elongated egg-shapes such as grains and seeds, because these produce the optimal results.

It is evident that the ancient Egyptians and Greeks, renowned for their logic and constructional ability, were well aware of this, because they stored their grains and liquids (oils, wines, etc.) in terracotta amphorae, sealed with beeswax. This despite the fact that the shape was wholly unsuited to compact and efficient storage in terms of space and ease of handling.

It is obvious that the selection of this form over any other was intentional and the result of certain knowledge of the long-term storage properties of such shapes. In many amphorae that have surfaced in archeological excavations over the last 100 years or so, grains of wheat have been found that were still viable and, even after storage over 2,000 years, germinated when planted.

Compared with cubes and cylinders, as shown in fig. 15.3 these shapes have no stagnant zones, no right-angled corners that inhibit flowing movement. By placing these terracotta vessels in shaded areas, exposed to air movement, the evaporative cooling effect will be significantly enhanced. Since all natural movement of liquids and gases is triggered by differences in temperature, so too inside the egg-shaped storage vessel, cyclical, spiral, vitalising movement of the water will be induced.

As we have seen, movement is an expression of energy and energy is synonymous with life. The external evaporation causes cooling of the outer walls and the water in their immediate vicinity. Being cooler and therefore denser, this water becomes specifically heavier and sinks down along the walls towards the bottom, at the same time forcing the water there to rise up the centre and move towards the outside walls. Continual repetition of this process results in the constant circulation and cooling of the contents.

With all existing installations for water storage, the main problem is that of exposure to light and heat. Where possible, all above-ground water tanks, whether of galvanised

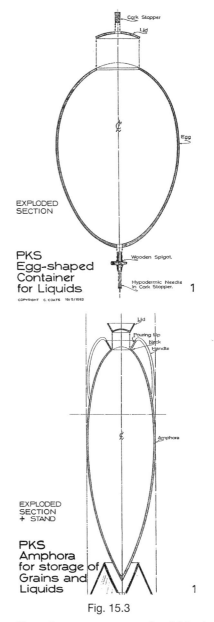

PKS Egg-shaped Container for Liquids

COPYRIGHT C. COATS 19/5/1982

PKS Amphora for storage of Grains and Liquids

Fig. 15.3

iron, fibre-glass or concrete, should be insulated on all external surfaces by applying sprayed foam or an equivalent thermal barrier, to a minimum thickness of 75mm. If not already white or of a light, heat-reflecting colour, then they should be so painted. For tanks set into the ground, only the top surface need be insulated and painted white.

For many people, dams or rivers provide the main source of water and certain simple measures can be taken to improve the quality of the water obtained from them. Providing the surrounding soil is porous, a hole of about 1,000–2,000 litres in volume should be dug, about 5–10 metres from the bank of the dam or river. If possible the depth should be equal to the depth of the latter. The tops of such wells should be above the highest water level of the dam or river to prevent flood contamination.

If the soil is sufficiently permeable, water will percolate through the intervening soil and into the newly excavated well. Depending on the stability and load-bearing capacity of the soil (a structural engineer should be consulted it there is any doubt), a small concrete, perimeter footing should be placed at a safe distance from the rim of the well. When the concrete has cured and set firmly, then a minimum of one course of blocks should be laid to prevent the entry of any surface water.

The well should then be totally enclosed and sealed with a well-insulated timber and sheet-metal roof, or a concrete slab, and provided with an access hatch to service the pump and/or suction pipe and foot-valve. The pump should preferably be located outside the well-space to avoid any possible oil pollution.

The reason for the 1,000–2,000 litre storage capacity is that it may only be possible to pump water intermittently, because the rate of replenishment from the main water source will depend on the permeability of the soil.

If the soil surrounding a dam or a river is impervious, then it would be necessary to excavate a channel about 600mm wide, to the full depth of the well, between the well and where the water percolates freely, or the main water body. The lower part of this and the bottom of the shaft itself should be filled with clean, quartz sand to a depth of about 600mm and the upper part back-filled with the excavated material and compacted. As the water percolates through either the existing soil or the sand, most suspended matter will be filtered out. Furthermore, because the water reaches the well from the lowest level of the river or dam, it will be obtained at the coolest possible temperature, and less likely to harbour aggressively harmful, pathogenic bacteria, which tend to populate the upper, warmer and more highly-oxygenated strata of the main water body.

In the early 1970s I built such a well on my own property at Montville in Queensland which produced an extremely clear, clean, odourless and good tasting water. The people who have since bought the property report that the quality and quantity of water has not changed. It is advisable to have such water tested for quality, purity and any possible contaminants, pesticides, etc., by the competent authorities.

River water is generally far richer than tank water (rainwater) in terms of its mineral, salt and trace-element content. In most cases it will be necessary to supplement the mineral content of rainwater, if this is the only source of drinking water, to prevent the extraction of minerals and salts from the drinker's body. Here the suspension of an artificial-fibre sack (rot-proof) containing the dust of crushed basalt or other igneous rock used for road building (commonly known as 'crusher dust' – see chapter 19) would do much to enhance the quality of the tank water, because it will absorb those elements it requires to become mature.

However, before adding any crusher dust to the water, it would be again advisable to test the resulting change in the quality by analysing the difference between two samples of tank water, one with crusher-dust added and one without, as a control. Both samples should then be placed in a cool, dark place and left for at least a week before an analysis of the mineral content and bacterial purity is carried out. This should be done by a suitably qualified specialist.

These ideas about water will be regarded by many as controversial, but let us hope they have given you much food for thought and action. Water should never be viewed or treated as an inert and lifeless liquid for, in so doing we debase ourselves, and the rest of life on this planet, ignorance of such magnitude will demand of us an awesome penalty.

Our life, however, is not merely supported by water, but also largely by the forest. In the following chapter we shall examine the all-encompassing service the tree so unselfishly extends to all living things. It too has been equally badly mistreated through our ignorance of its vital functions and its necessity for a healthy, fruitful life.

Notes

1. *Our Senseless Toil*, Pt.II, p.6.
2. From *Water – The Mirror of Science* by K.S. Davis & J.A. Day: Heinemann Educ.Books, London, 1964. *Biology* by C.A. Villee, E.P. Solomon & P.W. Davis: W.B. Saunders, Philadelphia, U.S.A.: ISBN 4-8337-0277-0.
3. pH is the measure of hydrogen-ion concentration in a given substance and indicates the degree of acidity or alkalinity. Like human blood, with a pH of 7 pure water is neutral. Above pH 7 alkalinity increases; below it, acidity increases.
4. "The Mechanical Generation of Life-Force" ("Maschinelle Erzeugung der Lebenskraft") by Viktor Schauberger in *Implosion* No.57.
5. Amer. Jour. of Health as reported in *The Australian* newspaper of 2 July 1992.
6. Letter from J.E. Allen to the *The Gympie Times*, 9 March 1990.
7. *Acres USA* magazine, March 1993.
8. *Our Senseless Toil*, Pt.II, p.17.
9. Austrian Patent No. 142032, granted 11th June 1935.
10. Silver also has a natural anti-bacterial function.

16

TREES AND LIGHT

16.1 The Entity 'Tree'

One of the problems seriously affecting real progress today is the emphasis on over-specialisation, particularly in the sphere of the Earth Sciences for which an overview is absolutely essential. All the research work carried out presently and historically is almost totally irrelevant, if the subtle interdependencies cannot be perceived and the knowledge applied and combined with research in other spheres. Preoccupation with analysis inhibits perception of the whole and prevents us from drawing conclusions we might otherwise draw were we at the same time more general in our approach.

While the next three chapters describe the interaction between trees and light, the part that water plays in the growth of vegetation remains a dominant feature of our discussion. Nature, after all, knows no boundaries, and any discussion of natural processes inevitably involves a number of interdependent aspects which should always jointly be taken into account.

In contrast to currently held doctrines, Nature is founded far more on cooperation than on competition, because it is only through harmonious interplay that physical formation can occur, that things can come together and structures can be built up. Without attraction between two or more atoms there would be no water, no plants, no chemical compounds, no living substances at all. In essence attraction is a form of love, so that in the polygamous relationship between two hydrogen atoms and one oxygen atom, their mutual attraction and interaction gives birth to the marvel of water.

Because of this attraction another entity is created, something greater than its component parts. In the absence of attraction nothing would have happened; if the hydrogen atoms were competitively oriented towards the oxygen atoms there would be no synthesis – and no life. While there are many other examples of symbiosis, Robert Auguros and George Stanciu in their recent book *The New Biology*[1], which elaborates the findings of their research into the cooperation between species, found that there was a far higher level of cooperation in Nature than we have hitherto been led to believe.

One of their graphic examples is the tree in fig. 16.1, which is inhabited simultaneously by several different species of bird, whose areas of activity really do not clash or overlap, but are all harmoniously integrated into the overall form of the tree. Here, at least, even if on a very small scale, it is evident that, instead of competition and survival of the fittest, wise Nature has developed an evolutive system of increasing diversity in which there is a place for everything. It would seem quite illogical and unintelligent to create so many different life-forms and have no room for them to exist.

The prevailing emphasis in biological education is that Nature is competitive, which blinds us to her other realities. In human beings the necessity to compete has often led to deep-seated feelings of inadequacy and inferiority, which frequently seek compensation in material acquisition. We are taught that we live in a hard, cold, competitive world, a world that has largely become so because we have made it so, although this does not necessarily represent natural reality.

For our own survival, the whole concept of the primacy of competition needs to be re-examined. It should be restricted to one's own performance in relation to the outer world; by developing one's talents, and by exercising them for the benefit of others. If we are going to prevent our own extinction, we must abandon this divisive, competitive ideology and return to a more *centripetally* (integrative) *organic* rather than a *centrifugally* (disintegrative) *mechanistic* way of living, limiting quantity in favour of increasing quality, and in particular the quality of giving.

What is an exchange? As a completed transaction, an exchange can only then take place when 'giving' and 'taking' come together in the proper and appropriate amounts. Without giving, there is no taking. If evolution is to continue its forward unfoldment, the giving must be greater both in measure and quality than the taking, to ensure a surplus of creative potential energy, without which no manifestations can occur. There is a contradiction here for, generally speaking, when the amount or quantity of a substance or energy is increased, one does not necessarily expect its quality to grow in the same measure, since quantity x quality = unity. However, as we have seen, the supply of essentially creative energy, emanating as it does from other dimensions, is not necessarily limited by the Conservation of Energy Law, and thus in this instance there is no reason why quantity should not increase in step with quality.

In this instance, however, measure is related to an intangible magnitude, a concentrated outpouring of love or giving (or in-*form*-ation). One learns (intake or uptake of information) in order to disseminate what has been learned that is considered desirable or

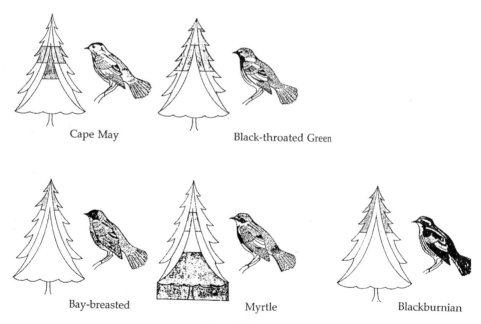

Fig. 16.1

Derived from a classic study by ecologist Robert MacArthur, this diagram illustrates how five species of warblers, similar in size and shape, feed on bud worms in the same spruce trees. They avoid competition by occupying subtly different niches. The shaded areas indicate where each species spends more than half its time. The birds also use different methods of hunting. This pattern of noncompetition is typical of naturally coexisting species.

Clearly the processes of suction and pressure need to be examined. No beneficial, natural exchange can take place solely under conditions of pressure. The effects of pressure (centrifugal thinking) and suction (centripetal thinking) can be explained with two simple diagrams.

1. PRESSURE +> <+ RESISTANCE ————> Friction-*in*ducing process
2. PRESSURE +> > – SUCTION ————> Friction-*re*ducing process

as a higher synthesis. As is the case with the development of juvenile into mature water, without this 'taking' one would not be in a position to 'give'. The countless forms of manifestation in Nature and evolution could therefore be construed as the material product of open, energetic, spiritual syntheses of 'giving and taking'.

As co-aspect of competition, the effects of pressure should be considered in the mechanics of an exchange. Pressure is the exertion of an unwanted force by one system on another unwilling to receive it. As an immediate reaction, *resistance*, the affected system will close off. This means that the system exposed to pressure will take to itself neither the information, nor the nature, nor the impulse of the pressurising system. All possible means of access are blocked and only under excessive coercion does the second system submit to the will of the first.

Friction is the inevitable consequence. If there are weak points or cracks in the system placed under pressure then, under certain circumstances it can be split apart or disintegrated, leading to its total destruction. This is a completely unnatural, mechanical process which in no way corresponds to natural processes of association and combination. Everywhere today we can observe the effects of such inhuman, technological methods. The whole phenomenon represents the worst aspects of a closed system.

However, if this process takes place under natural conditions, then resistance, viewed as a necessary counterforce to suction, should not be interpreted as an obstacle to progress, but rather as a catalyst which moderates and alters the direction and quality of movement, building up life in a new way.

Suction, on the other hand, evolves through the interaction of the forces of attraction between two complementary polarities,

and represents more, qualitatively speaking, than friction does as a force. A sucking system is first and foremost an open system. It opens itself in order to receive. It attracts a second system to itself, a system that wants to be drawn in.

With suction there is no friction or resistance. On the contrary, there is only the desire of two attracting forces to combine, which doubles the attracting energies and accelerates their coming together. It is in this way that Nature works, for all natural organisms must be open systems to be able to interact with the rest of life. All life is created out of eggs and orifices, or enclosures and openings, whose porous substance and structure permits the diffusion and passage of life energies.

As we have seen, water is created by the coming together of molecular hydrogen and oxygen in the regions below the surface of the Earth. It is the basis for the growth and development of all life-giving and life-carrying fluids such as blood, lymph, sap and milk. As such the development of tree is therefore closely connected to the evolution of water. Every living system is a water-column or container of the most unique kind.

The life history of a tree is also the life history of water. Trees are the highest and noblest plant form, whose giving is universal and unconditional. They should be an example for us to follow, for they are to the vegetable kingdom as human beings are to the animal kingdom. Trees, however, are not wholly like us, but they are autonomous; they do not need us to survive, but we need them. Through the process of photosynthesis they breathe out the oxygen we need to exist and in return, as we breathe out, we contribute to the pool of carbon-dioxide they require. The table – fig. 16.2 – further exemplifies this interdependent activity.

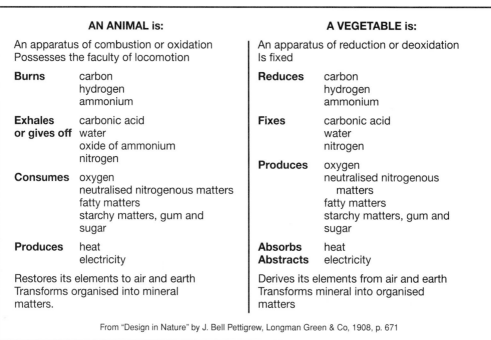

AN ANIMAL is:	A VEGETABLE is:
An apparatus of combustion or oxidation Possesses the faculty of locomotion	An apparatus of reduction or deoxidation Is fixed
Burns carbon hydrogen ammonium	**Reduces** carbon hydrogen ammonium
Exhales carbonic acid **or gives off** water oxide of ammonium nitrogen	**Fixes** carbonic acid water nitrogen
Consumes oxygen neutralised nitrogenous matters fatty matters starchy matters, gum and sugar	**Produces** oxygen neutralised nitrogenous matters fatty matters starchy matters, gum and sugar
Produces heat electricity	**Absorbs** heat **Abstracts** electricity
Restores its elements to air and earth Transforms organised into mineral matters.	Derives its elements from air and earth Transforms mineral into organised matters

From "Design in Nature" by J. Bell Pettigrew, Longman Green & Co, 1908, p. 671

Fig. 16.2   **The Respiration of Plants and Animals**

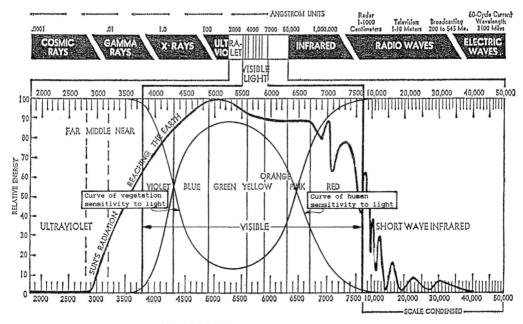

Fig. 16.3   **Electromagnetic spectrum**

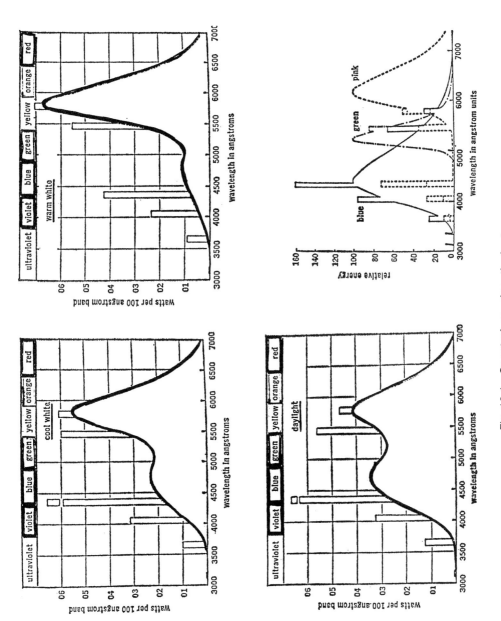

Fig. 16.4   **Spectral wavelength charts**

Cool white, warm white, daylight white and various colours of fluorescent tubes. (Source: Sylvania Electric Products Co.)

Of the total amount of oxygen they produce by photosynthesis, 60% is released and the remaining 40% is used by the tree or plant itself during the night to produce cool, structure-creating oxidations which the tree requires. Similar to many other inter-dependencies in Nature, this is a symbiotic exchange, a cooperative transaction. Without photosynthesis we could not survive, so our continuing existence is wholly dependent on this great gift of oxygen that only trees and other vegetation can provide. Were there no trees there would be no animal life, human life or micro-organic life on this planet. When trees are cut down indiscriminately, we not only harm them, but we harm ourselves as well for, by doing so we reduce the amount of oxygen *and* water available to us.

There are also other more subtle symbiotic interactions between trees and human beings in terms of colour. The graph in fig. 16.3 shows the relative intensities of radiation in the electromagnetic spectrum[2], which proceeds from the ultraviolet on the left through the visual spectrum and into the infra-red zone on the right. The very solid line depicts the intensity of solar radiation relative to

frequency or to the various categories of colour.

In the visible part of the spectrum there is a very high level in the green and, to the right, still has fairly high levels in the red, whereas it drops away quite rapidly in the ultraviolet to the left. A tree is a mirror of the quality of light in its natural habitat, as will be discussed in more detail later.

From the graph it can be seen that the highest intensity of solar radiation lies in the green to blue-green part of the spectrum. These are precisely the frequencies that the tree cannot use for its growth, for these colours induce a sort of torpor or dormant inactivity. Whatever colour or frequency is not absorbed, is reflected. A red surface, for example, absorbs all colours except its particular shade of red. Many metabolic processes are triggered by specific frequencies, and if the required frequency of light is not available or available only in limited quantity, then the response, the function or the reaction is impeded or does not occur at all.

In his book *Light and Health*[3] Dr. John N. Ott furnishes experimental evidence of the detrimental effects of colour or frequency-deficient illumination. The graphs shown in

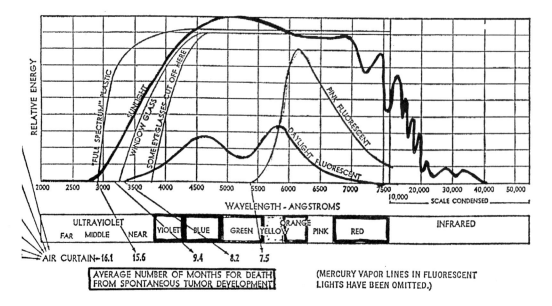

Fig. 16.5   **Influence of wavelengths of light on spontaneous tumor development in C₃H mice**

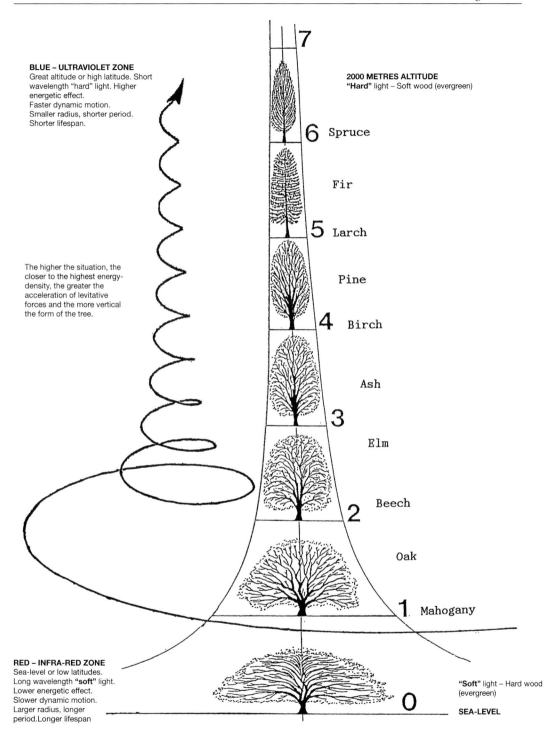

BLUE – ULTRAVIOLET ZONE
Great altitude or high latitude. Short wavelength "hard" light. Higher energetic effect.
Faster dynamic motion.
Smaller radius, shorter period.
Shorter lifespan.

2000 METRES ALTITUDE
"Hard" light – Soft wood (evergreen)

7

6 Spruce

Fir

5 Larch

Pine

4 Birch

Ash

3

Elm

Beech

2

Oak

1 Mahogany

The higher the situation, the closer to the highest energy-density, the greater the acceleration of levitative forces and the more vertical the form of the tree.

RED – INFRA-RED ZONE
Sea-level or low latitudes.
Long wavelength "soft" light.
Lower energetic effect.
Slower dynamic motion.
Larger radius, longer period. Longer lifespan

"Soft" light – Hard wood (evergreen)

0

SEA-LEVEL

Fig. 16.6   **The form of the tree in relation to levitative forces**

fig. 16.4 show the intensities of light and the light spectrum of the fluorescent tubes normally available and used commercially. When the light output of these is compared to the full spectrum of light from the Sun, it can be seen how deficient and limited are these various forms of artificial lighting.

In an experiment carried out with the use of 'pink' and 'daylight' fluorescent lights (fig. 16.5), the average number of months to the death of C_3H mice, due to spontaneous tumour development, under 'full spectrum' plastic was 15.6 months; under window glass, 9.4 months; under daylight fluorescent, 8.7 months and under pink fluorescent, 7.5 months. All this, simply because they were not receiving light energy in the right proportions. The light had been impaired, and one must therefore seriously question the effect of atmospheric pollution not only on us, but also on our life-support system – the tree.

The two smoother opposing curves I have added to this diagram are intended schematically to represent the different sensitivities to light of human beings and trees. A tree's greatest light sensitivity lies either in the ultraviolet or the red to infra-red portion of the spectrum. It is almost totally insensitive to green light and, if placed under green light, does not grow and appears to be in a state of suspended animation. The light sensitivity of the human eye on the other hand is exactly the opposite. It is not sensitive to the ultraviolet and infra-red areas, but extremely sensitive to the colour green.

Because we cannot appreciate the presence of any green in sunlight itself, were it not for trees and vegetation we would see little or no green at all. For us, green is a very soothing, healing colour, having a sedative effect on the nervous system and psyche, and if it does not form part of our general life, we can become irritable and indeed violent. We only have to look at large modern cities where few trees exist to appreciate the effect of the absence of green. Here then is yet another biological niche, as it were, where the interaction between human beings and trees is complementary.

On another tack, for many of us it is quite painful to see a dead tree left standing. Somehow, there is an innate desire in human beings to remove it, to lay its soul to rest as it were. It is as though a cadaver had been left lying on the ground. One wants to bury it. So we have certain feelings towards trees akin to those we hold for other human beings. A further parallel here is that, as we grow older, we become more fixed in our ways and often revert to child-like attitudes or those we held a long time ago.

Various stages of growth are reflected in the structure of the tree. It is a record of the tree's life-experiences and, in a sense this could be equated with the historical movement of sap (as lifeforce, spirit or intellect, over the full span of the tree's existence. As the life energy of the tree recedes, the sap sinks lower and lower, falling back through all the various stages of its previous development recalling and reliving these events and attitudes imprinted in bygone days. Moreover, because the tree has developed past maturity, like elderly human beings, its structure has become very stiff and unbending and is therefore unable to change and adjust to new conditions.

We forget, however, that the tree as an organism is probably the least adapted to rapid change. The average lifetime of a tree is the next longest after rocks, and therefore many centuries must pass before any real adaptation to changed conditions can occur. Changes in the environment, even if apparently of minor consequence, which may not be as detrimental to other faster-living living

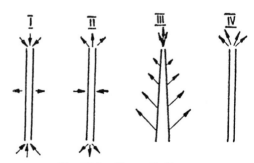

Fig. 16.8 **Magnetic flows:**
I inorganic. II organic. III dislocated biomagnetic flow in a tree. IV healthy biomagnetic flow in a tree.

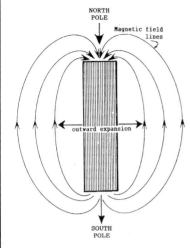

NORTH
POLE

Magnetic field
lines

outward expansion

SOUTH
POLE

Fig. 16.7 **Soft iron bar magnet**

When we think of magnets, our first image is usually of an *inorganic* one made of soft iron, where the magnetic lines of force enter and leave at the ends, (the north and south poles), and eloignate themselves from the bar at the centre (fig. 16.7). However, according to Viktor Schauberger, the tree, as an *organic* bar magnet, accumulates its energies laterally and discharges them in a vertical plane. Fig. 16.8 is his explanatory diagram which schematically depicts this and compares the inorganic magnet at *I* with the organic one at *II*. The antithetical functional mode of the biomagnet is apparent.

Fig. 16.9, is clearer where the direction of movement of the lines of magnetic force surrounding a wound steel hyperbolic cone-shaped electromagnet are indicated by the arrowed lines. In contrast to the bar magnet shown in fig. 16.7, the lines of force here actually enter the cone laterally in the upper more cylindrical portion and can been seen to charge and discharge vertically. The other two images, *III* and *IV*, in fig. 16.8 relate to natural or unnatural flows of formative energy and their effect growth, which will be referred to later.

things, can cause trees to wither and die and, in our ignorance of their necessities for life, we are ringing in their death knell.

We owe trees an enormous debt of gratitude for their silent, unceasing service in so many areas. Although extremely vulnerable to our depredations, they do not apparently protest, nor do they ever go on strike for better pay and conditions, but continue day by day unstintingly to provide the wherewithal for all forms of life. Amongst their many functions trees stabilise the climate and, were forest cover more widespread than it is today, they would be able to distribute water-vapour very evenly through the atmosphere, thereby ensuring an even distribution of heat or temperature, as was discussed in chapters 6 & 9. A mature beech tree, for example, has up to 7,000,000 leaves with an area of 1.47 evaporative hectares.

Not only do they draw up moisture and nutrients from deeper levels, but trees also break the speed of the wind, creating shelter for other life-forms and lesser species of vegetation. The planting of shelter-belts (best in spiral form) reduces both the speed of the wind and the dehydration of the soil, creating microclimates that help the soil through the provision of additional humus and protection against erosion. Indeed shelter belts can influence the evaporation rate over culti-vated land by as much as 30 metres upwind and 120 metres downwind, and Canadian research has shown that farms with $\frac{1}{3}$rd tree cover in the form of shelter-belts are more productive than farms of equivalent area where there are no trees at all.

These shelter belts also trap carbon-dioxide (CO_2), the heaviest naturally occurring atmospheric gas, which chiefly resides in the lowest levels of the atmosphere and which is one of the essential ingredients in photosynthesis. More CO_2 under the right conditions means more healthy photosynthesis. From this it becomes obvious that the removal of the clusters of trees and hedgerows between fields will significantly affect carbon-dioxide availability and thereby productivity, which will have the most drastic long-term consequences. Just as we should revere water, so too should we revere trees, which like water are also the givers of life.

16.2 The Bio-Magnetic Tree

In chapter 4 we discussed the connection between bio-magnetism and levitation. The tree is an important example of this, and there seems to be a certain correlation between altitude and tree species. The form, inner structure and lifespan of a given tree is

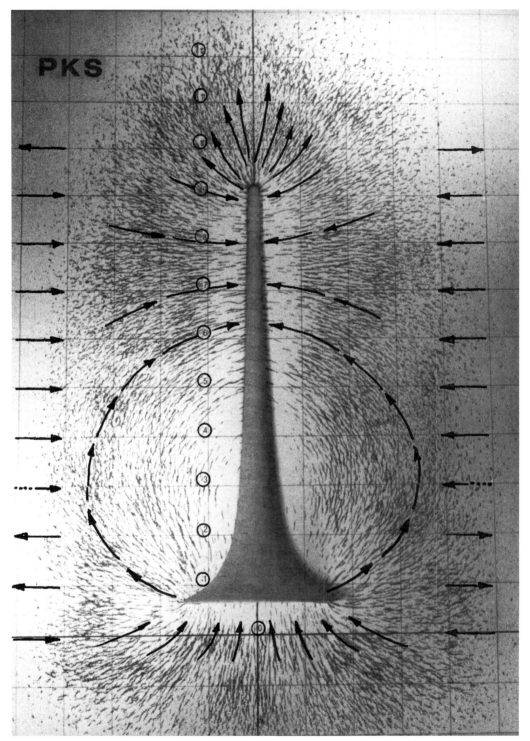

Fig 16.9   **Hyperbolic electromagnetic cone**

also dependent on the invisible movement of the energies in its natural habitat and is moulded by the interaction of gravitation and levitation.

It would appear that there is an increase in the levitative force with altitude, as depicted by the upward, convergent spiral in fig. 16.5. For example, if the tree is growing at low latitudes near the Equator or situated in a low-lying area, where the atmospheric density is greater and the dynamic movement correspondingly slower, (i.e. more harmonically structured energy in relation to dynamic energy), then, if not in a rainforest, the branches tend to spread out more horizontally than upwardly. These species of timber – longer living hardwoods, such as beech, oak, elms, etc, whose lifespans lie between 200 and 800 years in reflection of the denser, less dynamic energy field and the weaker influence of the upward energy spiral (levitative force) active in their lower altitude environment have a tendency to be more robust.

As we progress towards higher latitudes, or higher altitudes, or a combination of the two, then the trees gradually assume a different, more vertical form, reflecting this up-lifting energy path. Since the levitational forces increase as gravity weakens with altitude, the higher the altitude of the habitat, the less the atmospheric density and the greater the dynamic component of the ambient energetic field and the faster the dynamic movement. Where the atmospheric density is least, the more vertical forms of the trees correspond to the more rapid upward flow of the forces of buoyancy, of levitation; the wood is softer and the lifetimes of the trees shorter (pine, fir, larch and spruce with an average span of 120–300 years).

Like all other organisms, trees are also the product of electromagnetic forces, their various forms reflecting the particular balance between the two opposing forces. In this case, however, we are not concerned with the more common conceptions of electromagnetic forces associated with today's technical devices and machines, but rather with bio-electric and biomagnetic energies, the latter also being described as *diamagnetic* and harmonically related to levitation.

In step with the alternation between night and day – the living pulsation of the Earth's inbreathing and outbreathing – this discharge of immaterial energies is either upwards by day or downwards by night. The energies the tree absorbs into the trunk horizontally are those female, fructigenic energies and animating currents propagated laterally and in their greatest intensity immediately above and below the ground surface, having been stimulated by the fertilising energy of the Sun as discussed in chapter 3. In their interaction with the seminal essences of the Sun, their formerly horizontal disposition is changed and produced vertically, in the physical process we normally describe as 'growth', which is the material result of unseen energetic interactions.

The immaterial energies, however, continue their upward or downward paths in a more subtle form, having now been purged of the more physical impurities which constitute physical growth. In their levitational ascent these energies sweep up the various higher resonances and essences of the substances in the tree, producing the qualitatively different evapo-transpiration from the trees mentioned in the discussion of the full hydrological cycle in chapter 9.

16.3 Tree Types

Trees can be classified generally into seven major categories (fig. 16.10). They can be subdivided in terms of latitude, altitude, whether they are light-demanding or shade-demanding species, the former having a thick, rough bark and the latter a smooth thin bark, and whether they are hardwood or softwood, broad-leafed, conifer, evergreen and so on.

Before we examine trees and their growth in relation to the above categories in more detail, it would perhaps be appropriate to have a greater understanding of the specific contribution that trees make to the general environment. We shall take the example of a 100 year-old tree, whose extraordinary performance was calculated by Walter Schauberger in the 1970s in relation to the average output of European species:

Trees can be categorised according to seven basic types.
These are determined to a great extent by:
latitude and **altitude**.

(1) **LIGHT-DEMANDING** timbers – **THICK**, generally rough BARK.
(2) **SHADE-DEMANDING** timbers – **THIN**, generally smooth BARK.
(3) **HARDWOODS** – thick and thin bark.
(4) **SOFTWOODS** – thick and thin bark.

GENERAL DISTRIBUTION*

(5) **CONIFEROUS**	(6) **DECIDUOUS**	(7) **RAINFOREST**
(evergreen)	(intermittent)	(evergreen)
(polar latitudes)	(median latitudes)	(equatorial latitudes)
(high altitudes)	(median altitudes)	(low altitudes)

*These boundaries are not necessarily clearly defined.

Fig. 16.10　**Basic Tree Types**

During the course of its life, this 100 year-old tree:

a) Has processed and fixed the amount of carbon-dioxide contained in 18 million cubic metres of natural air in the form of about 2500kg of pure carbon (C).

b) Has photochemically converted 9,100kg of CO₂ and 3,700lit of H₂O.

c) Has stored up circa 23 million kilogram-calories. (a calorific value equivalent to 3,500kg of hard pit coal)

d) Has made available for the respiration of human and beast 6,600kg of molecular oxygen (O₂).

e) Against the forces of gravity, has drawn from its roots right up to its crown and evaporated into the atmosphere at least 2,500 tonnes of water,

Every tree is therefore a water-column and if such a column, which continually supplies and recharges the atmosphere with water, is cut down, then this amount of water is lost.

f) Thereby fixing a mechanical equivalent of heat equal to the calorific value of 2,500kg of coal.

g) Has supplied a member of the consumer society with oxygen sufficient for 20 years, and its nature is such, that the larger it grows, the more oxygen it produces.

In view of such achievements, who in future could value this tree merely for its timber?

The combustion of 100 litres of petrol consumes about 230kg of oxygen. That is, after a trip of barely 30,000km (9.6lit/100km), this tree's entire 100 year production of oxygen has been squandered.

Driving an average size car 30,000km = 100 years of oxygen production.

If a person chooses to breathe for 3 years, to burn 400lit of petrol or heating oil, or 400kg of coal, then the production through photosynthesis of 1 tonne of oxygen is required.

1 tonne of O₂ = the O₂ content of 3,620 m³ of air (+15C° at 1 atm)

The photosynthetic production of 1 tonne of oxygen necessitates:

a) The building up of 0.935 tonnes C₆H₁₂O₆ (carbohydrate),

b) which process requires 1.37 tonnes CO₂ (carbon-dioxide) and 0.56 tonnes H₂O (water)

c) The transpiration of 230–930 tonnes H₂O

d) Light energy equal to 527 x 10⁶ quanta (v = 440 x 10¹²) which represents 3.52 million kilocalories.

[Walter Schauberger]

Not a small achievement by any stretch of the imagination!

16.4 Trees – the Mirrors of Light

As an expression of energy, the effect of light on growth has two principal functions. Firstly it in part determines the structure of the timber and, secondly, it influences the form and character of the tree itself, depending on whether it is a shade-demanding or a light-demanding species, all of which are also related to latitude and altitude as indicated in fig. 16.6.

Since whatever we observe in Nature is a reflection as well as a product of a certain form of energy, then trees are also a mirror of the quality of light that falls in their natural habitat. Not only do their various colours reflect those frequencies of light harmful to them, and thus not absorbed (repelled) but, as a rule of thumb, where the incident light has a greater proportion of high-frequency, high-energy, ultraviolet light, in other words *hard* light, the wood is *soft*. Conversely, where there is a greater preponderance of low-frequency, low-energy, infra-red, *soft* light, the wood is *hard*.

We can observe this very clearly in Australia's native timbers, famous for their hardness. Because of the obliquity of the Earth's axis to the ecliptic (ca. 23°27"), the eccentricity of its orbit and Australia's position on the Tropic of Capricorn in the southern hemisphere, at perihelion (when the Earth is closest to the Sun – in January), the intensity of infra-red light is greatest as Australia experiences its high summer. This intensity is further augmented by the additional infra-red radiation resulting from Australia's semi-desert condition. Australia, along with other countries in the southern hemisphere, is therefore exposed to more intense infra-red light than their counterparts in the north, which experience more moderate conditions.

There appears here to be a seemingly anomalous effect, however. In our awareness of light, we generally limit our consideration to the seven principal colours of the visible spectrum, which does not comprise a full octave in terms of frequency, proceeding upwards as it does from wavelengths of 740–390 nanometres (nm=1/1,000,000,000 metre) or frequencies of 4.3–7.5 x 10^{14} cycles per second (cps) or hertz (Hz) [8.6 x 10^{14}cps would represent the full octave]. We cannot perceive the full spectrum of the octave in which light is manifested, because our eyes are only sensitive to the light frequencies lying between red and violet. We have no awareness of the light spectrum lying between violet and the higher octave of red, of which bees, certain other animals and insects seem to be aware.

In terms of the frequencies themselves, there will be a point somewhere above violet, whose lower octave lies in the infra-red zone. When two systems are in an octave relationship, two musical strings, for instance, they are in a direct resonant relation and the energy transfer between them is unimpeded. As their vibratory patterns are virtually identical they therefore give rise to near identical forms and structures (see fig. 3.3 p. 43). So somewhere in the frequency spectrum an infra-red frequency may be in a direct octave relationship with an ultraviolet frequency. Thus, in some forests, at the equator for example, certain species of timber, such as balsa, have the softest wood of all. This suggests that the wood-quality-determining frequency has proceeded past the point where hardwoods are created and has re-entered the resonant conditions of the softwood-generating frequencies, although one full octave below, because balsawood is a magnitude softer than the softest of normal softwoods.

Similarly, the colour of the new growth of many species of Australian timber has a peculiar hue, being comprised of a mixture of red, violet and blue, reflecting the necessity to resist the potentially harmful penetration of these various light frequencies. In Europe, on the other hand, where light conditions are completely different, with some exceptions (such as copper-beech), most new growth is light-green in colour.

For the trees themselves and their relation to the various light zones, the location of the blue-to-ultraviolet zone of high-energy, high-frequency 'hard' radiation is related to both altitude and latitude; the lower the latitude, the higher the altitude and vice versa. That is to say that softwood species, such as pine, in the main are to be found at low altitudes in high latitudes, and at high altitudes in low latitudes. Conversely hardwood trees, with some exceptions, are

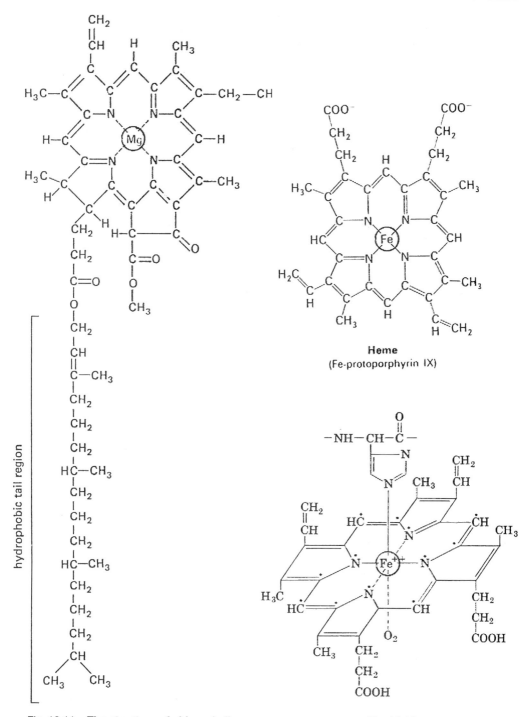

Fig. 16.11   **The structure of chlorophyll**

Heme
(Fe-protoporphyrin IX)

Fig. 16.12

generally to be found at low altitudes in low latitudes (Amazon basin and rainforests) and at low to median altitudes at low to median latitudes.

Ultraviolet, shortwave 'hard' light has a higher energetic content, a faster dynamic motion and the spiralling movement of the light itself has a smaller radius, shorter period. This suggests that, as a result of this greater dynamic, the life-processes in such a zone should take place at a faster pace; indeed high-altitude trees, such as spruce, do have relatively short lifetimes compared to some of the deciduous species, beeches and oaks, for example. These high-altitude trees are often evergreen and the wood soft. In the opposite light zone, at sea level or low latitudes, where long wave-length, low-energy, low-frequency, 'soft' light predominates, the wood is hard and the trees generally longer lived.

16.5 *Photosynthesis*

The sap responds in its ebb and flow, like tides, to the attraction of the Sun and the Moon. Sometimes the powers of

Nature works through pulsation, through inbreathing and outbreathing. When the Sun rises, then the sap, charged with trace-elements and gases, is drawn up due to the energetic stimulation or information of the Sun's waxing influence in order to further the processes of photosynthesis through the supply of minerals, etc. Photosynthesis, however, is intimately connected with the amount and the quality of the incident and available light. When the level of light falls or the presence of the full light spectrum is absent due to atmospheric pollution, then growth, photosynthesis or the creation of chlorophyll diminishes and less oxygen is transformed and released into the atmosphere.

In photosynthesis a certain portion of the upwardly streaming water or sap is transformed into carbohydrates, the remaining water being employed for evaporation and the cooling of the tree. Cooling is the process of energetic concentration or densification (= tensioning), which has nothing to do with technical, thermodynamic vaporisation. In its simplest form the photosynthetic reaction, where molecular oxygen is released for the respiration of man and beast alike, takes place as follows:-

(1) Carbon-dioxide (CO_2) + Water (H_2O) + LIGHT = Photosynthesis + $O_2 \uparrow$

in this way carbon-dioxide and hydrogen combine and molecular oxygen is released as is shown by the upward pointing arrow.

(2) CO_2 + H_2O ——> CH_2O (theoretical carbohydrate) + $O_2 \uparrow$

($C_6H_{12}O_6$ = glucose = the simplest form of carbohydrate.)

these luminaries are in unison, at other times in opposition. This fluctuation from above to below and back again correspond to concepts of yin inward movement and yang outward movement and their boundary conditions of exhaustion. That is to say, when the combined downard pull of both Sun and Moon reaches the extreme limits of its effect, like the physical limit of an inward breath, its influence weakens. It then gives way to the opposite function of their combined upward pull whose strength increases until its power culminates (limit of outward breath).

With the powerful coherence of the water-molecule in the earlier discussion of electrolysis in chapter 8, it seems most likely here that it is the carbon-dioxide molecule that releases its molecular oxygen, but not the water molecule its single oxygen atom. Through this process the otherwise excessive quantities of CO_2 and O_2 are fixed both in the short and long term, so that the correct proportions between the atmospheric gases comprising CO_2 (0.3%), oxygen (20.95%), nitrogen (78.08%) and the noble gases (0.93%) are maintained. All living systems can thus be viewed as Nature's energy-refuse heaps and purification plants, through which no element can remain in harmful excess or overdose.

Photosynthesis, as a process, is closely associated with the production of chlorophyll. If we study the molecular structure of chlorophyll in fig. 16.11[4], which is the molecule principally responsible for the green colour of the vegetation, we can see that it is comprised of 137 atoms and at the centre of the nitrogen ring there is one atom of magnesium (Mg). In photosynthesis the positively charged magnesium atom, the very core of the chlorophyll molecule, is brought into contact with water (H_2O) and carbon-dioxide (CO_2) through which the chlorophyll molecule as such can first come into being. Surrounded by a chain of 4 nitrogen (N) atoms, the magnesium atom is king of the chlorophyll molecule, which in vegetation, it is one of the essential bases for life on this planet. Human blood, equally a life-giving fluid, has a similar central molecular structure, but at the centre of its nitrogen ring in figs. 16.12[5] there is an atom of iron (Fe) (also shown circled) in lieu of magnesium. Known as haemoglobin, it is the active part of animal blood and performs the same function in animals as chlorophyll does in plants. Indeed in an experiment carried out with rats, their blood was replaced with liquid chlorophyll and they showed no signs of either distress or disease, but continued to go on living as though nothing had happened.

If we now expand on the photosynthetic reaction above by including the key magnesium atom, discounting for the moment the other elements in the chlorophyll molecule, then in essence the following happens:

---

(3) $Mg+H_2O+CO_2$ **+ plus LIGHT** —————————> Chlorophyll + O_2 ↑
   (green pigment +)
   (molecular oxygen)

With the same elements in (3) above there two further reactions, however, both equally important in their final product:

(4) $Mg+H_2O+CO_2$ **– minus LIGHT**—————————> $MgCO_3+H_2$ ↑
   (magnesium carbonate)
   (+ molecular hydrogen)

or (5) $Mg+H_2CO_2$ [carbonic acid] **– minus LIGHT** ——————> $MgCO_3+H_2$ ↑
   (magnesium carbonate)
   (+ molecular hydrogen)

In the last two chemical reactions (4) and (5) the magnesium can be replaced with calcium (Ca), which produces calcium carbonate ($CaCO_3$) in lieu of magnesium carbonate, but with the same release of molecular hydrogen.

These two almost identical, but still different combinations of magnesium, CO_2 and H_2O are the prerequisites for the two principal carriers of life, namely water and photosynthesis (creation of chlorophyll and carbohydrates). One of these takes place in the zone of daylight (the visible world) and the other in the zone of darkness (the invisible world). In the day zone, O_2 is released and the overall quantity of oxygen increased, whereas in the night-zone, the release of hydrogen takes place leading to the rebirth of water through its combination with oxygen.

---

addition contains an assortment of carbon (C), hydrogen (H) and oxygen (O) atoms, making a total of no less than 137 atoms.

It is interesting to note that 137 is a prime number, i.e. a number divisible only by itself or by 1. Chlorophyll is thus a very stable molecule, securely rooted as it is in the indivisibility of a prime number, and rightly so since, as a fundamental building block of

16.6 Why Growth Occurs at the Extremities

To clarify this process, let us briefly re-examine the movement of rainwater. When rain falls, each droplet represents an accumulation and agglomeration of **like**[6] molecules of H_2O. Having both positive and negative charges and having become collectively more massive, i.e. more material in the matter-energy balance, in their descent as dipole molecules, which simultaneously orbit along their spiral paths, rotate about their own axes and circulate their energies internally, these raindrops are no longer able to float in the particular energy field where aggregation occurred and fall earthwards.

On their downward spin they not only absorb increasing quantities of atmospheric oxygen, nitrogen and other trace-gases, but at the same time generate increasingly intense bioelectric and biomagnetic fields. They are thus endowed with a certain tension (life potential), which is ultimately 'given' to the plants upon which they fall. When the oxygen and other gases thus collected and concentrated reach the ground or fall upon leaf structures, they are absorbed and, together with the accumulated immaterial energies, provoke heightened activity in all processes of transformation and growth. This is why plant growth responds with much greater vitality and activity after a fall of rain than it does with conventional systems of irrigation, in which the fall-distance is considerably shorter in relation to that of the raindrop, and, consequently, also such water has no possibility of beneficial exposure to the higher immaterial energies of the Sun present at an altitude of 4,000 metres.

When rainwater reaches the ground under a positive temperature gradient, it penetrates into the soil. The overabundance of oxygen is gradually absorbed and dispersed into the surrounding soil, initially to activate humus functions and micro-organism activity in the upper layers of the soil. This activity diminishes as the rainwater sinks deeper into the substrata and progressively releases the excess oxygen, as it gradually cools towards the $+4C°$ anomaly point. Having been almost totally expelled from the water at this temperature, the residual free oxygen meets with the free hydrogen, which has been released in the combining of either magnesium (Mg) or calcium (Ca) with carbon-dioxide (CO_2) and water (H_2O), forming either magnesium- or calcium-carbonate; calcium being inter-changeable with magnesium in reactions (4) and (5) above.

Due to the coolness of the ambient temperatures, the oxygen is in its most passive state and thus is easily bound by the hydrogen. New water molecules – H_2O – are formed as a result, i.e. water is born and created. From which it follows that the amount of available water **is not constant!**

Once again, this is pure water unpolluted by any other substances or ingredients. Born under temperature conditions of about $+4C°$ (level of highest energy density and the so-called anomaly point), this juvenile immature water, which has all the attributes of insatiable youth, begins to rise up through the various energy-horizons (the most finely differentiated temperature strata), accumulating more and more information in the form of other energetic systems and resonances.

As it slowly ascends, it gradually begins to warm, dissolving more and more minerals, salts and trace-elements on its way. These become ionised in the process and brought into a condition in which they can be taken up by the plants and their micro-organisms. Salt, for example, is dissociated into its two components of chlorine (Cl) and sodium (Na), which develop negative and positive charges respectively. From a so-called 'inorganic' substance, two living polarities are created. Without these charges, these now separated elements could not combine with other positively or negatively charged substances. The necessary attraction would be missing.

The water is now able to give to life instead of taking from it, creating life-imparting macro water molecules. These various macromolecular nutrients are then further activated by the increasingly available oxygen. Growth activity rises as these molecules themselves are drawn up through the capillaries of the plants or trees, becoming more and more refined as energy and nutrients are progressively imparted to the various structures and chemical processes on the way up. The more these macro-molecules of mature water become refined, the more their potency increases until, at the forefront or workface of growth itself, when their material quantity is at a minimum and of such size as to be able to pass through the extremely minute foramen and stomata, their potency, energetic quality and action reachs a maximum at the material level. Thus the greatest growth, development and unfoldment occurs at this point, namely at the furthest extremities of the tree, plant or blade of grass.

It is therefore along this upward developmental path from the deeper strata towards the surface that water is transformed from a seeking, 'taking' system into a ripe, information-rich condition, when it is at any moment ready to distribute this new quantity of transformed, qualitatively improved in-*form*-ation to the living systems of its environment. An immature, 'taking' system has been transmuted into a radiating, 'giving' system, possessed of and offering the widest variety of ionised elements in homeopathic doses.

Precisely at the point now reached by this alive, mineral- and trace-element-rich water, full of promise for the future, the next, young, 'taking', information-seeking systems are to be found, namely, the fine hair-roots of the plant systems and their micro-organisms, or 'micro-transmuters'. Here the water is first taken up as a fluid by the micro-organisms which, as catalysts, transform the raw materials, elements, CO_2, oxygen, nitrogen, etc. into larger molecules and fluid compounds.

These do not only serve the rapid extension of the hair-roots themselves (the receivers of mineral nutrients and more subtle energies), but also as the principal substances for the inner growth of the plant as a whole as they rise through the enlarging capillaries, ducts, arteries and canals in the roots. These coarse macro-molecules are sucked towards the centre and deposited in order to build up the central structure of the plant or tree. The hair roots act like the small tributaries of a river, contributing formative fluids to the main channels of the major roots. This increasing, but slower-flowing quantity of formative material is built into the tree structure up to the level of the ground-surface, where suddenly the supply of quasi-solid physical matter (minerals, salts, trace-

elements, etc.) from sources external to the plant ceases.

Here the threshold of the unseen world of the root-zone is reached and the visible, energetic world, endowed with a higher dynamic and suffused with radiant, fertilising energy from the Sun, is entered. Perhaps it is here, precisely at the surface of the ground, that the actual 'heart' of the tree is to be found. This is the point where the two aspects of the tree, the two systems of distribution, the seen and the unseen, meet and are united.

In the human body, the veins and arteries enlarge in the direction of the heart and narrow towards the capillaries, all of which is ordered by subtle differences in temperature or by differences in charge, energy density and energetic activity. The human body possesses two principal, pulsating circulation systems; to the lungs and to the rest of the body via the heart. The former seeks renewal of oxygen and discharge of CO_2 and water, whereas the latter delivers oxygen as well as nutrients to all parts of the body and on its return journey collects and transports CO_2 and waste matter.

The tree, however, has no pulsating heart as such. The 'pulsators' responsible for the movement of its sap are the Sun and the Moon. As the world rotates, the direction of the Sun's and the Moon's attraction fluctuates from above to below, through which a discontinuous pulsation between the boundary conditions of inhaling and exhaling arises.

From the ground up, the various sap-ducts and capillaries begin to narrow in hyperbolic measure and according to their physical size and consistency, the coarser elements, which are unable to be raised further, are built into the tree's structure at the point where their upward movement ceases. The higher and the deeper the sap flows, the smaller the diameter of the sap vessels and the faster the sap streams both upwards and downwards. The greater the homeopathic potential, the smaller the material quantities, so that ultimately only the most minute particles, which are hardly to be counted as matter, stream up towards the crown or down to the roots with increasing spiral gyration, dynamic and energetic effect.

Right at the very extremities of crown and root zones, the growth activity is at a maximum, because all that here is active are the most highly potentiated homeopathic quantities and resonances, which can still be described as structured matter. However, this upward or downward stream of energy does not stop here. The very pinnacle of the growth process, where physical extension ceases, could perhaps be described as the jumping off point, namely the point where the physical, harmonically structured visible aspect of the plant terminates and where the purely energetic, form-controlling aspect, the spirit of the plant reunites with its wholly invisible path, now released from the constraints of matter. There is a complementarity here between the unseen extremities of the root zone, where the energetic polarity seems to be that of life seeking life, and, at the other extremity, at the crown of the tree, life giving life.

Being the finest of the fine, all that eventually exits from these extremities is the water molecule, but in the case of the crown zone, a water molecule which carries within it all the no longer material, but highly active, highest overtone resonances of the trace elements previously taken up in the root zone. Having become refined to the point of being almost pure energy and an almost pure water molecule again, albeit with ultra-high potency, homeopathic, ethereal, trace element overtone resonances, it then ascends from the leaves through the minute stomata, drawn ever upward towards the higher level of energy at an altitude of 3000–4000 metres, once more to reach its energy anomaly point, or that energy field-density commensurate with its own internal energy density or quality. Here it is once more in a 'taking' mode in order to equip itself with yet finer and more spiritual energies obtained from the Sun and from the very cosmos itself.

This further accumulation of information in addition to that already borne aloft, represents a large increase in both the power and quality of the information that drives evolution. Here too it floats until attracted once more into association with its peers, eventually to fall again to the Earth as rain, enriched with new energy and new vitality, bringing with it all the new information and formative energy it has accumulated, thus providing a fresh impulse for further evolutionary processes and development.

Notes

1. New Science Library, Shambhala, 1987, ISBN: 0-87773-364-3.
2. *Health and Light* by Dr. John N.Ott: Devin-Adair, Greenwich CT, USA, 1973, ISBN: 0-671-47433-2.
3. *ibid.*
4. "Chlorophyll Structure" in *The Molecular Biology of the Cell* by B. Alberts, D. Bray, J. Lewis, M. Raff, K. Roberts & J.D. Watson, p.517, fig. 9–46: Garland, New York, USA, 1983. ISBN 0-8240-7282-0.
5. *ibid*. p.495: Fig: 9–19, "Heme structure".
6. Here we are confronted with an apparent paradox, where in the physical world of polarities, systems with like charges and like potential or the same sex repel each other. Only those systems with complementary polarities are drawn together and a new synthesis for creation and regeneration is made possible. In this type of more animal magnetism, individualities merge to produce a new third system or entity. On the other hand, at a more spiritual level under the influence of the higher dialectic counterpart, bio-magnetism, those systems that attract each other are imbued with the same desires, the same interests and the same goals. This is an attraction that extends beyond their purely physical differences.

This is what happens with raindrops. It is a more immaterial attraction and it could thus be construed that the agglomeration of water-molecules into raindrops is ordered from a much higher source through bio-magnetic, upbuilding and uplifting forces operating at a completely different level. Evolution can therefore be seen to evolve in a positive sense only when the lesser physical opposites are over-ridden or guided and united by a higher purpose. If this order is reversed and the attraction between like systems occurs at a level below the level of the attraction of opposites, then evolution is doomed to become unproductive. Here like attracting like is genetically unfruitful and devolutionary (viz.homosexuality and lesbianism).

17

FORESTRY – A NOBLE OR IGNOBLE ART?

The forest should only be cared for by people who love it. Those who view the forest merely as an object of speculation, do it and all other living creatures great harm, for the forest is the cradle of water. If the forest dies, then the springs will dry up, the meadows will become barren and many countries will inevitably be seized by unrest of such a kind that it will bode ill for every one of us.[1]

Viktor Schauberger

17.1 Contemporary Forestry

Before the advent of the science of forestry, which had its earliest beginnings in Switzerland about 160 years ago, the health and regeneration of the forest was largely left to Nature. Under normal circumstances in the high forest a vast mixture of species of overstorey and understorey flourish in harmonious interaction, each contributing in its own special way to the well-being of the whole.

Those species with deep root-systems bring up valuable nutrients from below, which are beyond the reach of the more shallow-rooted, and through the casting of their leaves in autumn, enrich the biomass and enhance the development of the layer of humus on the forest floor. Here, with the cooperative activity of the myriads of micro-organisms inhabiting the humus, the nutrients are transformed into a state in which they can readily be taken up by the vegetation. Due to the presence of the protective canopy of dense foliage overhead, the ground remains cool and moist and in a condition to absorb and retain up to 85% of whatever rain falls, thereby ensuring the recharge of the groundwater table and the full cycle of water.

Those trees and other species of vegetation very sensitive to light and heat are shielded from these degenerative influences by varieties of tree whose structure is designed to resist them and which, as guardians of the forest, range themselves around the edges of it. Under this protection and that of the mother trees the young saplings grow up healthily in the diffuse light and coolness of the CO_2-rich atmosphere below the crown cover, which shields the young growth, not only from the harmful effects of direct sunlight and heat, but also from the buffeting of strong winds and the impact of heavy rain. Only when the mother tree finally dies is space and light made available to the rising generation, who by this time, in their adolescence, as it were, are ready and fully equipped to assume the role of their parent trees.

Under these conditions the life of succeeding generations takes place in its fullness, each able to reach full maturity and live out its allotted span in the ceaseless cycle of life and death. The seeds of these mature trees, from which the up-and-coming new growth are to evolve, are therefore of the highest quality, thus ensuring the continuing fertility and healthy reproduction of their offspring. In this highest state of order founded on wide bio-diversity, Nature is in a changeable, lively, wholesome and productive state of equilibrium.

All this vibrant tranquility rapidly began to vanish, however, as humanity made further and further inroads into the resources of the forest. Larger and larger surfaces were laid bare for agriculture but, as long as this was on a relatively small scale, the damage to the environment was slight. Sometimes this clearing was for other purposes. When Henry VIII ordered the massive expansion of the Royal Navy in the early 16th century, for example, two thousand mature oak trees were required to build each vessel, virtually denuding England of the vast oak forests, whose size and density was recorded by the Romans at the time of their invasion in 54BC. The forest thus was seen as an unlimited repository of useful materials, and no thought was given to the conditions vital for its continued existence or to the effect of its removal. This was despite the fact that in many ways there was a greater affinity for Nature in earlier times and a greater knowledge of timber, as the following quotation taken from the records of an Austrian master cartwright written in 1843 shows[2].

There are only three days suited to kiln-drying in the year: April 3rd, July 30th and St Catherine's day. The latter is also good for casting ball and shot.

To make sure that timber is solid and firm it should be felled during the first 8 days after the new moon, if this is in a 'soft sign' (i.e.in any of the zodiacal signs of Virgo, Pisces, Gemini or Libra).

To make sure that timber does not rot after felling, there are only three days in the year when it can be felled. The first day after the Conversion of St. Paul (26th January) and the 10th and 13th of February.

To obtain incombustible timber, it should be felled the first day in March, when the Moon still has 48 hours to wane.

The best day for felling timber so that it does not shrink is the third day in autumn when daylight is reducing and the Moon waxes above the first quarter.

In order that there should be good regrowth, firewood should be cut in October during the first quarter of the rising Moon.

Saw logs should be cut under the rising sign of Pisces. They should be leached out in water under the sinking signs of Pisces or Cancer.

So that it does not shrink, timber should be felled when the Moon is three days old, on a Friday and under the sign of Cancer.

The straight and true wood required by cartwrights, coopers and the like, should be felled under a new Moon and the signs of Scorpio or Cancer. The wood will then remain firm and solid.

To ensure that timber does not swell up, it should be felled in November on the first and second days before the new Moon.

Over the centuries, however, the rape of the forest grew apace, deserts were created where legendary fertility and productivity once held sway. Forests always precede civilisation, and deserts are the evidence of its passing. Whole nations were uprooted and had to move elsewhere in their search for subsistence. Fortunately in those days there was somewhere else to go, because the world's population was still relatively small. But such is not the case today when we are so many and yet, despite all the historic proof of the effects of deforestation on a large scale, we still continue to remove it at an alarming rate as though, like lemmings, we wish to hasten our own extinction.

When someone dies the bell tolls. When the forest dies and with it a whole people, then no-one lifts a finger.[3]

Viktor Schauberger

Forestry, the husbanding and conserving of the vital national and international assets of the forest should be regarded as foremost amongst professions. Apart from water resources management, it is forestry, above all other disciplines, that is responsible for maintaining the stability of the global climate and Earth's land surfaces.

The science of forestry was born in the early 19th century as the Swiss inaugurated a large-scale reafforestation program to rectify the enormous depredations caused by the massive removal of great trees during Napoleon's passage through the Alps. With a greater sense of place and belonging than exists today, they formulated strict laws forbidding the planting of species where they did not grow naturally. Spruce and other high altitude trees could not be planted in the valley and the planting of beeches, oaks and other deciduous trees at high levels was equally restricted by law. This legislation still applies in Switzerland and has also been adopted by Austria, although as in other countries, forestry there too has largely devolved into the commercial production of timber chiefly for the manufacture of cheap furniture, wood chipping and firewood.

In the process of mass production, all connection and understanding of the natural processes which provide high-quality timber have been lost. Vast areas of land are cleared of trees completely, exposing the soil to the direct heat and light of the Sun, thereby destroying the delicate soil-capillaries – the vital furnishers of nutrients and soil-moisture – as well as raising the ground temperatures and drastically lowering the groundwater table. Any kind of tree is planted anywhere regardless of its origins and the conditions of its natural habitat, and the home and sustenance of myriads of creatures, whose very existence depends on natural mixed forests, are irrevocably lost.

While the highest quality hardwoods are cleared wholesale for the production of the highest quality paper and furniture, relatively few are replanted because they take a longer time to grow to maturity; in other words the natural period of rotation is too long for commercial exploitation. Any reafforestation that does occur is generally done with softwoods such as pine, for forestry, in its ignorance and as an instrument of government, worships short term financial gain, caring nothing for the long-term consequences.

Rotation is reduced to an absolute minimum and biologically speaking represents a denial of the future, because no tree is allowed to reach full maturity. It is a process akin to the killing of a child. While the age of a mature redwood is about 2,000 years, today it is felled after 60 years of growth. This means that it has been cut down when only 3% of its full potential has been realised

and before it can be fruitful. As an act of violence it is equivalent to slaying a human being with a life expectancy of 70 years when it is just over 2 years old. As a result there is no longer any mature seed and gradually the genetic base of the seed deteriorates to the point of infertility. The consequences of this madness are far-reaching, for as the biological diversity is depleted of its highest quality organisms, so too are the qualities, energetic and otherwise, that support higher forms of life. The destruction of the forest goes hand in hand with the destruction of water, and as we have seen in earlier chapters, the consequences of this insanity are appalling.

The death of the forests is only the tip of the iceberg and is a reflection of the deeper deterioration in humankind itself.

Ernst Krebs

17.2 Monoculture

In a natural mixed forest, all the available elements and influences required for growth and development are distributed evenly and apportioned to each organism according to its needs. Here differentiation and diversification are at a maximum; nothing is wasted, and nothing is in excess. In Nature order is so complex that it appears chaotic, but because it is order and tranquility it satisfies the eye and uplifts the spirit – the eye requiring the most complex 'mirror' for its own balance and equilibrium).

One of the reasons why young, same-age plantations of pine trees disturb the eye is because their level of order in no way matches the much more complex order to be found in natural forest. All their branches are at the same height, producing a disturbing, buzzing horizontality wholly absent in mixed forests. The self-evident, thriving sustainability of old-growth forests which existed on this planet before the advent of humankind, this natural complexity, which represents the very highest state of order, has been completely disregarded. The life-contributing undergrowth in managed forests is cleared on the assumption that more water and more nutrients will be made available to the commercial crop of trees. Instead of the natural synergetic cooperation between different species, divisive competition is introduced, pitting one plant form against the other.

In a monoculture situation, all the trees strive for the same nutrients and frequencies of light to survive. Here, truly, we are confronted by the survival of the fittest, because the amount and quality of the nutrients specific to a particular species are limited. There is only a certain amount of each element and chemical compound available and all the trees whose lives are wholly dependent on them must fight to get it. The energies change, the pulsation and harmonious interaction are disrupted, disease, discord and dissension prevail, extending their insidious and pernicious effects to all other creatures. Embedded in systems of order of much lower complexity, more highly ordered systems lose their stability and even become extinct. Humankind please take note!

Because the trees or plants in a monoculture only absorb certain frequencies from a fairly narrow bandwidth of frequencies in the available spectrum, only the percentage specific to them is used by the particular species and transformed into creative growth, the remainder being reflected in many cases as additional ambient heat. When, through changes in vibratory patterns the physical form changes, this means quite simply that the previous form has been destroyed or has metamorphosed, sometimes forcibly. In other words the later forms are different to the earlier ones.

Energy as movement is indestructible and thus eternal, there being no such thing as 'neutral' energy in the sense of static energy. Therefore if any energy-path is in any way abrogated or truncated, or in any other way diverted from its naturally-ordained path or form, then such energy is perverted and cannot fulfill its creative functions.

Any function which in any manner maintains a given system in a state of stable health and balance, is the outer expression of an inner creative force. Were it not creative, then such a system would deteriorate. Thus if energy, in this case the light and energy from the Sun, cannot dispose itself creatively, then it inevitably becomes destructive. Here the destructive effects result in the overheating of these monoculturally planted trees.

Once the internal metabolic processes have been distorted through unnatural temperatures either received externally, or induced internally through excessive oxidation, then the plant's naturally ordained metabolism can no longer operate in a healthy fashion. In other words, if the natural standing-wave pattern of frequencies, which supports a particular manifestation changes as a result of an increase in internal temperature (see fig. 7.1), then, in the case of the tree, or human being for that matter, the new picture no longer represents that of 'healthy tree', but 'sick tree + parasites'.

As human beings we are generally considered healthy and do not have a 'temperature' when our body temperature is +37°C. However, as soon as our temperature rises to say +37.5°C, then we start feeling ill, perhaps a little dizzy, but at all events slightly feverish. Suddenly we are in a disease-prone condition. What has happened? A very minute change in temperature has occurred and we are sick; we are malfunctioning. Because we are sick, our internal temperature has altered to a temperature conducive to the development of a life-form that is otherwise alien to us.

At all times we are the carriers of most known diseases, it is just that they are dormant and remain so, because our healthy body temperature is unsuited to their existence and propagation. When we get a temperature for some reason or other, or we get a chill, then the body temperature reaches a level where bacteria can unfold and develop. The virus emerges from its crystalline state and becomes active and organic. But here Nature is very clever and, in order to dispose of these unwanted alien systems, the body raises the temperature even further to a level lethal to the bacteria or the germs, whose normal temperature range may lie between say +38.2°C and +38.6°C. This is why, once a climactic temperature has been reached, the affected person often recovers very quickly.

From this it becomes clearly apparent that, like us, the tree does not sicken because of parasitic and fungal attack, but because its state of indifference has been disturbed and its condition of highest health and vitality disrupted. The tree thus attracts those parasites because the changed energetic vibrations, resulting in abnormally high internal temperatures, are conducive to their procreation and propagation. Parasites are therefore what Viktor Schauberger called "Nature's Health Police", whose job it is to remove all genetically degenerate organisms in order to safeguard the future. In the case of the tree, however, the principal cause of this genetic degradation is a total misunderstanding of the tree's responses to light and heat, which will now be addressed below.

17.3 Light- and Shade-Demanding Trees

The table [fig. 16.10] on p. 216 shows that there are two categories of tree labelled shade-demanding and light-demanding. Modern forestry practice does not recognise this, with dire consequences for the overall health of the forest. In its quantitative approach, contemporary forestry considers that if a tree grows rapidly, puts on a profusion of branches and gains quickly in girth, then it is getting value for money. What forestry is actually getting is *quantity*, but not *quality* for its money.

Through lack of understanding of the light factor and its associated effects of increased temperature, forestry has completely overlooked the reason for the increased incidence of disease, not only in logged natural forests, but more particularly in plantation forests, where shade-demanding species are exposed to the damaging effects of direct sunlight and heat almost from birth. But how can we determine whether a tree is a light-demander or a shade-demander? There are two principal ways:

1. Shade-demanding species generally have thin smooth bark for, being normally resident in the inner areas of the forest, they do not need to insulate themselves from the heating effect of direct sunlight. Light-demanding timbers on the other hand have thick, coarse, thermally insulating bark, which is Nature's way of protecting them from the same potentially harmful influences.

2. Shade-demanding trees grow additional branches on the trunk when exposed to light and heat, whereas light-demanders do not.

As an example of this, fig. 17.1 shows two trees on the author's property in Australia; one is a shade-demander (*a*) and the other a light-demander (*b*). The whole area shown in the photograph was covered over with dense lantana (which as an introduced exotic species goes berserk in hot climates) up to a height of about 4 metres. The trunks of both trees were therefore protected from the light of the Sun for the first 4 or so metres above the ground.

Since this area was only recently cleared for the first time after many years, the youngish shade-demanding tree had lived all its life with its trunk protected from the heat and light of the Sun. Six weeks after clearing operations, the shade-demanding tree (*a*) (see also fig. 17.2) started to grow some extra branches on the lower part of the trunk on the sunny side. It had to do this in order to protect itself from the new and unwanted heat, which disturbs the orderly flow of sap.

In most cases, therefore, when trees or shrubs are pruned and continually regrow branches quickly in those areas where they were cut off, you know that you are dealing with a shade-demanding species. The reason they put the lower branches on is not because they want the sunlight, but because they do not want it on the trunk. When sunlight bathes the trunk, all the metabolic processes within the tree are disrupted. The tree becomes overheated, the sap no longer flows as it should and the general structure of the tree becomes very coarse, leading to malformations, cancerous growths in the interior,

Fig. 17.2   **Six weeks after clearing the tree starts to grow more branches**

Fig. 17.1

Fig. 17.4   **A tree protects itself after a forest fire**

rough bark
of tree (b)

Fig. 17.3   **The light-demanding tree puts on no new growth**

and so on. Conversely, during the same period, the light-demanding tree (*b*) (see also fig. 17.3) was not affected by the additional exposure, and put on no extra lower branches at all.

As with all other organisms, what is vital to every tree, indeed all vegetation, is the maintenance of an even inner climate, of its healthy state of 'indifference' or 'temperaturelessness'. If this is in any way disturbed, then the tree becomes disease prone. As far as they can manage it all shade-demanding trees, and under certain circumstances light-demanders too, will do everything they can to maintain or reinstate this temperatureless condition.

This is particularly evident after a forest fire and explains why trees that survive such a conflagration quickly cover themselves with a profusion of small shoots as shown in fig. 17.4. The fire has blackened their bark, so that, instead of reflecting the heat, it absorbs it and other radiation. Without the rapid restoration of protective cover the interior of

the tree would quickly overheat and the flow of sap would slow considerably and no longer reach the highest branches.

As a shade-demander the pine or fir in fig. 17.5 would normally grow in dense forest with no other branches of any significance except those of the crown. Because it is much taller than its neighbours, it must once have been surrounded by trees of similar height but, because it had not yet grown sufficiently to be of any commercial use, it was left standing when the area around it was replanted.

What has happened to this poor tree is quite evident. At a fairly late stage in its growth, its protective surroundings have been removed, leaving it exposed to excessive light and heat. As a result it has had to divert the energies employed in upward growth in order to erect extra branches all the way down the trunk in self-defence. This malformed growth produces a very knotty timber, because an abnormal number of branches have to be grown in areas of the

Fig. 17.8 **Beeches growing at the edge of the forest**

Fig. 17.6   **This shade-demander grows branches only on the sunny side**

Fig. 17.5   **This shade-demander would normally grow in dense forest**

Fig. 17.7   **This beech stoops its crown to protect itself from sun**

Fig. 17.9   **A small beech (arrowed) protects itself at the forest edge**

trunk normally branch-free, severely disturbing the whole process of growth. Under normal conditions all the growth of such a tree would be concentrated in the crown, the trunk would virtually be free of branches and take on a cylindrical shape.

Fig.17.6 shows an evergreen conifer, where the branch development is very one-sided. Observing this with our conventional eyes, we would normally attribute the lack of branch-development on the left hand side to the fact that this area is shaded by other trees, i.e. because there is no sunlight the tree has produced no branches to catch it. This is not correct, however. The tree does not develop any branches because there is no sunlight from which to *protect itself*. On the outside, however, where there is sunlight, there is also a burgeoning development of branches and foliage.

The extent to which shade-demanders, as organic and therefore intelligent entities, are prepared to go to protect themselves is

shown in fig. 17.7. Here the lower branches have been cut off and the higher ones have subsequently folded themselves down towards the ground in order to shield the trunk. As far as the tree is concerned, this extra, unwanted growth sucks the energy from the tree and diverts it from its normal path. This downward curving protective movement shown in fig. 17.8 is also characteristic of shade demanders growing on the outer fringes of a forest.

Fig.17.9 on the other hand shows a very small beech tree (indicated by arrow), also a shade-demanding species, growing right at the edge of the forest. The profusion of small lateral branches all the way up the trunk is symptomatic of its fight to protect itself from the Sun and, although it may look very pretty, the tree is actually severely deformed. As a result the overall growth, and the quality of growth in particular, suffers to a greater or lesser extent.

Here a further parallel can be drawn between human beings and trees on a more psychological, behavioural level. The shade-demanding tree could be viewed as an introvert. Introverts are reserved and extremely sensitive to external influences. Their mode of expression tends towards introspection, mental activity (predominant development of the tree's crown) and they are inwardly preoccupied and absorbed. They need a certain shielding and protection, peace and quiet to develop to maturity and their full potential.

The extroverts on the other hand are represented by the light-demanders, the trees that can happily stand on their own, reflecting the extrovert's need for light and space around them. Their mode of expression tends towards the physically active, outward radiance (branch development) and they are less sensitive to their external environment. They need this outer interaction and exchange to grow. In other words, they are independent, outgoing individuals, who tend to be more capable of standing on their own feet without support.

17.4 Light-induced Growth

Dendrology the branch of science related to the study of trees, is concerned with the analysis of the annual rings in trees in order to determine the climatic conditions under which they grew. Some trees, such as the *Sequoia gigantica* of northern California, which grow to heights in excess of 300 feet (91 metres) and live for 2,000 years or so, provide dendrologists with an accurate record of climatic changes and the trees' response to them. The period where the annual rings are more widely spaced are considered 'good years', because of the quantitative approach to analysis. If they are more closely set they represent the 'bad years', when life for the tree in question was supposedly more of a struggle.

While such analyses may accurately record variations in ambient temperatures over a period of time, the assumption that a tree had to struggle for survival or not is generally incorrect. The true interpretation of the spacing of the annual rings is quite the opposite – where the spacing is larger the tree had

greater difficulty in growing and where smaller the growth was healthy.

This crucial factor, neglected in all contemporary forestry, is best explained by demonstrating the difference between natural and light-induced growth in shade-demanding timbers. The photograph from Viktor Schauberger's book, *Our Senseless Toil* (fig. 17.10), compares the girths of a plantation tree and two naturally grown trees. As can be seen, the separation between the annual rings in the light-induced growth is far larger than in the naturally grown timbers, in which these are barely perceptible. All three trees are roughly the same age, but substantially different in quality.

Because the initial growth of the naturally grown trees took place in very diffuse light under the protection of the mother-tree and in the proper soil conditions, the annual rings are very close together, the sap-ducts are virtually straight and the timber has what might be termed a 'resonant' quality. Incidentally this extremely fine-grained timber is the sort of timber that Stradivari used to make his famous violins. The actual timber that he used was mulberry wood that had fallen into streams in the southern Italian Alps.

This wood had been transported in cold naturally flowing water and had lain in it for quite a considerable period. Its high quality confirms Viktor Schauberger's assertion that when materials are transported in natural streams or double-spiral pipes their quality can be significantly improved. Just lying in this energised water the quality of the timber was enhanced, which is why the Stradivari violins achieved their exceptional tone-colour.

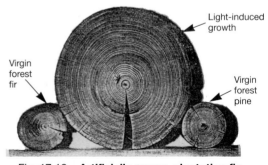

Fig. 17.10   **Artificially grown, plantation fir**

The effect of excess light and heat on the growth of a shade-demander is schematically depicted in fig. 17.11. The annual rings on the sunny side of the trunk are very widely spaced, whereas on the shaded side they are very close. Because the metabolic processes taking place in the shaded area have not been disturbed, the wood has not been forced to expand with heat. On the left-hand, shadow side, the diurnal temperature fluctuation is relatively small and on the right-hand, sunlit side, is much larger due to the exposure to light and heat. These large extremes of temperature are not conducive to the uniform and regular growth found on the left-hand side.

An example of the depletive effects of deforestation is shown in the box overleaf.

17.5 Other Man-made Depredations

Apart from the well-documented effects of acid rain, which will not be addressed here, there are other man-made factors which affect tree growth. Here the use of the term 'man-made' is quite specific and refers to one particular gender on this planet as will become apparent in the final chapter.

According to research by a German electrical engineer, Dr. Wolfgang Volkrodt, a tree is a communication system that functions at much lower energy levels than high-frequency, short-wave emissions in use throughout the world's communication systems. If a tree as a communication system is forcibly overloaded with stronger signals, which were not present 20–30 years ago, for example, then its whole internal communication and organisational system becomes incoherent. This dissonant artificial electromagnetic stimulus affects the proper function of the bioelectrical and biomagnetic circuits in the tree's cells, resulting in wrongly programmed growth and, if the tree is exposed to ultra short-wave frequencies and transmissions long-term, it is destroyed.

The chief culprit in this additional scourge of the forest and the one responsible for the alarming death of the forest in Germany, (or 'Waldsterben' as it is called) is radar. Dr. Volkrodt's survey of 'Waldsterben' determined that it was most widespread around military and civilian airfields and in frontier regions, where the use of radar was greatest. The impulse strength of civilian and military radar installations amounts to about 20,000,000 watts, the radiation limits in the West being about 10,000 times stronger than in Russia. Each sweep of the radar beam the tree experiences as a periodic whiplash from which it cannot escape. In Canada, for example, large tracts of forest have been destroyed by the DEW-line (Defence Early Warning) radar installations.

Microwave directional communication transmitters are equally destructive, having a signal density of 100 watts/cm² near to the

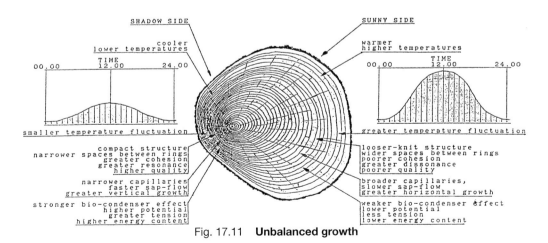

Fig. 17.11 **Unbalanced growth**

Some mention should be made of the climatic effects of deforestation. The transpiration rate of an average rainforest tree, for example, is about 600 litres of water per day. Assuming 200 trees per hectare of rainforest, this represents a water loss to the atmosphere of 120,000 litres per hectare (ha) per day, or a loss in potential rainfall of 12mm/m^2 per day. In other words, if all the water transpired from a single tree were precipitated to the ground within the ambit of its drip-line, then 12mm would be delivered daily per square metre of ground surface.

Not all forest is rainforest and in Algeria, with a climate similar to much of Australia, a 14 metre high eucalypt delivers 375 litres of water a day to the atmosphere through transpiration [data from *Sahara Challenge* by Richard St. Barbe Baker]. According to the 1977 Australian Forestry Report, the quantity of hardwood removed annually since 1973 amounts to 13,819,000m^3. Assuming an average yield of 1.5m^3 of useful timber per tree this = 9,212,667 trees. At say 150 mature trees/ha, the area of tree cover cleared annually = about 61,420 ha or 614.2km^2. On the basis of 150 trees/ha, the daily

transpiration loss at 375 litres/tree = 56,250 litres/ha or 5,625mm/m^2, totalling 2,054.6mm/m^2/year. Over the full 61,420ha cleared annually at a rate of say 168.25 ha/day (61,420ha/365 days), the cumulative loss over 365 days would amount to about 632,150 million litres or 632.15 million tonnes of water per year. If this felling rate has been constant over the last 22 years, then discounting any replanting, the total loss of potential rainfall due to deforestation would total about 13,907,345.2 million litres or 13,907.3 million tonnes of water, or an area 13.9km wide, 1,000km long and 1m deep. Not an insignificant amount of water by any standards for a dry continent. When the trees are removed and people wonder why they are stricken by drought then, in view of this, it easily becomes understandable.

Replanting of trees and global reafforestation on a massive scale is therefore imperative at this late hour if humanity is to be saved from disaster. As for the necessary work-force, there are millions of people available for such work. In actual fact there are not enough unemployed at present to do all that needs to be done.

transmission tower. In order to check the efficiency and proper function of a microwave transmitter, or a high-tension power-line for that matter, a neon tube is held up parallel to the direction of transmission. If it lights up, the system is in order. Aware of all these pernicious effects as a result of his studies, Dr. Volkrodt made it his business to keep track of all proposed new microwave transmission towers. He discovered that after a new microwave sender had been commissioned, the trees on the slopes exposed to and lying directly in the path of the signal suffered severe damage within a few weeks of the transmitter's operation. On the reverse or shadow slopes, the trees tended to be unharmed.

One of the apparent reasons for this deterioration is that microwave transmitters operate with wavelengths between 2cm and 50cm, exposure to which has dangerous biological consequences, i.e. thermal or other

effects such as electro-smog. Microwaves have energetically chaoticising and disruptive effect, triggering changes in crystal structure such that the elements dissolve and are reduced to a lower state of complexity. Domestic microwave ovens operate on similar wavelengths to radar and produce similar decomposive, disintegrative effects due to the vibrational heat they generate in the molecules of the irradiated substance.

The natural wavelength of hydrogen, however, is 21cm and well within the bandwidth of current microwave transmissions. As hydrogen is one of the constituent atoms of the water molecule it is therefore quite possible that it is greatly disturbed or even destroyed due to the excessive excitation arising from internal microwave-induced heating. In the case of the tree this leads to the breakdown of the structure of the sap, which like our blood, is about 80% water, while at the same time increasing the quantity of available oxygen within the tree, leading to wholly unnatural metabolic acceleration. Unfortunately for such a tree, it is rooted to the spot and cannot escape the radiation emitted by microwave towers and high-tension transmission grids.

As a case in point, the tree I photographed in November 1987 near Munich in fig. 17.12 has evidently been exposed in its later life to constant irradiation by nearby civilian and military radar as well as to microwave transmissions, which have now become the norm for almost all telephonic communication, television, etc. As we can see its growth is chaotic and it is grossly deformed. Although human beings are more mobile, if they too are constantly exposed to such radiation, then they too become increasingly prone to blood disorders. In several recent scientific studies it has been shown that people living in close proximity to high-tension cables have a higher than normal incidence of disease.

That this internal microwave-induced warming is becoming more widespread and accelerating could be inferred from an ongoing study of the space between the annual rings of Huon pines carried out by the Commonwealth Scientific & Industrial Research Organisation (CSIRO) in Australia, which showed that in the last 25 years the increase in tree ring width has risen more rapidly than in any other period since 900AD. What happened then is not known, but it may have been a period of large volcanic eruptions or there may have been a massive increase in cosmic radiation for some reason.

The article in question "Global warming rings true"[4] attributes this expansion to increases in ambient atmospheric temperature which may well play a role, but fails to take into account the amount of radio, television, microwave, radar and other forms of electromagnetic transmissions that, over the last 25 years, have reached almost saturation proportions. Nowhere on this planet today is any organism free of permeation and penetration by the disturbing vibratory influences of these insidious radiations. To this can also be added the less publicised radioactive leakages from nuclear power stations and waste dumps, to say nothing of the baleful rotting corpses of Russian nuclear submarines. It would therefore seem far more likely, in the light of Dr. Volkrodt's research, that the increase in tree ring width in these Huon pines is due to electromagnetic rather than thermal effects.

The hope for the future of forestry, however, lies in the involvement of concerned individuals and ecologically-oriented citizen groups, rather than government organisations which rely on so-called 'expert' advice. As we have seen, in relation to Viktor Schauberger's battle for the Rhine and the subsequent construction of unnatural hydraulic structures, these 'scientists' have a vested interest in supporting those in power. If Viktor Schauberger's knowledge and the theories and practices of these various citizen organisations were combined and implemented on a global basis, then much would be done towards turning the presently ebbing tide of life on this planet.

Fig. 17.12 **Tree near Munich damaged by radar**

In Australia and in many other countries around the world, for example, Permaculture[5], an environmental movement founded by Bill Mollison and David Holmgren in Australia in 1974, has been growing enormously. The theories and practices espoused by Permaculture encompass the creation of an integrated environment at both large and small scales and, in their practice have proved very successful. It is a particularly 'hands on' approach, designed for individuals and families from all walks of life and is therefore, well within the means and capacities of those interested in enhancing their own immediate environment.

Apart from improving the quality of life in so-called civilised countries, the application of Permaculture methods in countries stricken with enormous poverty has made it possible for many people who would otherwise have perished in the most miserable conditions to survive with increasing abundance and quality of food. In Permaculture all use of artificial fertilisers is forsworn and natural methods of composting and fertilisation only are employed. If the implementation of this well thought-out system was more widespread it would begin to have a significant effect first on local and then on more general conditions.

Permaculture seeks to replicate as far as possible the biodiversity of plant types found in Nature, rather than the orderly gardens of modern fashion. In these artificially created natural habitats, agriculture, silviculture, animal husbandry and whatever water is available are combined into a harmonious and sustainable whole. Species are chosen according to which grows best in association with another. Shelter belts and groves are placed in order to provide the optimum conditions for growing vegetables along with other plants and pastures for domestic animals in the prevaling climatic and soil conditions. Each family or group is thus provided with the means to become more and more self-sufficient.

Reafforestation is now required on a massive scale globally. Charles Peaty[6], of Western Australia, has developed a system for the successful mass planting of trees in arid conditions. In view of the vast areas of existing deserts and their rapid expansion and incipience in previously productive regions due to the near total removal of tree cover, Charles Peaty's methods most certainly provide a viable solution. These systems actually work, and there is now no valid reason why any government threatened by desert and drought should not immediately implement them, if it is truly concerned for its economy and the well-being of its people. With this system Charles Peaty guarantees a survival rate of 92% and, over recent years, has planted 60,000 million trees in Kuwait, Pakistan and Western Australia. If any climatically and agriculturally restorative measure is worthy of United Nations and World Bank support this one qualifies par excellence!

Notes

1. "The Dying Forest" ("Der sterbende Wald"), by Viktor Schauberger, Pt.I: *Tau* mag, Vol.151, Nov.1936, p.30.
2. *Implosion* mag, No.78, p.29.
3. From the Schauberger archives.
4. "Global warming rings true", *New Scientist*, Sept.1991.
5. Permaculture Inst, P.O.Box 1, Pyalgum 2480, NSW, Australia. Permaculture Intern'l Ltd., P.O.Box 6039, South Lismore 2480, NSW, Australia.
6. Charles Peaty,B.Sc.(Forst'y), Afforestation Pty.Ltd, 5 Luth Avenue, Daglish 6008, W.Australia.

18

THE METABOLISM OF THE TREE

All the processes that take place in water are reflected once again in the individual forms of vegetation.[1]

Viktor Schauberger

18.1 The Movement of Sap

It is appropriate now to examine the actual movement of the sap under both the conditions of natural growth and of unnatural light-induced growth. As with everything else in Nature, this is also determined by the temperature gradient, in this case within the tree itself, as well as in its relation to external factors such as light, heat and cold.

We saw in chapter 9 that the solution, transport and deposition of nutrients are all functions of the temperature gradient. When light and air are excluded the precipitation of salts and minerals occurs with cooling, whereas with exposure to light and air, precipitation takes place with heating. It should also be recalled that, under a positive temperature gradient, the highest quality nutrients are precipitated last as the sap cools towards +4°C or is maintained at this temperature. Under a strong negative temperature gradient and with light and heat, the opposite happens and the lowest quality nutrients only are expelled, the highest quality not being transported at all.

In the last chapter we described how the natural course of growth and development of a shade-demanding species takes place largely in the crown. The overall shape of the trunk is cylindrical, with very minimal lower branch development (fig. 18.1), because there is no need to protect the trunk against light. The air temperatures at the level of the crown is usually significantly higher than the temperature at ground level. Because there is no horizontally incident light, the trunk is also never exposed to massive and abrupt fluctuations in temperature; as a result the annual rings are very closely set, sometimes so closely as to be indistinguishable with the naked eye.

The temperature gradient of the trunk is positive from the outside inwards, the cooler interior temperatures ensuring that any deposition of growth material is evenly distributed, of high quality and relatively small amount. The direction of growth and development is therefore upwards with little lateral extension, reflecting the proper, natural movement of sap and the levitational energies that are part of it. According to Viktor Schauberger these can be so strong in a healthy, mature and naturally grown tree that it is almost impossible for a storm to uproot it. It is these energies that return the tree to its normal vertical stance once the gusting fury of the wind has passed. This also explains the extraordinary slenderness of the trunks of some young saplings in natural old-growth forests, which seem to defy the forces of gravity in their long reach for the sky.

In mature, natural, old-growth forests the light available for the growth of saplings and young trees comes from the diffuse source above. However, because a typical plantation tree, usually a shade-demander, is planted out in the open (fig. 18.2), to survive it has imme-

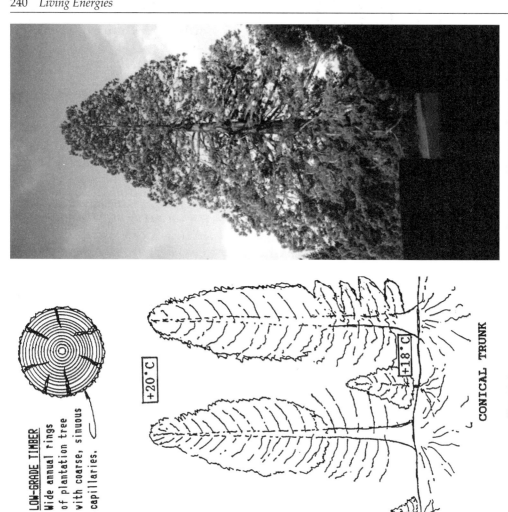

Fig. 18.3 Unnatural cone shape

HIGH-GRADE TIMBER
Narrow annual rings of healthily grown forest tree with very fine, straight capillaries.

LOW-GRADE TIMBER
Wide annual rings of plantation tree with coarse, sinuous capillaries.

+20°C

+15°C

CYLINDRICAL TRUNK

Fig. 18.1

+20°C

+18°C

CONICAL TRUNK

Fig. 18.2

has immediately to cope with unnatural levels of illumination and heat, covering itself as quickly as possible with branches right down to the ground at the expense of its upward growth. Its form is cone-shaped, sometimes excessively so; as fig. 18.3 shows, there is massive development of branches on the lower part of the trunk. On closer inspection it can be seen that the distribution of branches is unbalanced, that there is a greater density of branches on the sunny, left hand side of the trunk and, although this shape may be appropriate for a Christmas tree, it is actually grossly misshapen.

In a plantation setting, as a tree grows it eventually receives a certain degree of protection from its neighbouring trees, the need for lateral branch development diminishes and the predominant direction of growth is once again upwards. However, in the conventional management of plantation forests, after the prescribed period of rotation, the trees are selectively thinned, those considered suitable as constructional timber going to the sawmill and the remainder to the pulp-mill.

The effect of this thinning out on the remaining trees is disastrous! Once again, and very suddenly, they are exposed to excess heat and light. In order to survive, all the growth energy is directed laterally towards the development of branches all the

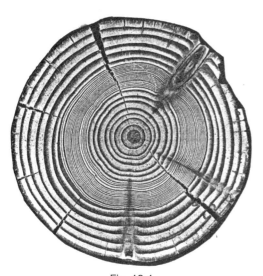

Fig. 18.4

way down the exposed part of the trunk, predominantly on the sunny side, producing a second profusion of knots, shakes and twisted, spongy grain. Note in fig. 18.4 the large variations in the space between the annual rings and the inner and outer coarseness in the grain on the trunk cross-section, the healthiest growth in this instance having taken place roughly during the middle third of the tree's life, when the annual rings were closest together. In the early stages of development this 33-year old tree was obviously exposed to unnatural levels of light and heat. As its trunk gradually became protected from these excesses by its companion trees, the annual rings drew together, only to expand again abruptly and hugely when this protection had been removed.

Any resonant timber would only be obtainable from the area of closely spaced rings, but a board cut from the full width of the trunk would suffer non-uniform shrinkage. In terms of their suitability for constructional purposes, the naturally grown, narrow-ringed timber is far superior, more consistent, firm and regular in its structure, and far less prone to warping or irregular shrinkage. Plantation timber or shade-demanders suddenly exposed to light in natural forests, on the other hand, exhibit not only irregular spacing of the annual rings, but the heart of the tree is frequently off-centre and prone to the development of heart-rot and ring-shakes, the latter being cleavages along the lines of and between the annual rings.

Moreover, not only does the spongy consistency of the inter-annular spaces result in excessive and unequal shrinkage, making such timber virtually useless and totally unsound as strong structural material, but the associated abnormally high internal temperatures also provide an ideal breeding ground for bacteria and parasites, to which the tree will eventually fall victim. All these necrotic phenomena are what Viktor Schauberger referred to as 'tree cancer' and is evidently what afflicted the tree in the two photographs in fig. 18.5, which has suffered a lethal infestation of heart-rot as shown by the fungal growths (arrowed) half way up the trunk, causing its fracture.

Disease in shade-demanding timbers through excessive exposure to sunlight

An example of the damage inflicted on a shade-demanding beech tree, when it is planted out in the open in plantation forests and exposed to the full impact of direct sunlight in its early youth. Such trees can only grow and develop healthily under the protection of the mother-tree.

The upper part of the trunk and the whole of the crown have broken off about half way up the trunk.

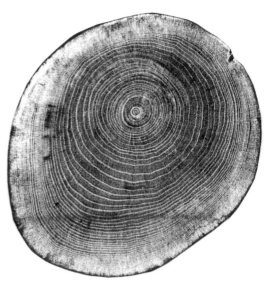

Cross-section through a 60 year old beech, showing the development of wide, oversize, annual rings during the first 25 years of its growth. The structure of the wood between such large annual rings exhibits a spongy texture, which is highly absorbent and leads to heart-rot.

Tree in the adjacent photograph has suffered a major attack of heart-rot, as evinced by the fungal growths (arrowed) on the trunk, which caused the fracture about half way up.

Fig. 18.5

According to Viktor Schauberger the actual movement of the sap is not through osmosis as is presently supposed:

On many occasions I have already stated that the rising of sap in trees cannot be explained by the physical factors hitherto put forward alone, such as the effect of the external air pressure, etc., but that its explanation is to be found in the on-going metabolic processes in constant pulsation in every cell of the tree and is therefore a result of the vital activity of the capillary tree-cell. Professor Kurt Bergel of Berlin came to similar conclusions in relation to the activity of the heart and the blood in animal life.[2]

Apart from the animating pulsation, the healthy movement of sap is also encouraged by the extreme fineness of the capillaries to be found in a completely naturally grown tree (fig. 18.6). The diameter of these capillaries is tiny. With slight warming the carbonic acid contained in the water and sap is converted into carbon-dioxide and forms bubbles, which completely close off the full bore of the capillary, and actually pump the water with the nutrients and the sap right up to the furthest extremities of the crown. These bubbles fill the capillaries like corks and, as they rise, push the intervening packets of water, sap, etc, ahead of them.

In this way the sap can be raised up the towering 91m (300ft) height of for example, a Tasmanian Mountain Ash, the tallest hardwood in the world. The upward movement of sap can neither be due to osmosis, whose absorbent raising action is limited, nor to mechanical suction alone, however, since it has long been established that a column of water cannot be drawn up higher than 9.81m (32.18ft).

The ascent of sap is a daytime process. The tree breathes out oxygen during the day through the process of photosynthesis, but at night the direction of movement reverses and it breathes in oxygen (like we do) in order to provide for the development of the root-system and the lignification of the trunk. When the Sun sets the temperature drops and the level of dynamic energy diminishes.

This initiates the retreat of the sap, which now becomes specifically denser through cooling and is drawn down in the direction of the sinking Sun and the root-zone. The sap ducts and capillaries in the crown are evacuated and a biological partial vacuum is created as the CO_2 gas-bubbles condense and begin to sink. Together with the sugars and starches formed during daytime photosynthesis, this suction draws down oxygen, nitrogen, sugars, starches, CO_2 and other trace-gases through the minute stomata and pores in the leaves and all the way down to the hair-roots. Here they nourish the life-functions of the tree during the night and provide the material for its structure-building activities, the formation of the annual rings and the lignification of the inner fabric of the tree as a whole. When the crown-zone and the trunk cool down, the root-zone warms up and vice versa. In this way the soil is kept warm during the night and in winter, and cooler during the day and in summer. As a result, excessive fluctuations in the ground temperature, which are detrimental to the microorganisms in the life-giving layer of humus, do not occur.

The same process applies to light-demanding timbers as long as the light is not

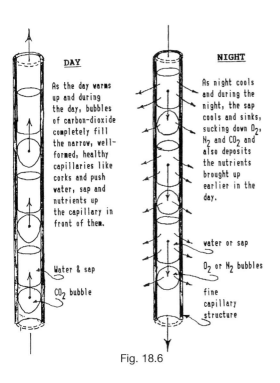

DAY

As the day warms up and during the day, bubbles of carbon-dioxide completely fill the narrow, well-formed, healthy capillaries like corks and push water, sap and nutrients up the capillary in front of them.

Water & sap

CO_2 bubble

NIGHT

As night cools and during the night, the sap cools and sinks, sucking down O_2, N_2 and CO_2 and also deposits the nutrients brought up earlier in the day.

water or sap

O_2 or N_2 bubbles

fine capillary structure

Fig. 18.6

excessive, because they have a protective mechanism in the form of very thick bark or, in some cases, a light-coloured bark with a high reflective factor.

Figs.18.7A and B show these activities in greater detail. The so-called 'cambium layer' could be viewed as a 'proto-annual-ring' and at the same time as a dielectric, as will be addressed later. This active zone is where the growth of the tree takes place through the interaction of two variously constituted and electrically charged fluids, i.e the negatively charged phloem containing oxygen, carbon-dioxide, nitrogen, etc, flows down the inner side of the dielectric, whereas the positively charged xylem, containing ionised minerals, salts, trace-elements, carbonic acid or CO_2, etc, flows up the outside. Between these two streams and through their interaction, the proto-annual-ring is transformed into a proper annual ring. These annual rings carry within them the imprint of the life-experience and history of the tree.

This whole process takes place in darkness under the protective cover of the bark so that, as far as possible, disturbances to this delicately balanced metabolism, through the excessive irradiation and increased temperature of direct sunlight, are avoided.

18.2 Temperature Gradients in the Tree

Here too temperature plays a major role. The active areas of growth in the outer peripheral zones of the trunk and branches require a certain warmth and level of energy to maintain the various formative elements in a productive, ionised and fluid state. All healthy processes of combination and re-combination taking place there, are wholly dependent on the orderly configuration and relative proportions of the temperature gradients.

With a positive temperature gradient from the outside inwards during the day as shown in fig. 18.7, C, the cooler more internal sap rises faster and carries the finest nutrients up to the top of the tree. This is for the highest quality growth, in the foliage, small green shoots, flowers and reproductive elements.

This upward flow can be as fast as 3m per hour, or 50mm per minute, as recorded by Viktor Schauberger. The lower quality, coarser nutrients present in the outermost layers of the cambium ring, which are required for the structural formation of the tree, can only be carried upward as far as their degree of coarseness permits, the coarser being deposited earlier in the formation of the trunk, the finer later in the branches. Both the graduation of quality and the height to which these elements are raised are dependent on temperature and the extent to which the negative temperature gradient, in its function as depositor or precipitator, is active from the outside inwards.

As the morning progresses the overall temperature of the atmosphere rises, causing the point of intersection between positive and negative temperature gradients within the tree to shift to deeper levels. The sap-flow begins to slow down and, according to their quality the various positively charged nutritive elements are held in near stationary suspension at various heights to await the arrival of the negatively charged elements from above. This may be why, for instance, the oxygen production in the Amazonian forest ceases towards midday. Due to the rapid development of high external temperatures during the morning, the positive nutrient-transporting temperature gradient soon gives way to a negative one. The uplift of elements for photosynthesis therefore ceases and with no photosynthesis, the evolution of oxygen no longer occurs.

As night falls, and with external cooling, the temperature gradient reverses and a positive temperature gradient arises from the inside outwards (left to right as shown in fig. 18.7, C), i.e. the outer layers become cooler than the inner. The sap begins to sink, the sap in the higher portions of the tree more quickly than in the lower because cooling in the crown takes place more rapidly. In the case of the Amazon above, the greater evaporation associated with the higher temperatures results in the accelerated cooling and densification of the sap, which then sinks after midday and does not reverse direction until the following day. In both instances the effect of this is to draw the oxygen and other

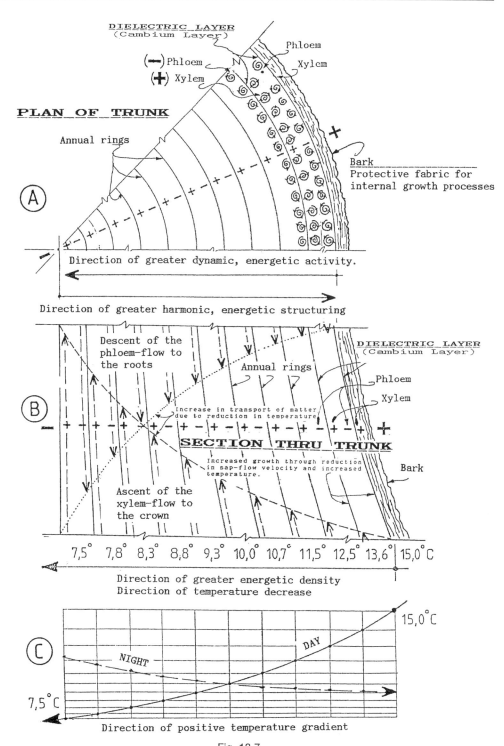

Fig. 18.7

gases and substances contained in the negatively-charged phloem down towards the root-zone. Oxygen, as the forcing agent in all growth and decay, is thus made available for the lower metabolism of the tree.

In its gradual descent the phloem encounters the suspended positively-charged material with which it interacts, an interaction which is enhanced as the positively charged xylem is drawn towards the exterior under the influence of the prevailing positive temperature gradient (fig. 18.7, A and B). This gives rise to various metabolic processes including the lignification of the trunk which, coupled with the densifying and consolidating effect of winter cold, by the end of the year leads to the hardening of the proto-annual-ring into annual ring proper. It is at night therefore that the girth of the tree increases and the root system develops.

The movement of the sap in a shade-demanding plantation tree, however, is markedly different. With the whole structure of the tree deformed by the necessity to grow more branches, the sap that would normally rise directly to the top is not only diverted into the unwanted branches, but its normally unimpeded flow is dislocated as it is forced to curl and twist around the extra knots in the trunk. This hindrance is further compounded by the fact that, expanded by excess heat, the sap ducts themselves are much larger in diameter and too large for the carbon-dioxide bubbles to fill them completely, as the size of the bubbles does not increase commensurately.

Instead of spiralling upwards virtually in a straight line within the duct, as in cylindrical trunks, the sap describes a larger helical path around the periphery of the enlarged duct and the CO_2 bubbles are only able to raise a fraction of the fluids required for healthy growth (fig. 18.8). They are no longer able to raise sufficient quantities to the crown of the tree and, because the nutrients themselves are of lower quality, having evolved through sub-normal or abnormal metabolic processes, naturally no high-quality wood can be produced and the life of the tree itself cannot be sustained for the usual span. This is what occurs with die-back. The sap is no longer

carried to the top of the tree or to the extremities of the branches and die-back sets in. The places where foliage still sprouts indicates the extent to which the sap can still rise.

The chief effect of this feebler movement of sap is the premature deposition of nutrients due to the unnaturally high internal temperatures. These are also responsible for the formation of inferior chemical compounds and are the cause of accretions that gradually block up the sap-ducts as shown in fig. 18.8. An analogous human condition is arteriosclerosis or varicose veins in the legs and feet, which happens for the same reason, namely faulty blood constitution and flow.

In the process of deposition these coarse materials increase the girth of the tree, the most inferior being deposited near the base of the trunk for, due to the higher temperatures, they cannot be carried any further up. The overall effect of this is the formation of a cone shaped trunk, which not only affects the quality of the wood but, recalling image *III* in

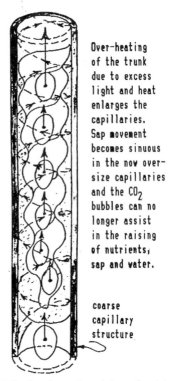

Over-heating of the trunk due to excess light and heat enlarges the capillaries. Sap movement becomes sinuous in the now over-size capillaries and the CO_2 bubbles can no longer assist in the raising of nutrients, sap and water.

coarse capillary structure

Fig. 18.8   **Inadequate raising of nutrients**

Viktor Schauberger's diagram in fig. 16.8, also distorts the pathways of the immaterial energies essential to the health of the tree and the atmosphere as a whole. Instead of strengthening the tree's vertical stance and spiralling up to great heights where they are further endowed with ethericities in the form of dynagens and qualigens, they are scattered unproductively to the four winds. With its levitational energies thus weakened, such a tree more easily falls victim to storms.

18.3 *The Tree as a Bio-condenser*

A full discussion of trees cannot merely entertain what is seen externally, but must incorporate the unseen energetic aspects which, as has been said before, are primary; the externally manifested form being the secondary effect. Having previously discussed the tree's biomagnetic force field, here we shall look at the way in which the tree's bio-electric energies are increasingly potentiated towards the tips of both branches and roots.

In the discussion of bio-condensers on p.89 (sec.6.2), it was shown that the charge density on one side of a dielectric membrane could be amplified by reducing the size of the charge-surface, while the potential could be increased simultaneously and exponentially by reducing the separation between opposite charges. It was also seen that, with concentric, spherical charge-surfaces, the charge-density and potential increased automatically. In the case of the tree, however, we are not concerned with concentric, spherical charge-surfaces, but with concentric, cylindrical ones, in which the same automatic increase in charge-density and potential applies. Proceeding from the outside inwards, both these magnitudes increase correspondingly (See figs. 6.8, 18.9 & 18.10).

While some growth occurs in the more central body, it is always at the ends of the new shoots of both root and branch alike that the most energetic growth occurs. As the tree grows higher, its overall diameter naturally decreases, which automatically reduces the distance between the annual rings. On reaching the top of the tree, they are extremely close together and the potential extremely high. Moreover the capillaries transporting the sap are almost infinitesimally small in diameter, so that the only substances that can pass through and along them are the very highest qualities of nutritive material and energies. This is because coarser matter, which goes towards building up the lower part of the tree, cannot pass through them. Therefore, around the periphery of the tree, not only are the very finest sap vessels to be found, but also the very highest quality of energy.

This harkens back to the previous discussion of homeopathic dosages where, with virtually non-existent material, a tremendous output or reaction can be effected. It is also the area of the tree which receives the highly energised drops of falling rainwater, which represent a direct and immediate transfer of pure energy and charge or life-force, which after all is all that energy really is. Thus it becomes clear why the most intense growth activity takes place at the extremities of the tree, both in the crown and in the root system, the former being an outward movement and the latter an inward one.

However, if these extremely sensitive, finely structured layers of densation and bio-condensers are pierced or disturbed by dissonances, excessive warming and other harmful factors, then the bio-condenser collapses, heart-rot and other diseases set in and the tree dies. In other words, the minute differences crucial to the life and continuing existence of the tree, through which life was able to emerge in the first place, have all been reduced to zero. There has been another biological short circuit.

This life-charge has actually been measured in experiments carried out by Walter Schauberger using a multiplex galvanometer and two insulated metal (zinc and copper) probes. One of the probes was inserted into the heartwood of the trunk, while the other was placed at the outer surface of the cambium layer. By the careful adjustment of the positions of their respective points, relatively high voltages were detected. Indeed Walter was able to obtain voltages sufficient to light

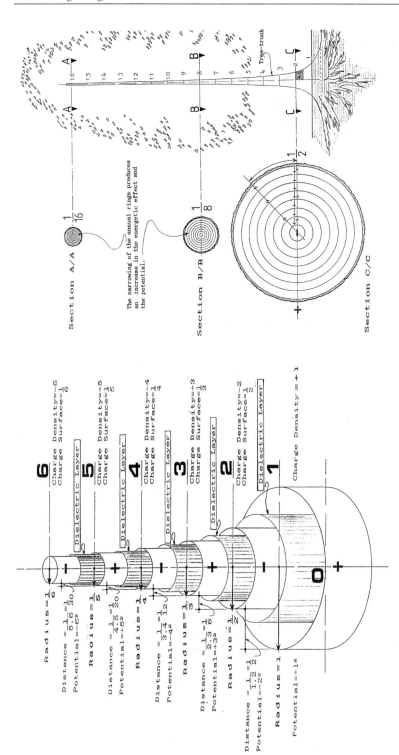

Section A/A

$\frac{1}{16}$

The narrowing of the annual rings produces an increase in the energetic effect and the potential.

Section B/B

$\frac{1}{8}$

Section C/C

Fig. 18.10 **Bio-condenser principle in relation to the tree**

layers of fatty material, which separate positive and negative bioelectric charges. In section C/C at the bottom of the trunk, the annual rings are spaced relatively widely apart and relative to its radius at ground level the trunk radius at this point = 1/2. In section B/B, however, the radius has been reduced to 1/8th, the annual rings commensurately closer together and both potential and charge-density correspondingly increased. At section A/A, the radius is now only 1/16th and the magnitude of the potential and charge-density begins to reach enormous proportions, for the narrower the ring-spacing, the greater the potential and the greater the amount of available energy waiting to be unleashed.

6 — Charge Density = −6
Charge Surface = $\frac{1}{6}$

Dielectric Layer

Radius = $\frac{1}{6}$

Distance = $\frac{1}{5.6} = \frac{1}{30}$
Potential = −6²

5 — Charge Density = +5
Charge Surface = $\frac{1}{5}$

Dielectric Layer

Radius = $\frac{1}{5}$

Distance = $\frac{1}{4.5} = \frac{1}{20}$
Potential = +5²

4 — Charge Density = −4
Charge Surface = $\frac{1}{4}$

Dielectric Layer

Radius = $\frac{1}{4}$

Distance = $\frac{1}{3.4} = \frac{1}{12}$
Potential = −4²

3 — Charge Density = +3
Charge Surface = $\frac{1}{3}$

Dielectric Layer

Radius = $\frac{1}{3}$

Distance = $\frac{1}{2.3} = \frac{1}{6}$
Potential = +3²

2 — Charge Density = −2
Charge Surface = $\frac{1}{2}$

Dielectric Layer

Radius = $\frac{1}{2}$

Distance = $\frac{1}{1.2} = \frac{1}{2}$
Potential = −2²

1 — Charge Density = +1

Dielectric Layer

Radius = 1

Potential = +1²

0

Fig. 18.9 **Hyperbolic bio-condenser principle**

The tree as a bio-condenser with a series of concentric, cylindrical, charge-carrying plates separated by cylindrical dielectrics is illustrated in fig. 18.9, the latter being indicated with vertical hatching. Elaborating this, fig. 18.10 shows enlargements of three cross-sections – A/A, B/B and C/C – through the trunk of the tree on the right hand side of the diagram and depicts the disposition of the annual rings, shown here oversized for ease of understanding. These could be construed as the dielectric layers separating the positively charged xylem, (the ascending, nutrient-rich fluid) and the negatively charged phloem (the descending, gas-rich fluid).

As in all cell structures the dielectric layers themselves are formed of very thin

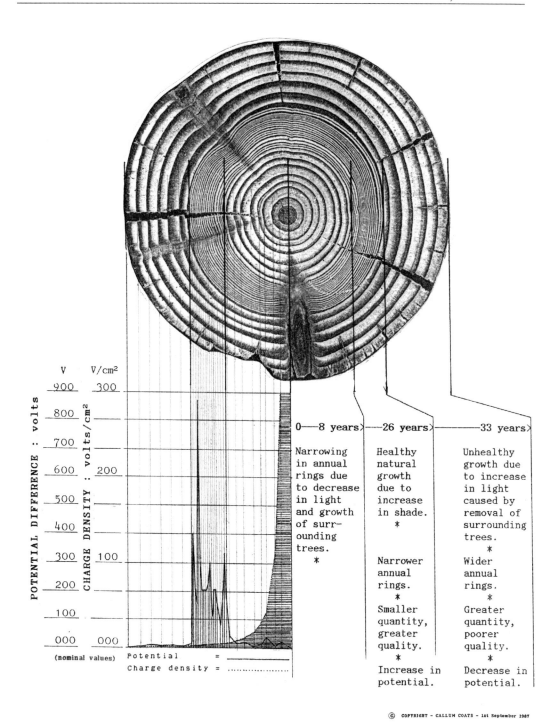

Fig. 18.11   **Bio-condenser effect in relation to a 33 year old tree under various conditions of growth**

a small torch or flashlight bulb. The brighter the light, the healthier and more naturally had the tree grown.

Fig. 18.11 shows that, if the potential (which increases in an inward direction) is measured across the annual rings from the outside inwards, at first it is relatively low, due to the wide spacing. But, as the rings gradually draw closer together, the potential and the energy increase. Creative energy is always a structuring process and the narrower the rings are together, the the more resonant they become; the higher the quality of the structure and the quality of the characteristics of the timber. Once the more widely spaced, central rings are reached, the potential suddenly drops away almost to zero. The charge-density, on the other hand, continually increases towards the interior, although not uniformly, due to the irregular structure of the trunk.

18.4 Root Systems

Every tree, plant or blade of grass is an energy pathway which exchanges, mediates and transforms the negatively-charged energies of the Earth (the Earth is essentially a receptive, female system) and the positively charged energies of the atmosphere and the Sun (a radiating, male system) as each penetrates the crown and root systems, from which the energies flowing upwards and downwards are approximately the same order of magnitude, but with opposite polarities. The zone of the crown is the energetic potentiation of the substance of the root-zone, and vice versa.

Potentiation means; ascent into higher frequencies, energetic functions and activity; the realisation of the invisible idea of the thing itself and the creation of the form of an individuality, an individual system, in this case a tree. Were this not so, then there would be neither growth towards the heavens, nor towards the centre of the Earth. In trees and other vegetation this growth first takes place downwards towards the roots and corresponds to the first independent action, the first inhaled breath as it were which, after the birth of a human being is also the first vital act, namely

a going within, a movement into the unseen. In this development, contrary to the age-old maxim 'As above, so below', we shall see that '*As above*' is actually **not** '*So below*'.

Here as everywhere it is the invisible that carries the visible. In the realm of mathematics, the intangible, indefinable, infinite series of irrational square-root numbers, which cannot be divided into 'rations', are those numbers, the so-called 'real' numbers, that can only be raised to rational whole numbers if they are potentiated, i.e. if they are multiplied by 'themselves'. With the tree the same mathematical game is played (fig. 18.12), because the invisible foundation must first be developed to enable the later visible manifestation to take place. Without the invisible, inner root-zone there would be no

Fig. 18.13

Fig. 18.14

Fig. 18.15   **For caption see p.251**

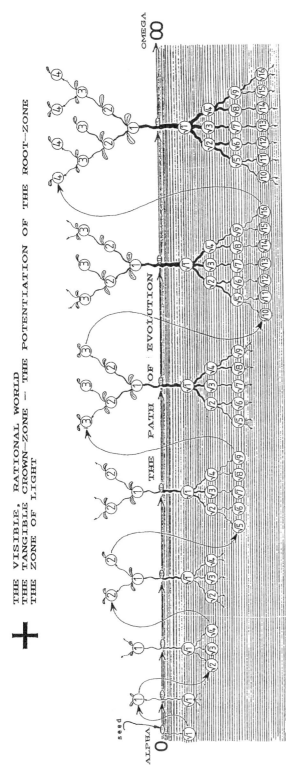

THE VISIBLE, RATIONAL WORLD
THE TANGIBLE CROWN–ZONE – THE POTENTIATION OF THE ROOT–ZONE
THE ZONE OF LIGHT

THE PATH OF EVOLUTION

Fig. 18.12

THE INVISIBLE, IRRATIONAL WORLD
THE INTANGIBLE ROOT–ZONE – THE FOUNDATION OF THE CROWN–ZONE
THE ZONE OF DARKNESS

Fig. 18.12 depicts this fluctuating, pulsating action. Starting at the left-hand side, when a seed is fertilised (a seed is the encapsulation of the DNA program for the growth of a future system), its first act of growth is downwards, or more accurately, inwards, as the 1st root – √1 – seeks to establish itself. Once this has been done and a solid basis for a movement in the opposite direction has been achieved, only then can the plant, be it a tree, a blade of grass, etc, begin to raise itself into the visible world. The square root of 1 is potentiated, out of which is born the whole number 1 – the stem, the first appearance of an individual system.

Once this first stage has been completed, then the further 3-fold series of roots – √2 —> √3 —> √4 – are developed until the foundation for the next visible stage of formation is achieved in the attainment of √4, which gives rise to the emergence of the whole number 2 (second stage of growth). With the completion of this second stage, then the creative energy moves once more into the unseen realm of the root-zone and proceeds upwards through the 5-fold series of square-roots – √5 —> √6 —> √7 —> √8 —> √9, which culminates in the outward manifestation of √9 in the whole number 3. The result of this latest invisible development is the unfoldment of

the magnitude 3 in the real world. From perusal of fig. 18.12 and the later fig. 18.16 it therefore becomes quite evident that the 'above' is not the mirror-image of the 'below'.

The series of images in figs. 18.13, 18.14 and 18.15 also appear to reflect this mathematical progression. In fig. 18.13 a seed was placed on a small piece of cotton wool floating on water enclosed between two sheets of glass at the interface between the light world of the seen and the lower dark world of the unseen. During the period between photographs a black card was placed over the latter zone and no light was able to enter laterally. When removed periodically for inspection, it was observed that the seed's first root – √1 – grew downwards into the water, into the unseen, to be followed later by the potentiation of √1 as the first sprouting appearing above it in the zone of light. As shown in fig. 18.14, this process continued to unfold according to the mathematical sequence in fig. 18.12, wherein the second sprouting into the world of the seen, marked with the number 2, only appeared after the lower 4th root – √4 – had grown. The experiment was finally abandoned when growth had reached the stage shown in fig. 18.15, after the development of the 9th root segment – √9 – and its corresponding third stage of growth marked with the number 3.

basis for the visible external aspect of the tree.

As we hardly ever see them, what do we really know about roots apart from the fact that they hold plants up? In fact there is the widest possible variety of root forms and systems, and their proper distribution is of vital importance to the whole process of tree growth, because each species of tree has a different pattern of root development according to the function it performs and the energies associated with it.

In the case of trees, these can be roughly categorised as flat-rooted, heart-rooted, taprooted and deep-rooted trees, the last evaporating more water than heart-rooted trees and flat-rooted trees evaporating least of all. Each plant species, therefore, has its own particular root structure, which penetrates and withdraws the elements it needs from particular horizons in the soil. Although not those of trees, the root systems of various plants shown in figs.18.16 (a)–(i) give some idea of this enormous complexity. These have been taken from the plethora of diagrams contained in two magnificent root atlases, exhaustively researched and painstakingly prepared in Germany by L. Kutschera and E. Lichtenegger[3].

When life first began on this planet, both soil and climatic conditions were probably very harsh. No high quality vegetation or life was possible, partly due to the strength of the winds blowing over virtually barren surfaces; and partly because the poor composition of the available soil, drenched and washed out by deluging rains, was unable to sustain them, for without humus there is very little micro-organic activity. Only the hardiest plants feeding on the salts and the coarse, unmodified minerals of almost bare rock were able to evolve and, little by little, they began to change the soil environment, thereby creating the preconditions for higher forms of plant to develop.

In this process, the most primitive plants, such as mosses or grasses, first take root at the surface of the ground at (a) in fig. 18.16. They can only extend their roots for a certain, relatively shallow distance below the surface, making use of the low-grade salts and nutrients available at this level for their growth.

These pioneer plants, however, not only trap the nutritive dust particles carried by the wind, but also have a cooling effect on the ground, thereby enabling the first beginnings of useful soil moisture to accumulate.

As they spread further over the ground, shading it from the Sun, the deeper ground strata where the higher grade elements reside, also begin to cool off. As a result, even though infinitesimally, the water table rises under this thin plant cover, lifting the whole body of minerals and trace-elements lying above the groundwater table and pushing slightly better quality salts and minerals towards the surface. With a richer mineral base to draw on, it is then possible for a higher form of plant to begin to grow such as that shown at (b).

As this higher plant form requires better sustenance, its root system descends further in search of it. In the process it draws its nourishment from a different horizon, so there is no competition between it and the pioneer plant at (a). Ultimately, through the progressive improvement of the soil and the coming into being of the more evolved plant systems depicted in (c) through to (i), which hold the soil together and provide the necessary protection for the slow build-up of humus, even higher species of vegetation can take root. Now provided with a more even climate within the growing humus layer, micro-organisms gradually proliferate and begin the task of breaking down the coarse minerals into finer and finer particles, thereby increasing the richness and fertility of the soil which, in the process becomes too rich for the pioneer plants, and they die off.

As some of this newer vegetation is very deep-rooted, yet higher quality elements are brought up from the depths and made available, further increasing the nutritive base for the later evolution of higher-grade plants. Hardy bushes and small light-demanding trees then take root and begin to tame the winds, creating areas of shelter for larger and more varied species of timber until finally the high primeval forest with its myriad root-systems is established in all its glory. Each root-system is inextricably connected with the others in a vast complexity that surpasses

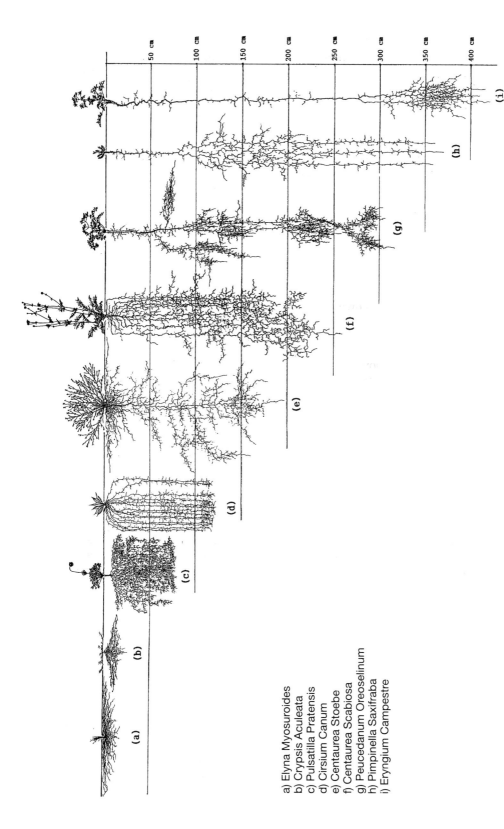

a) Elyna Myosuroides
b) Crypsis Aculeata
c) Pulsatilla Pratensis
d) Cirsium Canum
e) Centaurea Stoebe
f) Centaurea Scabiosa
g) Peucedanum Oreoselinum
h) Pimpinella Saxifraba
i) Eryngium Campestre

Fig. 18.16 **Various root systems**

even the legendary Gordian Knot. Each system, however, has is special part to play in this majestic orchestration of Nature and draws its vital substances from the soil horizons peculiar to its species, sometimes enhancing or providing for the growth of another variety of plant, but increasing all the while the overall amount of water and water-retentive humus in the soil.

Monoculture, however, does not exist in Nature. It is not a form of plant organisation to which Nature subscribes and it will always bring disaster in its wake. In monocultures, all this marvellous, harmonious interdependence comes to a screeching halt, because all the trees have the same root system and obtain all their nutrients from the same horizon in the soil. If one variety of tree or one species of plant is removed from a natural forest, then suddenly, within the midst of all this interdependency, a hole is created in the matrix of roots.

Suddenly a vital link has fallen out of the interconnecting chain between the depths and the surface, leading to a reduction in the capacity of some plants to raise water and minerals for the benefit of others. The store of available nutrients in a given soil horizon, which can now no longer be replaced, begins to diminish as the plants compete for them. Once this nutritive material has been exhausted, then those plants dependent on them die out. Further holes are created in the underground water reticulation system and, as a result even more species of plant succumb.

An appalling acceleration in the devastation of the former high forest ensues, which eventually drags everything, plants, birds, animals and ultimately humans in its wake. The former rich biodiversity of the forest has been destroyed and sterile uniformity prevails. No differentiation, no variation exists and life is reduced to its lowest possible level.

As we know, life can only be created through differences in form and potential. Therefore to restore all that once was to its former burgeoning glory, it will be necessary to start again laboriously, step by step, almost from the very beginning to recreate all that we have so foolishly destroyed.

This is not something that can happen overnight, but will require the cooperative effort of many generations to come and the universal use of all new and existing ecologically-harmonious methods of increasing soil fertility. Moreover the wholesale redefining of all current forestry and agricultural practices and laws directed towards short term gain, indeed of the whole of so-called economics, will have to be instituted immediately. There is now very little time left before the seesaw up which we are struggling and which we mistake for the long-waited economic recovery, will suddenly tip over and hurl us on an unstoppable downward path to oblivion, for the point of no return will then have been reached.

In our arrogance and pursuit of material growth we fail to see that, apart from the gift of water, green photosynthesis and the production of chlorophyll are the very foundation of our existence, without which there is no economy and no future at all, neither short, nor long term. If present methods and priorities continue unabated then what we face is extinction. Unfortunately those responsible for this horrific state of affairs, comfortably off, removed from the rigours of life and secure in their tenures and pensions, will mostly die in their beds, while those whose lives and futures they have ruined are left behind to suffer the most terrible privation. It is time therefore that we call them to account, that we get up and throw them out as Jesus did the money lenders in the Temple, if we wish to survive.

Notes

1. "The Forest and its Significance" ("Der Wald und seine Bedeutung"), by Viktor Schauberger: *Tau* mag, Vol.146, p.1, 1936.
2. *Our Senseless Toil*, Pt.II, p.34.

3. Diagrams from *Wurzelatlas; mitteleuropaischer Grunlandpflanzen*, Vol.1, "Monocotyledoneae" 1982, and Vol.2, "Pteridophyta und Dicotyledoneae", 1992 by L.Kutschera & E.Lichtenegger: G.Fischer, Stuttgart, Germany.

19

AGRICULTURE AND SOIL FERTILITY

Our primeval Mother Earth is an organism that no science in the world can rationalise. Everything on her that crawls and flies is dependent upon her and all must hopelessly perish if that Earth dies that feeds us.[1]

Viktor Schauberger

19.1 The Golden Plough

While in Bulgaria to construct a log-flume in the 1930s, Viktor Schauberger was also asked by King Boris to investigate why soil productivity and soil moisture, particularly in the northern parts of the country, had begun to decline since the introduction of modern mechanised farming methods. Touring the country to examine the problem in more detail, he found that in the north the fields were ploughed with tractor-drawn steel ploughs, whereas in the poorer south, populated largely by communities of Turkish origin, the fields were still tilled with wooden ploughs pulled in the main by teams of women. Here, however, in stark contrast with the north, the fields were still extremely fertile and produced abundantly healthy crops. From his study of water as a carrier of nutrients and aware of the generally detrimental effect of steel or iron on the quality of water, Viktor attributed the northern drop in soil fertility to the use of faster moving steel ploughs.

Using this as the starting point, Viktor began his postwar agricultural research in collaboration with Franz Rosenberger, an engineer, and began a series of experiments designed to increase soil fertility. But before going further, as with temperature, here we have to differentiate between two types of electromagnetism.

Type A: Comprises bio-magnetism and bio-electricity, the former more commonly referred to as diamagnetism. It is the form of electro-magnetism that energises and animates all living organisms. Diamagnetic elements are copper, bismuth and hydrogen.

Type B: Comprises ferro-magnetism, usually just called magnetism, and electricity, which here we shall refer to as ferro-electricity to give both terms a common root. This type of electro-magnetism is the one commonly in use in our technical world in electric motors and dynamos for the generation of electricity. Ferro-magnetic elements are iron, cobalt and nickel.

In Viktor's view the use of steel ploughs had many detrimental effects on the soil. As the steel ploughshares are drawn rapidly through the soil, minute ferro-electric and ferro-magnetic currents are generated in the interaction of hard steel against soil which decompose the nutrient-laden water molecules in the ground in a manner analogous to electrolysis, thereby discharging the soil's potential and reducing the surface-tension of the water molecule. This not only destroys the soil's subtler energies, but converts the nutritive elements or removes them from the mature water molecule. This was demonstrated in the discussion of the true facts of electrolysis in chapter 8, in which the end product of the process is pure juvenile water, which, as we have seen, is of little benefit to any organism.

In addition, small particles of steel are abraded from the shear-surfaces of the ploughshare, covering the ground with a thin film of rust. As we saw mentioned in the chapter on water supply with steel pipes, this provides an ideal breeding ground for the propagation of pathogenic bacteria, harmful to both soil and crops. This extra deposition of iron also increases the overall iron content of the ground and it is a known fact that soils high in iron are less water-retentive than soils where iron is not present, whereas soils high in copper have the capacity to retain greater quantities of water.

Furthermore, as they move, the ploughshares produce considerable warming friction and soil-crushing pressure-waves in the ground, due to the relatively steep angle of the share. This destroys the delicate soil capillaries responsible for the delivery of nutrients and water to the surface as well as some of the micro-organisms that process them, thereby cutting off the normal supply from below and, in consequence, soil fertility drops markedly. The application of fertiliser, natural and artificial, and other factors for the moment apart, the overall action of iron or steel ploughs is therefore extremely destructive of the natural balance of energies and potencies, to say nothing of soil moisture, and is yet another serious aberration in humanity's treatment of Nature, for as Viktor laments:

*Wherever we look, the dreadful disintegration of the bridges of life, the capillaries and the bodies they have created, is evident, which has been caused by the mechanical and mindless work of Man, who has torn away the soul from the Earth's blood – **water**.*[2]

To counter this insidious effect, which was having disastrous consequences for production of high quality food as well as productivity in general, Viktor started to experiment with copper, initially making use of a standard steel ploughshare overlaid with a sheet of thick copper as shown in figs.19.1 & 19.2 for which patents were later applied and which came to be known as the 'Golden Plough' because of the remarkable results it achieved. The use of copper replaced the destructive ferro-electromagnetic effects with

beneficial bio-electromagnetic ones which through processes of bio-electromagnetic ionisation enhanced growth and soil fertility.

This boost to soil fertility was decisively confirmed in field trials carried out in the vicinity of Salzburg in 1948 and 1949. Here fields were ploughed in strips, using steel and copper-plated ploughs alternately. The difference between the two types of plough and their effect became quite apparent. Where the copper-plated plough had been used, i.e. where there were no rust residues and where the water content and other energies of the soil had been increased, the corn stood about 6–8 inches higher with a much fuller head. Some yields in the strips ploughed with copper-plated implements increased by up to 40% in comparison with the control strips where conventional steel ploughs were used. This remarkable increase could only be attributed to the use of copper in lieu of steel, because all other factors of soil chemistry, orientation, furrow width, etc., were identical.

In one experiment, extraordinarily large ears of rye were grown carrying up to 104 grains each; a truly stupendous production, as is shown in fig. 19.3. In another parallel experiment at Kitzbühel in the Tyrol high quality, well-formed potatoes were produced weighing up to 430 grams, nearly half a kilo, containing as many as 20 'eyes', those portions of the potato that can be cut off and planted separately from which to grow the next crop (fig. 19.4). With such potatoes more food would be made available, not only on account of their larger size, but also because of the greater number of 'eyes', and fewer potatoes would be required for replanting.

Further research work was carried out which, in 1948, resulted in the development of the 'Bio-Plough' shown in figs.19.5 & 19.6; the model in fig. 19.5 was produced by a Hamburg engineer, Jurgen Sauck. The form and function of this plough is completely different to that in fig. 19.1. To reduce the damage to the soil capillaries to a minimum, instead of the pressure-wave forming and shearing crush-cut of the conventional ploughshare, here the blade is designed so as to create a long slicing cut before the soil is involuted through the centripetal action of the curving swan-like

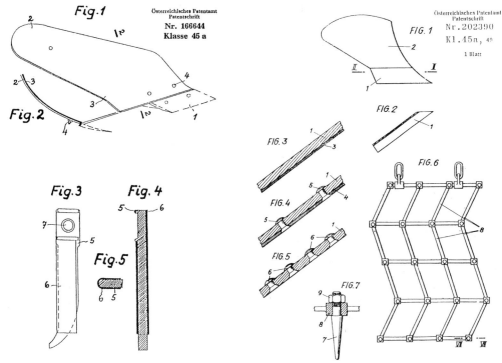

Fig 19.1 & 2 **Patent applications for steel ploughshare overlaid with thick copper**

wings of the ploughshare itself, emulating the burrowing action of the mole.

Furthermore, instead of presenting a steeply inclined barrier to the soil, this plough presented sharp cutting edges only, the soil gliding through between the curved foils and gently rotated left and right, or right and left as the case may be, in the figure-of-eight movement indicated by the arrowed, broken lines in fig. 19.6. The ploughshare itself is made of phosphor-bronze which is nearly as hard as steel and therefore almost as durable. In any event, the vastly increasing productivity arising from its use would well outweigh the costs of its eventual replacement. As a result of these experiments it was clearly established that the soil should never under any circumstances, be worked with naked iron or steel, but only with implements made of wood, copper or copper alloys.

Despite the obvious and proven benefits to the nation that would accrue from the use of this plough, it never went into production for, owing to the success of his Salzburg field trials, Viktor Schauberger once again came up against the corruption of politicians and the concerted opposition of entrenched interests. During the period immediately after the war copper was was a scarce commodity in Austria and, having been unsuccessful in obtaining further supplies through normal channels, Viktor approached the Ministry of Agriculture. There he was told by the Minister that more copper sheet would only be made available to him if he compensated the Minister financially for the losses he would suffer if he supported Viktor, because at that time the Minister was receiving large bribes from various manufacturers of artificial fertiliser to promote the use of their products. True to his upright nature, Viktor categorically refused, saying that he did not traffic with criminals. As a result all copper, particularly in sheet form, was denied to him and this whole area of research and development, potentially so beneficial to agriculture everywhere, came to an abrupt end.

Fig. 19.3   **15cm long ears of rye with up to 104 grains/ear**

Fig. 19.4   **Potatoes grown on alpine farm at Kitzbühel, Tyrol.**

Before moving on, another form of plough also needs to be examined. In an article by Kurt Lorek in *Implosion*[3] he discusses the plough shown in fig. 19.7, which was designed, built and experimented with in the vicinity of Munich at about the same time as Viktor's trials in Salzburg. It is not known, however, whether Viktor Schauberger collaborated with its designer but, as it used similar copper alloys in its construction it seems likely he did, since Munich and Salzburg are just over 100km apart.

According to Kurt Lorek, this plough produced equally astounding increases in productivity. The rotation of its 4 or 5 copper or copper-alloyed spiral blades was directly geared to the forward movement of the tractor, thereby slicing rather than ripping the sod as well as giving a slight impetus to forward motion. As can be seen from the diagram, the ground was also sprayed with water or liquid manure. This was to moisten the soil during ploughing operations in order to offset the additional evaporative losses caused by conventional ploughing, as well as providing for simultaneous fertilisation. All trace of this plough has since been lost but, in view of its apparent efficacy, its design is certainly worthy of resurrection.

19.2 Sun Ploughing

Always paying attention to the apparently insignificant, in his investigation of the drop in soil fertility in Bulgaria, Viktor Schauberger also noticed that, whereas the fields in the north were harrowed, those of the Turkish

communities were not, the people either being too poor to afford them or the women too weak to drag a harrow over the rough tillage. What he noted in particular, however, was that after ploughing had been completed, there were no straight, even furrows but, due to the single wooden tine, which was all the women had strength enough to pull through the ground, the furrows were not only rough and irregular, but also composed of very large clods that flopped over in different directions. Everything was higgledy-piggledy, yet out of this disorder the most marvellous, healthy crops were produced. Apart from the use of wood instead of steel, here was another factor that contributed to the evident fertility.

The irregularity of the furrows and the oversize clods gave rise to an even distribution of sunlight as the sun passed across the heavens. Very little of the soil, therefore, was constantly exposed to the drying and heating effect of

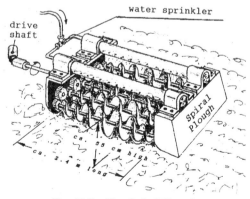

Fig. 19.7   **The Spiral Plough**

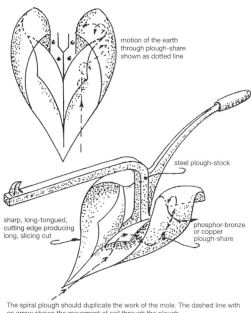

motion of the earth through plough-share shown as dotted line

steel plough-stock

sharp, long-tongued, cutting edge producing long, slicing cut

phosphor-bronze or copper plough-share

The spiral plough should duplicate the work of the mole. The dashed line with an arrow shows the movement of soil through the plough.

Fig. 19.5 & 6   **"The Bio-Plough", 1948**

direct sunlight, the clods and the convoluted furrows providing changing patterns of shade. In consequence far less soil became desiccated and the young sprouts thrived in the additional soil moisture and were protected for a great part of the day from overheating.

With harrowing, however, the clods are reduced to relatively small particles, which understandably not only dry out much more quickly, but the depth to which soil moisture is reduced is much greater. All this makes the germination of seed far more difficult as well as facilitating erosion, because the smaller particles can be washed away more easily. The solution to this problem lies not only in the method of ploughing, but in the overall orientation of the furrows.

Instead of ploughing in straight lines in any direction, the furrows should be sinuous, curving first one way and then the other, and oriented as far as possible in a north-south direction. Fig. 19.8 shows that no surface is thus exposed to uninterrupted solar radiation because of the ridging of the furrows and their curvilinear configuration. Similarly, the young shoots of the new crop receive a more

even exposure to direct light, each portion of the plant enjoying both light and shade as the day progresses. As a result, soil moisture is enhanced and the flow of sap is disturbed as little as possible.

19.3 Of Cows and Scythes

There is another aspect related to cows and the maintenance of fertility worthy of note here. In Austria and other mountainous countries, where cattle are driven to the uplands to graze during the summer months, until the introduction of artificial fertiliser and mechanised reaping the carrying capacity of these alpine pastures was virtually unlimited, due to the way they were cut with a scythe and how cattle actually graze. When a cow grazes it crops the tufts of grass in a special way. Viktor Schauberger carefully observed the movements of the cow's tongue and noticed that it gathered the grass-haulms together with a spiral enclosing sweep, finally separating them from the tuft in a clean break with a jerk of its head precisely at the point where

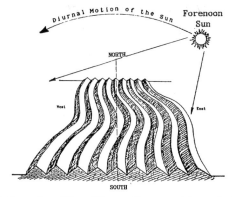

1. No portion of the soil has continuous, uninterrrupted exposure of direct sunlight.

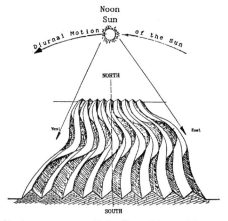

2. Shadow areas vary with the time of day and the seasonal height of the sun.

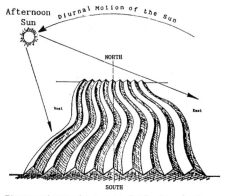

3. Plants and crops have even distribution of solar radiation.

Fig. 19.8   **Advantages of Sun Ploughing**

the haulm suffered the least damage. Having done so, with its soft muzzle and saliva, the cow then nuzzled the open wounds on the haulm, thereby sealing them and preventing any loss of moisture and energy.

With adequate winter fodder always a concern for these peasant farmers, while the cattle grazed they also harvested as much grass as the season permitted, sometimes cutting the grass three times before winter fell. Because of the steepness of the alpine slopes, the implement they used for this was the scythe which, for them, was a highly prized and very personal instrument, entrusting its use only to those they knew would look after it properly.

Looking after a scythe properly entails sharpening it not with a sharpening stone but by hammering the blade on a block of hardwood (fig. 19.9) which, as a non-conducting material, safeguards the accumulation and storage of the resultant energetic charge. To ensure that it does not leak subsequently the scythe-blade, which is mounted on an equally non-conducting wooden handle, is then wrapped in cloth and stored in the dark away from the heating effect of the Sun which would otherwise discharge it. This sharpening process, however, was always undertaken towards late afternoon or in the early morning immediately prior to harvesting, which was also done at these times to prevent the de-energising light of the Sun from striking the scythe blade. When the pastures were scythed in the growing darkness of the long summer evenings, it was possible to observe these accumulated energies in the form of minute glowing sparks, which leapt from one serration on the blade to another.

Most conventional mowers cut with an inclined blade against a sharp edge and, while this does cut the grass, it is a process akin to the action of the standard ploughshare mentioned earlier. In other words, it is a crushing ripping cut which damages the capillaries in the grass-haulm and shreds the top of the haulm for several millimetres. This exposes a large surface area to unwelcome bacterial activity and germs, as well as allowing the grass to bleed. As a result, instead of applying its energies immediately to new growth, the grass-haulm first has to heal the wound which in this case may take several days. The scythe, on the other hand, delivers a long, slicing cut, thereby keeping the wound-area to a minimum. Due to the energies inhering in the blade and implanted there by hammer-sharpening, the imparted ionisation quickly draws the elements in the material surrounding the wound together and rapidly seals it.

Fig 19.9   Scythe-hammering

It is clear that the centuries-long maintenance of fertility and productivity on these high alpine pastures was due to the combined effects of the correct use of the proper implement at the right time of day and the natural cropping of the grass by the cattle. This alone should give us cause to reassess presents methods of harvesting green fodder and the times of day when it should be cut. It may well be that a suitable mechanical reaper blade should take the form of the spiral blades of the plough shown in fig. 19.7, but the cutting spiral edges should be more closely spaced and mounted at right-angles to the direction of movement. The spiral blades themselves could likewise be made of phosphor-bronze, rotating forwards from the ground upwards so as to slice the grass as cleanly as possible.

Today, however, no account is taken of all these subtle effects and, despite massive artificial-fertiliser-induced overproduction in some countries, soil fertility and productivity are actually on a steep downward path, although at the moment we are not aware just how steep it is.

19.4 The Pernicious Effects of Artificial Fertilisers

Contemporary agriculture treats Mother-Earth like a whore and rapes her. All year round it scrapes away her skin and poisons it with artificial fertiliser, for which a science is to be thanked that has lost all connection with Nature.[4]

Viktor Schauberger

In the latter part of the 19th century, apart from his other achievements, Baron Justus von Liebig (1803–1873), a German chemist, carried out a great deal of research into the elements and chemicals required by plants for growth, no doubt in the sincere desire to rectify soil deficiencies and increase fertility. As in so many areas of science, however, analysis rather than synthesis is uppermost, the aim always to find the one factor responsible for a given phenomenon, whereas in reality all physical manifestation is the result of many synergetic influences. In the event, Liebig determined that the principal ingredients for soil fertility besides calcium (Ca) in the form of lime, were nitrogen (N), phosphorus (P) and potassium (K), frequently referred to today as NPK.

Nitrogen is supplied in the form of urea (CO[NH$_2$]$_2$); ammonium sulphate ([NH$_4$]$_2$SO$_4$) – a by-product of coal-gas production; nitrates, which are salts or esters of nitric acid (HNO$_3$); calcium cyanamide (CaCN$_2$), which is converted into ammonia by water and produced by heating calcium carbide (CaC$_2$) at a temperature of 1,000°C in nitrogen gas. CaC$_2$ on the other hand is produced by heating calcium oxide (CaO – quicklime) which in turn is made by heating calcium carbonate (CaCO$_3$), a substance occurring naturally in the form of limestone, chalk, calcite and marble.

Potassium (K) comes *inter alia* in the form of potassium chloride (KCl), potassium sulphate (K$_2$SO$_4$) and disodium hydrogen orthophosphate (Na$_2$HPO).

Phosphorus is obtained by heating calcium phosphate with coke and silica in an electric furnace and is introduced into the soil in other compounds such as phosphate (H$_3$PO$_4$), calcium phosphate as calcium hydrogen orthophosphate, better known as superphosphate (Ca[H$_2$PO$_4$]^{2}H$_2$O).

All of these products are soluble and the majority of them, sometimes in the form of slag, are manufactured from and as by-products of what Viktor Schauberger called 'fire-spitting technology'. In other words, they are produced with structure-disintegrating and energy-depleting heat. In their final preparation they are either made into solutions for sprayed application to the soil or thoroughly ground into fine deliquescent powders, their deliquescent properties enabling them to attract moisture from the air or the soil in order to liquify.

As another means of turning waste material to profit, these compounds were quickly seized upon by various chemical and other manufacturers. Despite Liebig's later recognition and admission that the elements required for healthy growth were far more complex than simple NPK and that further detailed analysis was vital lest irredeemable damage be done to the soil, his words went unheeded and the production of artificial fertilisers proceeded apace. With their use, the height of cereals and health of crops generally quickly diminished, each succeeding application further depleting the fundamental fertility of the soil as its organic base was gradually eroded. Applied as part of a highly mechanised farming system using steel implements, large tracts of mid-western America were reduced to dustbowls as a result, forcing the impoverished farmers to leave their land.

Today the use of artificial fertilisers continues unabated, but slowly and surely and just as inevitably they will finally reduce the soil to a lifeless mass. Naturally, the manufacturers of artificial fertiliser will point to the enormous production that has been achieved with its use, but this has been a production of quantity at the expense of continually decreasing quality, of profit at the expense of life. Artificial fertilisers act like stimulants and prop up production like narcotics to which the soil has unwillingly become addicted. Like drug addicts, who can neither function nor survive without frequent injections and who, as their physical condition worsens, require more and more shots to extend their lives a little further, the soil too is dying.

All the vital capillaries, which supply naturally derived nutrients, mature water and conduct rising immaterial energies, are being blocked up by these fine powders. The stultifying effects of the latter substances de-energise the soil and, at the same time, rob both the lower ground-strata and the young plants of moisture, for in their deliquescent state these chemicals use this moisture to become liquid. With insufficient moisture, transpiration is reduced and the plants' internal temperatures rise with the same unwelcome results as we saw in shade-demanding timbers exposed to sunlight.

The capillaries now choked, it becomes more difficult for rain to infiltrate. This in turn gives rise to more rapid runoff, quickly followed by faster re-evaporation, both of which make irrigation a necessity. Such irrigation, however, is carried out with virtually worthless water as mentioned in earlier chapters, and the produce grown under such conditions, while large and apparently healthy, is almost tasteless, their colour often as artificial as rouge.

Moreover, if excess nitrogen is introduced in any of the above compounds, it makes less ionised material available for root development, leading to further water starvation of the affected plant, because the negatively charged ions, the *anions⁻*, in the nitrates in artificial fertilisers take *cations⁺*, the positively charged ions of other elements, downwards away from the root zone, thereby robbing the trees and plants of positive cations⁺ such as magnesium and calcium ions. It is important to remember that the magnesium atom is the core atom in the chlorophyll molecule.

Nature quickly despatches the 'Health Police' in the form of parasites and other blights to remove the organisms which have now become diseased, necessitating the use and overuse of pesticides and fungicides. Once the crop thus treated has been harvested, apart from passing on the pesticides to the consumer, it then becomes necessary to fumigate the ground in order to eradicate these supposedly pernicious pests, which are none other than sure indicators of the ill health of both plants and soil. Areas of ground are sheeted with plastic and probes inserted into the ground to infuse it with poisonous gases.

Everything dies – earthworms, micro-organisms and beneficial bacteria alike. Life with all its differences is completely eliminated as total uniformity supervenes.

While it is often stated in defence of artificial fertilisers that the world population could not be fed if their use was discontinued, this is yet another smokescreen to ensure large profits, for there are other ways far more effective, far cheaper as well as environmentally sustainable, which not only increase quantity, but quality too, and to which we shall now turn.

19.5 Biological Agriculture

In sustainable agriculture the key factor is not so much the make-up of the underlying ground-strata, but rather the composition of the uppermost stratum referred to as the topsoil, which can vary in depth from a few centimetres to several metres. The long term fertility of the soil is wholly dependent, firstly on the depth of this stratum, and secondly on its content of organically processed material. Under natural conditions this friable zone is populated with an abundance of earthworms and other creatures, and culminates in a profusion of microbial activity in the surface layer of humus, which generally consists of decomposing leaves and other organic matter. Without all this mineral and chemical processing, fertility decreases rapidly and it is therefore in our vital interest to ensure that a suitable soil environment is not only maintained, but also increased wherever possible.

This can be done in several ways which will only be elaborated briefly here, since there is ample information readily available in most bookstores. Viktor Schauberger's contributions, however, will be addressed in more detail and while we are here concerned more specifically with food production and soil fertility, all the others factors and influences discussed in previous chapters should still be taken into account.

SOIL REMINERALISATION:
In 1894 Julius Hensel, an agricultural chemist and contemporary of Justus von Liebig, pub-lished an important book, *Bread from Stone*, elaborating the beneficial effects of fertilising with stone-meal, better known as 'crusher dust' or 'rockdust'. However, by this time the production of artificial fertiliser was well under way and as his book posed a significant threat to this new industry, just about every copy was sought out, bought up and destroyed, to the great detriment of both life and soil.

In essence, soil remineralisation is an inorganic approach to increasing soil fertility. While it may sound very much like artificial fertilising, it is, however, a fundamentally different process and involves the use of very finely ground, but otherwise untreated, mainly igneous rocks with a broad mineral spectrum, such as diabase, basalt, etc. Once ground in a cold process which retains its inherent energies, it is then spread over the cultivated land and, because of its wide variety of salts, minerals and trace-elements, it gives rise to the emergence of an equally large variety of different micro-organisms.

Although this system of fertilisation has been in use in Switzerland for nearly 150 years on a limited scale and, no doubt, contributed to the compiling of Julius Hensel's book, its more recent use has been pioneered with amazing effect by the American engineer, John Hamaker. In his book *The Survival of Civilisation*[5] written in collaboration with Don Weaver, he explains in detail the climatic importance of remineralisation, as it is the magnitude and mixture of the available mineral and trace-element base that is the determining factor in the growth and quality of vegetation, the latter being the vital moderator of climatic extremes. The book also describes the marked increase in fertility and depth of top soil that John Hamaker achieved on his Michigan property, which increased from about 10cm (4in) to about 1.2m (4ft) over a period of 10 years.

More recent experiments with this material by the 'Men of the Trees' under the direction of Barry Oldfield in Western Australia showed a remarkable increase in the growth and health of seedlings planted with it as against those without. Rockdust has already been produced inadvertently for most of this century in all quarries where gravel or blue road-metal is crushed for road making or aggregate produced for building. The plant and machinery for its larger scale production is, therefore, already at hand and, with a little extra investment in fine crushing mills where necessary, almost unlimited quantities can rapidly be made available relatively cheaply. Indeed, at the 1993 annual convention of the National Aggregate Association and the National Ready-mix Concrete Association in San Antonio, Texas, where Don Weaver gave an address, he was informed that the combined production of both organisations amounted to 2 billion tons of aggregate of which 200 million tons were rockdust 'fines', whose disposal was a recurring headache.

Though an initial application is preferable in extreme fineness, because it makes the greatest surface area immediately available to micro-organisms, a mixture of large and small particles also ensures a slow release of minerals over a long period. Another beneficial effect of rockdust is that it has been shown to be a buffer against nitrate, sulphur dioxide and nitroxide, and it absorbs and fixes anions-while leaving cations+ free for the the use of the plants. Under normal conditions rockdust need only be applied every five years or so, the quantity being determined through careful analysis of soil deficiencies, although whatever the soil condition, the effect has been shown to be beneficial[6].

That people and not only plants can benefit from rockdust is amply demonstrated by the state of health and well-being of the Hunzas of Northern Pakistan. Living in the high, clean air of the Himalayas, their fields are watered by cold glacier melt-water, rich in trace-elements ground from the rocks over which the glacier passes. Their fields were therefore constantly fertilised with a broad spectrum of minerals, which not only maintained a high level of productivity, but ensured that the produce itself was vibrantly healthy and disease-free. At the time of the British Raj, an army doctor was once stationed in Hunzacut for a period of ten years as resident medical officer. During his sojourn, apart from treating the occasional wound and fracture, he had nothing to do, such was the high state of health of these mountain people, whose average life-expectancy of between 130 and 140 years can only properly be attributed to the supreme quality of the food and water available to them.

A further pointer to the wholesome influence of rockdust, which has very interesting and positive ramifications for the improvement of drinking water, was demonstrated by the behaviour of the pet dogs of some friends of mine in Queensland. As rockdust enthusiasts they had been fertilising their fruit trees with it, using a bucket for transportation. While the dogs normally drank copiously from bowls on the veranda filled with rainwater from the tank, over a period of days it was noticed that the bowls were always full. Wondering where the dogs were getting water, they were followed and seen to drink out of the bucket used for carrying the rockdust. Left beside the heap, this still contained a small amount of rockdust and had filled with rainwater in the interim. As animals are far closer to Nature than most human beings and because they act on instinct, there can be little doubt that these dogs knew what was best for them, as was also the case of the cows whose behaviour is described below in the section on biodynamic farming. We would therefore be well advised to take a leaf from their book of knowledge.

ORGANIC FARMING:
Although, prior to the introduction of artificial fertilisers, organic farming, with the use of cow manure, farmyard liquor and composted vegetable matter was the norm, over this century these practices largely lapsed due to the less labour-intensive use of chemicals and the apparent resultant rise in productivity and therefore profitability, with the result that most farmers switched to artificial fertiliser completely. Others, however, steeped in the organic traditions of their forebears, were not swayed by the blandishments of artificial fertiliser manufacturers and held to their well-tried and trusted methods, thereby safeguarding the older knowledge, which, since the end of the Second World War, has experienced a renaissance, organic produce now increasingly being seen to be of far higher nutritive worth.

The underlying philosophy of organic farming is to return to the soil for reprocessing what was previously removed from it and, in this way, the fertility of the soil was successfully sustained for many centuries. Moreover, as the material is organic rather than so-called inorganic, it requires less of Nature's energy to reconstitute it into a form readily assimilable by plants, as the energies required to convert it from an inorganic to an organic state are spared.

With composting as generally understood today, however, instead of previously dried material, green sap-laden vegetable matter interleaved with layers of earth is used, which generates considerable heat in the compost heap itself. Indeed this warming is generally taken as a sign that the composting process is progressing properly.

While the product of such a heap is eventually broken down and well-fermented at completion and while it does maintain the current level of fertility, according to Viktor Schauberger it does not increase it markedly, except in cases where no compost has been used previously. One of the reasons for this is that the relatively high internal temperatures prevent the entry and activity of the earthworms, always sensitive to heat, until the latter stages, when the heap has cooled sufficiently for them to be attracted into the decomposing material.

Furthermore, there is no consideration given to the effect of rainfall which, as mentioned earlier, is juvenile, element-hungry water and avidly seizes upon whatever material it can find in order to become mature. By constructing a compost heap differently and by protecting it from rain, the end-product will be of far higher quality, not only as a result of cold rather than hot processes of fermentation, but also due to its higher content of protein and other immaterial, fructigenic energies.

Although shown here on a small scale, the same principle can be applied to larger compost heaps. In Viktor Schauberger's view, a compost heap should be egg-shaped, reflecting the life-giving properties of the egg, and should ideally be built up under a large fruit-tree with a broad canopy as shown in fig. 19.10. Protected by the foliage above, a cavity is scooped out of the ground around the base of the tree into which a 20cm thick

layer of sun-dried or otherwise desiccated leaf-matter and vegetable residues are laid. It is important that this material is thoroughly dried before being added to the heap, for excess water will trigger unwanted heat during fermentation. The whole is then covered with an equally thick mixture of earth, fine sand and river gravel. Use of the latter elements not only harks back to the system of remineralisation above, but also to the improved quality of material carried by naturally flowing streams. To this mixture is added a small quantity of copper and zinc filings, whose function will be explained later.

Before this is done, however, the trunk is first wrapped loosely with several layers of newspaper or other suitable decomposable material, which not only protects the tree but, once decomposed, then provides a duct surrounding the trunk for the entry of air. The heap is then temporarily covered with clay or an impermeable material to prevent the entry of rain and its content of raw oxygen. Since this is a cool process, earthworms, insects and other aerobic micro-organisms are at once attracted into the heap and begin their reprocessing activity aided by the diffused oxygen, nitrogen and other trace gases entering through the newspaper or sacking round the trunk and the overlying mixture of earth and sand.

Gradually, as more vegetable refuse becomes available, the heap is built up into the stable form of the egg shown in fig. 19.9. Once finished, and to ensure the wholesome completion of this cold decomposition, the entire heap is then faced and smoothed over with clay to prevent the entry of rain which, due to the near vertical external surfaces, is more inclined to drain down the side than infiltrate through the clay. The final act of maturation then begins.

Having by now infiltrated the whole of the compost heap and thoroughly aerated it, the microbial life and, in particular, the earthworms which by this time have populated the compost heap in their thousands, begin to die off, their decomposing bodies giving an additional nutritive boost to the end-product with the provision of large quantities of animal protein. In late autumn the strength of the Sun's light and heat dimin-

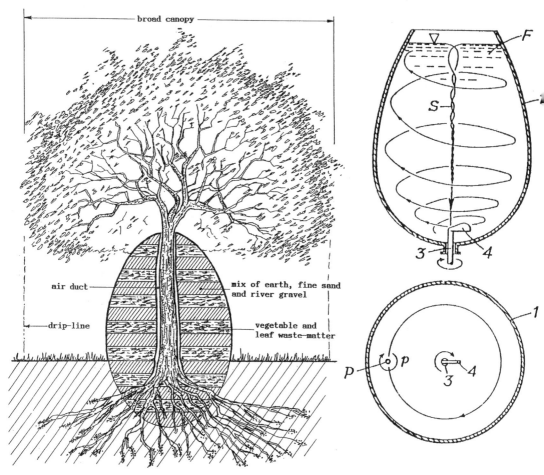

Fig. 19.10 **The egg-shaped compost heap**   Fig. 19.11

ishes, the ground begins to cool more markedly and a strongly positive temperature-gradient is established between atmosphere and ground. This is when the compost heap is demolished to ground level, the residual matter being left in the cavity around the trunk and roots of the tree. Towards evening, the material is spread evenly over adjacent fields, for under the positive temperature-gradient – most powerful at this time – the nutrients are carried below with the infiltrating rain or dew.

In this way the land is provided with far richer and higher-quality, natural fertiliser, which not merely maintains but increases fertility. At the same time, the host tree also benefits enormously and produces an abundance of healthy, blight-free and tasty fruit. By constructing such compost heaps under different trees each year, eventually all the fruit trees are well fertilised. Where no suitable trees are available, however, compost heaps can be built up in similar fashion, but in the form of dome-like humps or barrel-shaped clamps, which should not only be suitably protected against the entry of rain-water, but insulated from the heating effect of the Sun.

BIODYNAMIC FARMING:
Biodynamic farming is a system of agriculture devised by Dr. Rudolf Steiner (1861–1925), a teacher and philosopher born in Austria, and founder of the Anthro-

posophical Movement. Anthroposophy sees the human being as the highest exponent of the Divine on Earth, embodying all the instruments and agencies of creative power and patterns of physical manifestation; it studies the world through the inner and outer nature of humanity. Its approach to farming basically assumes energy to be the primary cause, and growth the secondary effect. To what extent Rudolf Steiner and Viktor Schauberger mutually influenced each other's thinking is not recorded, although it is known that they did have fairly lengthy discussions.

Biodynamic farming's attitude to fertilisation is to exalt the energies in decomposed and organically transformed organic matter by filling empty cow horns with a base material of cow manure. These are then buried *en masse* about 60cm underground in autumn, when the Earth's geospheric energies sink into the ground as the repose of winter approaches. Due to the vortex-like and vortex-enhancing shape of the cow horns, the transformative, horizontally propagated fructigenic emanations in the ground are focused on the contents of raw dung and, in the coolness of the ground over winter, are transmuted under cold processes of fermentation. In early spring, when the fields require fertilisation, the cow horns are dug up, their contents having been transformed into a sweet-smelling, highly active substance as a result of their sojourn in this zone, permeated by geospheric energies.

This transformed material is then used in the production of the natural fertiliser known as '500 mix'. Due to the sustained efforts of Alex de Podolinsky in Victoria[7] and others such as Terry Forman in New South Wales, it has been increasing widely used as fertiliser, at least since 1947. To date over a $1\frac{1}{4}$ million acres are fertilised in Australia using this system and, seen from the air, those properties where it has been applied stand out clearly from neighbouring farms, due to the greater abundance of green pasture. Indeed on Alex de Podolinsky's farm the grass was so lush and wholesome that several of his neighbour's cows broke through the fence to eat it. Discovered some four hours or so later, they were rounded up and returned to their own paddock. It was noticed that they did not eat for two or three days, so high was the quality of the grass they had eaten on the biodynamic farm.

The fertiliser '500' itself is produced with a pulsating movement similar to the homeopathic process of succession, in which the state of energy or order is progressively increased through the successive creation and recreation of order and chaos. A small quantity of the transformed cow dung is added to water and mixed in such a way as to create vortices rotating about the vertical axis of the mixing vessel. Here the liquid is stirred in, in one direction until the vortex has been formed. The direction of mixing then reverses until another vortex is created. This process of repeated reversal of direction not only imbues the liquid with the opposite charges arising from opposite directions of rotation, but also draws in inseminating O_2 while gradually building up and structuring the liquids internal energies in a process best explained by the art of sword making.

Apart from the various alloys used in the Japanese art of swordmaking, the base material is first made red hot and then beaten out or 'structured' with a hammer as it cools. It is then further heated to incandescence, folded over on itself, fused together and beaten out again. Here the reheating represents the chaoticising aspect, whereas the beating is the structuring aspect. Little by little, with continued repetition of the two processes involving order and chaos-creation, the structure of the blade increases and the level of chaos diminishes, ultimately producing a razor-sharp blade whose structure is both laminar and flexible. In similar fashion with the fertiliser, as the vortices are alternately formed and destroyed, the level of energy rises and the degree of chaos decreases until, after about an hour, the product is ready for use. This is applied to the fields in spray form towards evening within two to three hours after preparation and before the accumulated energies have dispersed.

In many mixing devices, when not mixed by hand, the vortices are created by motor-driven paddles rotating first in one direction and then the other. Many of the mixing vessels are cylindrical but it would obviously be preferable if these vessels were of egg shape (as discussed earlier). Moreover, in lieu of the paddles to generate vortices, a simple single-bladed impeller like the head of a golf club mounted through the bottom of an egg-shaped vessel (as shown in fig. 19.11[8]) would achieve the same results with greater economy of motive force.

The apparatus shown here is of a type Walter Schauberger used to infuse carbon-dioxide permanently into water under a partial vacuum. Instead of steel or galvanised iron, the vessel should be made of fired clay, wood or copper, and mixing should be carried out in the open on the ground (not on reinforced concrete slabs) so as to permit the insuction of both cosmic and geospheric ethericities.

If stirred by hand the quality of the energies generated can be further enhanced by classical or Indian music or by what was known and practised by some of the older Central European peasant farmers in a ritual called 'Tonsingen'. The German word 'Ton' has a two-fold meaning, as either clay or tone as in music. Here Viktor relates an event where one evening he came upon a farmer bent over a wooden barrel stirring the contents. This peasant's farming methods were very unusual, but he nevertheless achieved extraordinary results with them, far surpassing those of his neighbours, which was why Viktor went to see him.

As Viktor watched him stir the contents to the left with a large wooden paddle, he sang in rising tones, only to change to descending tones when stirring to the right, but all the while crumbling pieces of aluminum-bearing clay into the water. After about an hour of these not wholly musical sounds, the peasant declared that he was finished and that the mixture was now ready for spreading over the meadow the following morning. This was done by dipping a bunch of small, leaf-covered branches into the barrel and then flicking the energised clay-water emulsion over the ground in a manner similar to the sprinkling of Holy Water with palmfronds on Palm Sunday.

In essence, the energies generated in this way are the result of the combination of two phenomena already discussed. The energies derived through the bio-dynamic procedure of forming and re-forming vortices are essentially the same as those created by the longitudinal left-hand/right-hand alternating vortices in naturally flowing rivers (discussed in chapter 13 with regard to Viktor's 'Energy Cannon' (fig. 13.14)). With 'tonsingen', however, we are more concerned with the encapsulation of the harmonies of the chanting (as formative energy) in the water's 'memory' (see discussion on homeopathy, chapter 9), which must be transferred to the waiting plants before the resonances abate and the water 'forgets'.

Notes

1. *Tau* mag, Vol.146, p.11, 1936
2. *Our Senseless Toil*, Pt.I, p.13.
3. "The Spiral Plough" ("Der Spiralpflug") by Kurt Lorek, *Implosion* No.8, published in Germany by Aloys Kokaly (dec'd). Publication of *Implosion* now continues with Kurt Lorek, Windschlägerstr. 58, 77652 Offenburg, Germany (tel: +49 781 73541).
4. From the Schauberger archives.
5. *The Survival of Civilisation*, self-published by John Hamaker and Don Weaver.
6. Further detailed information on rockdust can be obtained from:

– Don Weaver, P.O.Box 1961, Burlingame, CA 94010, USA.
– Joanna Campe, ed. of *Remineralise the Earth*, 152 South St, Northampton, MD 01060, USA.
– Barry Oldfield, Pres."Men of the Trees", 3 Over Ave., Lesmurdie 6076, W. Australia.
– *Das Buch von Steinmehl* by Helmut Snoek: Orac-Pietsch, Germany.
7. Alex de Podolinsky's work is fully elaborated in *The Secrets of the Soil*, by Christopher Bird: Harper, New York
8. Austrian Patent No.265991.

20

THE GENERATION OF FRUCTIGENIC
ENERGIES

Viktor Schauberger also had concepts similar to Rudolf Steiner's biodynamics for the production of natural fertiliser. His ideas and their practice, however, do not necessitate the use of the thousands of cow horns presently employed by de Podolinsky. Those millions of horns are only available through the increasingly widespread consumption of beef and other meats, which from about 2 million tonnes in 1950–52 rose to 11 million tonnes in 1984[1]. This expansion, however, has taken and is continuing to take a serious toll on the ecology and environment of the producing countries. A recent scientific study in Costa Rica, for example, showed that for every beef carcass exported, 2½ tonnes of top soil were irretrievably lost through erosion. Quite obviously, such widespread damage is totally unsustainable.

Moreover, in view of the increasing movement away from a predominantly meat-eating diet in many Western countries, a gradually accelerating decline in meat consumption can be envisaged, which will eventually put a stop to the supply of cow-horns. This movement is now growing very fast due to the increase in heart disease and cancer associated with the overconsumption of animal protein and the moral implications of intensively cruel industrialised methods of meat production, so graphically depicted in all their horror by C. David Coats in his book *Old MacDonald's Factory Farm*[2]. Amongst other countries in the so-called 'civilised' world, in Great Britain for instance the number of vegetarians has doubled since 1990, representing 7% of the population or 3.1 million people[3]. This is an enormous acceleration in changed awareness which, if manifested on a world-wide basis, would inaugurate equally far-reaching changes in the present balance between pastoral and arable agriculture.

Purely from the point of view of acreage economics, which must be taken into account in view of the rising world population, whereas a meat-eater requires the produce from about 1.6 acres to survive annually, a vegetarian needs only 0.66 acres, or about 41% of the first figure. Any system therefore, which enhances fertility both quantitatively and qualitatively without the need of large animal-based inputs is certainly preferable.

In our examination of biological farming methods, we have moved from the inorganic to increasingly higher organic and energetic processes. In addition to those already discussed, there are further ways to enhance and strengthen growth and fertility. These involve the amplification of the Earth's fructigenic, qualigenic and dynagenic ethericities, which were described in chapters 4 and 5 as aspects of the Sun's fertilising role, and which are the spiritual driving force of life.

Because of their close intercommunion with the higher dimensions of being or existence (viz. levels c^4 to c^6, chapter 4 – 4.6), these energies operate at extremely high frequencies. This means that their formative influences are correspondingly more powerful and their effect on the pattern of physical manifestation greater, for they are the messengers of the Will-to-create and the power source of the idea of what is to be created. If these ethericities can therefore be multiplied artificially, but according to the laws of Nature and the nature of the ethericities themselves, then it should be possible greatly to promote healthy growth and fertility.

Thus, apart from a purely sexual process of procreation, we are here confronted by a process of higher genesis with the ability to endow quantity with quality.[4]

Viktor Schauberger

To recapitulate on these ethericities briefly, fructigens are those essences that produce greater fertility, whereas qualigens create greater quality and dynagens generate higher intrinsic energy. To some elements at a lower more immediately physical level Viktor Schauberger ascribed certain male and female attributes or temperaments, silver, zinc and silicon being paternally oriented and gold, copper and limestone maternally oriented.

As we saw on p. 84 (fig. 5.2), the natural movement of the female essences expands outwardly from the centre of the Earth, propagating horizontally at the Earth's surface. At all levels, however, they interact or interbreed with the seminal substances of the Sun, whose natural direction of movement is along a plane perpendicular to that of the female, the energetic residues thus produced being expelled as physical growth.

Here the form of growth itself is dependent on the relative proportions of the differently oriented energies. If the plants to be fertilised have a predominant tendency to vertical growth, such as wheat, sugar cane and maize, then more paternally oriented elements should be added to the mixture as these are associated with vertical (i.e. phallic) movement. If the natural form of the plant is more horizontally inclined, then the emphasis should be towards the maternally oriented elements.

The seeding of the soil with immaterial energies was also long known to the Tibetans who buried their so-called 'Treasure Vases' in the ground in certain propitious places. These, filled with precious stones and metals, were believed to emit wholesome energies which enhanced and protected the environment. The Tibetans also considered that gold and other precious metals were best left undisturbed in the ground, similar to the way the Australian aboriginals and the Hopis feel about uranium as an emitter of energy.

Viktor Schauberger's vision for promoting a greater abundance of creative animating energy, of fertility and rising quality, involved the creation of what he referred to as 'amniotic fluid'. This required the liquid intermixture of the above elements of silver, zinc and silicon (male) and gold, copper and limestone (female) together with other vegetable or animal residues in a suitable galvanic container. The respective negative and positive polarities of these substances gave rise to certain anodic and cathodic functions enhancing the dissociation, association and higher reconstitution of the contained elements into a liquid brimming with germinating potency.

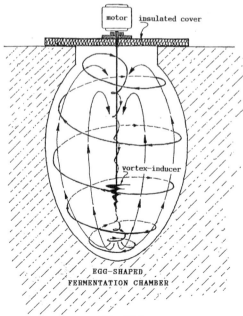

Fig. 20.1

Once again this requires the use of egg-shapes and, in particular, the arrangement shown in fig. 20.1. This egg-shaped cavity or fermentation chamber is scooped out of the ground, about 2 metres deep, and faced with aluminium-bearing clay. As a more permanent installation it may also be lined with natural materials such as wood or stone. Burnt material such a brick, having been exposed to fire, is less desirable. If timber is used and the chamber is constructed with wooden staves like a barrel, the whole should be held together at intervals with copper or copper-alloy bands and bedded in sand in the same way as the wooden water mains described in chapter 14.

Once completed and ready for use, then all varieties of waste matter such as stable-manure, kitchen refuse and even human excreta are added, in as fresh a state as possible and broken down into the finest particles. These should then be mixed with liquid manure, when available. After filling the lower third of the chamber in this way, the remaining space should be filled with well-oxygenated, juvenile rainwater or surface water, well exposed to the Sun. The whole arrangement should be thoroughly insulated against light and heat, so that the developing concentration of energies arising through the interaction of cosmic and geospheric ethericities can neither escape nor be dissipated.

Having been created out of the most thoroughly rotted elements of former life, these emanations are the most natural fertilisers, which have metamorphosed their erstwhile spaciality (spacial volume) to such a degree, that they can only manifest themselves as highly dosed (concentrated) energetic matter.[5]

Viktor Schauberger

As with the egg-shaped compost heap described in chapter 19, powder or filings of copper and zinc, with small quantities of silicon and limestone, should also be added to stimulate the immaterial energies of different potential. Particles of gold and silver can also be beneficially introduced, the very much higher financial outlay probably being well

repaid by a corresponding increase in health, fertility and productivity.

Towards late afternoon or at night, a small electric motor is switched on which drives a vortex-inducer made of a biometal (silver-plated copper). The vortex-inducer itself is mounted on a hard copper or phosphor-bronze shaft and is located in the bottom third of the fermentation chamber, its rotation causing the cyclical vortical circulation of the contents. In other words, the liquid is moved in the 'original' or planetary way, which, according to Viktor Schauberger, has the following effect:

....'planetary motion' is characterised by forces that strive to reach the central point and reduce the outward pressure on the peripheral wall-surfaces. They generate reactive forms of cold and lead to specific densation. Planetary motion involves the natural, animating, centripetalising acceleration of mass, which initiates higher-grade fermentation processes of an invigorating nature in the bipolar mixture of basic elements. The end-product is biomagnetism, a reproductive, regenerative and upwardly evolving form of energy.[6]

Not only is biomagnetism generated, but the overall energetic potential of both paternally and maternally oriented substances is increased through the alternation between centrifugal (outbreathing) and centripetal (inbreathing) pulsations, during which process the contents are vortically cooled towards the all-important +4°C anomaly point. As the chamber is egg-shaped, no particles are left unmoved and, ultimately, all the waste is atomised into the smallest possible particles, thereby producing a very high homeopathic rarefaction, Viktor stating in this regard that:

In terms of homeopathic principles and attempts to produce super-dilutions in order to still the "specific' hunger of the plants, the more dilute the fertilising agent, the more it approximates the character of the above ethericities, thus facilitating further interactions that in turn result in increased growth.[7]

By mixing the elements of Earth and Heaven in this way, what Goethe called the 'connecting link' is created, which in turn gives rise to the generation and accumulation of a high geospheric charge which cannot escape, due to the external insulation. In the form of a highly active negative or fructigenic potency, a condition that Viktor described as "a hungry voluptuousness akin to nymphomania",[7] it combines with the water, which becomes crystal clear. Like de Podolinsky's '500 mix', it is also free of unattractive odours and indeed is sweet-smelling.

Viktor compares this process to wine-making, where sweet and turbid grape-juice matures into clear, relatively dry wine in a cool cellar. The maturation of good wine, however, may take a year or more, whereas this extraordinarily procreative liquid takes only two to three nights to prepare, weather conditions permitting. When broadcast over the fields in the evening, it attracts the predominantly paternally-oriented atmospheric energies in preparation for fertilisation by the Sun's energies the following day.

Here again we are concerned with the interaction of almost non-spacial energies through which the ur-genesis or out-fall of physical matter takes place through the partial solidification of the discharged precipitates (energetic waste products of the higher, 5th dimensional energies, due to the expulsive effects of heat and light, which Viktor Schauberger called "4th dimensional mediatory substances".) However, because these precipitated energies are non-spacial, the extent to which the chamber can be charged with them is virtually unlimited.

In this fourth-dimensional state these ethericities, whose natural direction of propagation is horizontal, enter the plant itself through the root-protoplasms, the little sacs or vesicles of proto-water or amniotic fluid attached to the root-tip. Like dew, another form of proto-water formed on the tips of blades of grass during the night and early morning, these vesicles, too, collapse if exposed to light and heat. This is why the greatest care must be taken when replanting small seedlings or saplings, which should only be done at night in order to keep injury to a minimum.

These delicate fragile root-protoplasms act as mediators and transform the nutritive energies that the plant will absorb. Depicted in Viktor Schauberger's charming sketch in fig. 20.2, he describes the process as follows:

No plant is actually nourished by dissolved matter, but rather with 'ascended', nutritive entities of geospheric provenance in a fourth dimensional state. These diffuse ethericities can only enter the sap-stream via the root-protoplasms, where they are fertilised by diffuse oxygenic ethericities. The higher outbirth of this emulsion (ur-procreation) is an ethericity that belongs to 5th dimension. These concentrations of matter-energy emit negative, hyper-charged emanations in all directions and bind the positively-charged ethericities entering through the skin or the bark. Some of this emulsion solidifies and whatever is subsequently manifested, is what we call 'growth'.[8]

Another version of this egg-shaped in-ground fermentation chamber is shown in fig. 20.3. This one, however, is not power-driven and fermentation takes up to six weeks, once again depending on external climatic factors, hotter periods having a retarding effect on the necessary cool or cold maturation processes. This chamber is not sealed and insulated in quite the same fashion

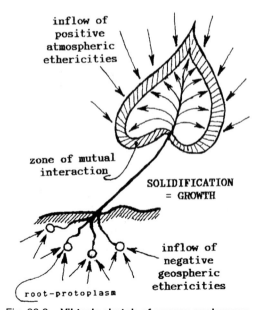

inflow of
positive
atmospheric
ethericities

zone of mutual
interaction

SOLIDIFICATION
= GROWTH

inflow of
negative
geospheric
ethericities

root-protoplasm

Fig. 20.2   **Viktor's sketch of energy exchanges**

as that in fig. 20.1, but is exposed to atmospheric and therefore male fertilising influences through the diffusing fabric of jute sacking or something similar, secured over the opening.

Virtually the same paternally- or maternally-oriented elements are introduced, but internal vortical circulation is slower, driven by variations in external temperature. Owing to the currents generated between the substances of opposite charge and potential, and due to the lack of insulation, lateral pulsations of energies are produced which are fructigenic either paternally- or maternally-oriented, *pulsation* being inherent in all life processes.

Their direction of movement is either away from the chamber or towards it, according to the time of day or night. In the process, these emanations fill the germinating zone with the fructigenic stimuli vital for growth. The extent of the surrounding environment that is affected by each chamber and its life-giving formative potential will depend on the amount and the relative proportions of these male and female elements. According to Viktor Schauberger, one or two such fermentation chambers are sufficient to permeate the soil over several square kilometres with fertile substances imbued with the will to germinate.

One other soil-restoring method of Viktor Schauberger's which should also be mentioned briefly, is for restoring the health of the soil in so-called 'sour' pastures, thereby increasing their fertility and attraction for grazing animals. In a process akin to the in-ground cisterns above, a largish wooden barrel held together by ropes or cord, but not with metal straps or fittings, is buried in the ground near the ailing field. The depth to which it is buried must be such that rainwater can be channelled into it along shallow trenches dug for the purpose. To prevent the entry of unwanted soil, the barrel it then covered with a lid to which dependent copper and zinc rods are attached in the ratio of 2 copper to 1 zinc. A hole about 5cm in diameter is cut in the lid and covered or otherwise closed with a good quality, diffusive material such as linen or jute sacking. After a while, a layer of green algae-like growths cover the surface of the water, which indicates that the contents of the barrel are ready for use. The sour field is then watered with this liquid and gradually the pasture grasses become 'sweet'.

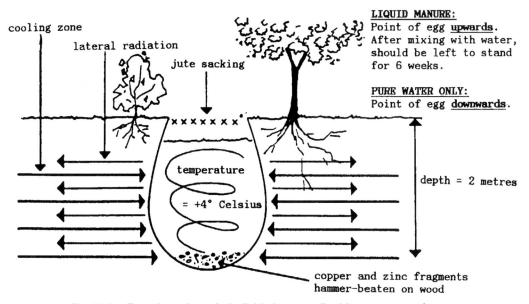

cooling zone

lateral radiation

jute sacking

LIQUID MANURE:
Point of egg **upwards**.
After mixing with water, should be left to stand for 6 weeks.

PURE WATER ONLY:
Point of egg **downwards**.

temperature

= +4° Celsius

depth = 2 metres

copper and zinc fragments hammer-beaten on wood

Fig. 20.3 **Egg-shaped amniotic fluid cistern or liquid manure transformer**

With these and the other natural methods of fertilisation discussed in the preceding chapter, there is therefore much that we can do to promote healthy and sustainable growth in agriculture. With this technology we have the ability to restore the soil, our only source of wholesome food, to its former state of high productivity and fertility, and even to increase it.

These means are not only far cheaper than the use of harmful artificial fertilisers and noxious pesticides, but they increase both the quantity and quality of food. At the same time, this will usher in the possibility of growing the same amount of food on a smaller area, thereby permitting the urgent reafforestation of those areas presently employed for meat production. Moreover, since the products of this new agriculture are of extremely high quality and vitality, it would be possible to satisfy the world demand for food with a smaller amount and still maintain healthy life. The systems of agriculture and food production that have been described here would well be able to support a world population even higher than the present, if that were deemed desirable.

The far greater abundance of food would greatly reduce people's fears for the future, modifying the defensiveness in our actions and behaviour towards others; for they are founded on the the the desire for self-preservation, still a strong instinct in humankind. By eating such vastly improved produce and drinking healthy and properly constituted water, we shall, at the same time, increase our own personal qualities and potential as individuals.

As we pointed out earlier, the finer intuitive and perceptive thoughts, capable of comprehending the intricacies of Nature's workings, can only be produced by high quality brains. If we are earnest in our desire to recreate the future and enter into a cooperative rather than a competitive association with Nature, then it is our duty to understand her ways thoroughly and hearken to the words of the English philosopher and student of Nature, Francis Bacon (1561–1626), who stated some 400 years ago, *We cannot command Nature except by obeying her.*

We cannot obey her laws, however, nor can we apply them towards the alleviation of all the present misery unless we can understand them. The first priority must be to implement these new methods on a worldwide basis for, in doing, so we shall be able to remove the scourge of hunger and destitution for all time. This will demand a complete reorientation in the present approach to agriculture, forestry and water resources management. Only then can truly economically, sustainable development and open peaceful human interrelations on a global basis be achieved.

A free people can only grow out of a free Earth. Any people that violates Mother-Earth has no right to a homeland, because in soils destroyed by speculation, high-quality races can find no abode, i.e. they are physical masses divorced of all connection with the Earth. Masses without roots perish. They have to travel the terrible road of decay until, like unsuitable fertilisers, they lose their stubborn wills and only when they have reached this condition, and starting again from the very beginning, will they be allowed to re-enter the mighty course of evolution.[9]

Viktor Schauberger

Notes

1. *Our Common Future*, p.119: Oxford Univ. Press, Oxford, New York. ISBN 0-19-282080-X.
2. *Old MacDonald's Factory Farm* by C.David Coats (quite incidentally my brother): Continuum, New York. ISBN 0-8264-0439-1.
3. *The Independent*, London, 21 Aug.1993.
4. *Implosion* No.37, pp.2–3.
5. *ibid*, p.3.
6. *Implosion* No.45, p.3.
7. Excerpt from a letter from Viktor Schauberger to Dagmar Sarkar in the mid-1950s; the diagram has been redrawn and annotated by the author for greater clarity.
8. *ibid.*
9. *Implosion* No.37, p.8.

You can find us at the following address:

21

IMPLOSION

Before we begin our examination of the processes of implosion and its associated apparatuses, it is necessary to state at the outset that the specific description of Viktor's devices is rather problematic. This is because none of the diagrams, where there are any, precisely conforms to the descriptive material in the various texts. These tend to overlap, producing many blurred areas.

Moreover, on occasion, what appears to be the same apparatus has been referred to by a different name and the whole chronology of the development of each of these machines is very hard to unravel, some texts referring to what appears to have been a 1940s development, while the middle 1930s are mentioned in others containing similar information. It has therefore been extremely difficult to determine precisely which description refers to which device, or indeed how many devices there are. These have variously been called the "Repulsator", the "Repulsine", the "Klimator", the "Implosion Motor", The "Suction Motor,", the "Trout Motor" and the "Biotechnical Submarine".

What all these machines have in common, however, is very silent and cheap operation as they all make use of similar principles. For lack of space here to address the full range of information[1], we shall examine them on a more general basis, using the name that seems most likely to apply. What is here very important, however, is that all the various aspects and factors such as male and female ethericities, the function of vortices in rivers, bio-electricism and biomagnetism, temperature gradients, etc., which have already been discussed, must also be borne in mind when considering the functioning of Viktor's machines because, in his philosophy nothing is to be seen in isolation or to be divorced from anything else. Central to Viktor's theories and the functioning of his machines is the creation of what he called the "Biological Vacuum" and we shall therefore begin by addressing it first.

21.1 The Biological Vacuum

In its simplest form, its mechanical effect is akin to the suction we experience when we place one of our hands over the plug-hole in a full bath after removing the plug. By uncovering and covering the hole with the palm of the hand, we can get some idea of the enormous power of suction, or the forces of **implosion** which, according to research by Prof. Felix Ehrenhaft, who helped Viktor Schauberger periodically, are 127 times more powerful than explosive forces.

In the case of the bath plug, we are concerned with suction produced by gravity. Gravity, however, as we learned in chapter 4 is octavely related to centrifugence, the counterpart of which is centripetence. In a manner akin to the interaction between suction and pressure on a common axis, the essential dimension of the jet engine, Viktor's apparatuses make similar use of centrifugence and centripetence to produce a biological vacuum.

This involves a vortical cooling process, sometimes in a sealed vessel, in which the contents are cooled to such an extent that, because of their extraordinary densation, a very powerful vacuum is created. If water is the medium used, for example, then for every 1°C of cooling the volume of its contained gases reduces by $\frac{1}{273}$ rd. On the other hand if normal air, which contains a certain quantity of water vapour, is used as the medium, the compaction of air to water involves a volumetric reduction of 816 to 1. At +4°C 1 litre of water weighs 1kg, whereas 1 litre of normal air weighs 0.001226kg.

An example of this implosive reduction is what happened to the American airship, the Akron, in the early years of airships. Filled with the inert gas helium instead of hydrogen, the latter having caused the explosion of the Hindenburg through self-ignition, the Akron mysteriously imploded on a cool and misty morning as its helium reverted to water. The reversion in this case means an almost instantaneous 1800-fold decrease in volume. This reduction in volume which is caused by a series of chain-reactions, is the biological vacuum and an ideal, environmentally harmless source of motive power. As a biological vacuum forms under conditions of continuous cooling, aeriform gases are transformed into water and the gases contained in the water itself are further transformed into volume-less substances.

In Viktor's machines, however, we are not only concerned with the spacial reduction of physical matter, but also with the concentration of its content of immaterial energies for, in its extreme form, the biological vacuum causes these elements to lose their physicalness and revert to their higher ethericitical nature (transition from the third to the fourth or fifth dimensions). This higher realm of being is what Theosophical teaching refers to as the 'laya point', the point of extreme potency, the eye of the needle as it were, through and from which all manifesting energies are propagated. Viktor called this process a 'higher inward fall', noting in his diary on August 14th, 1936:

I stand face to face with the apparent 'void', the compression of dematerialisation that we are wont to call a 'vacuum'. I can now see that we are able to create anything we wish for ourselves out of this 'nothing'. The agent is water, the blood of the Earth and the most universal organism.[2]

This process of 'higher inward fall' Viktor was able to induce in varying degree in most of his devices, but principally in the so-called 'flying saucer' and 'biotechnical submarine' described later. Through the interaction between centrifugal and centripetal forces functioning on a common axis, he was able implosively to return or re-transmute the physical form (water or air) into its primary energetic matrix – a non-spacial, 4th, or 5th dimensional state, which has nothing to do with the three dimensions of physical existence. It was therefore possible in this way to remove matter or physical quantity from the physical world (creation of physical vacuity) and, owing to the non-spacial, other-realm quality of such a vacuum, to pack it as almost unlimited amounts of pure, formative energy into an energetic matrix akin to memory, or the progenitive idea of the thing itself. In the manner of a holograph, this conformed in every respect to the physical configuration of the reverse-transmuted substance. All that was required to release this huge potential, to unleash an enormous power and expansion back into physical existence, was the appropriate trigger, such as heat or light.

In terms of what is here involved and at what levels it operates, a recent paper on cold fusion that came my way in the middle of writing this book, provides new and interesting insights. This paper on low-temperature nuclear fusion, published by the Russian Journal of Chemistry[3], refers to the 'layered spaces', in which all truly fundamental natural phenomena and energetic interactions take place. Affirming the earlier discussion in chapters 3 & 4 on the causality of higher non-spacial dimensions of energy that give rise to physical genesis, this paper further states:

In our 'laboratory' space we observe only the result of a process, but it takes place in another layer of the enveloping layered space. The authors then go on to state that *...a physical vacuum is not a 'curved void', as generally assumed, but a real material substance consisting of elementary vacuum particles resulting* *from annihilation conversion of, for example, a proton and an antiproton or an electron and a positron. In other words, proton-antiproton and electron-positron vacuums are a physical reality. However, elementary vacuum particles **exist not in our laboratory space, but in another layer of enveloping space**, and for us, making observation in laboratory space, they are virtual particles. Such, according to FFT[4], is the real nature, and not the formal nature, of virtual states: particles that really exist, not in our space, however, but in a space complementary (in the mathematical sense) to it. **Elementary vacuum particles (EVP) and other virtual particles are states of the microworld that manifest themselves indirectly in laboratory space through the results of processes taking place in other spaces**.*

[My emphasis – CC]

I am almost tempted to say 'Q.E.D.', because this gives a very clear notion of what Viktor Schauberger conceived as the essential nature of the biological vacuum, although he produced it *inter alia* by rapidly cooling the medium of either air or water through the combined pulsating application of vortical centrifugal and centripetal forces on a common axis. In addition the "layered spaces" referred to in the above quotation also give a more concrete conception of those realms of reality Viktor referred to as the 4th and 5th dimensions, analogous to the higher vibratory energetic states of c^4, c^5, proposed in chapter 4. As primary formative instruments, they could be likened to the unseen inner shells of an onion, which furnish the energies creating the outer form.

21.2 The Repulsator

The device shown in fig. 21.1 is a later development of Viktor's 1943 egg-shaped spring water-producing machine, which was constructed in Sweden by the Biotechnical Research Group headed by Olof Alexandersson (the author of *Living Water*). The purpose of this apparatus is to regenerate old, stale water or create new mature water from distilled water by in-rolling and out-rolling it through the creation of alternating right and left hand vortices, emulating the sequential alternation of negatively and positively charg-

ing longitudinal vortices at the bends of naturally flowing rivers. This takes place in a manner similar to the biodynamic production of '500 mix' described in chapter 19.

The whole idea is to make the water breathe and inhale various trace-elements and carbon-dioxide in a particular order to become mature. This is done by a simple one-bladed impeller at the bottom, the pointed end of the egg, which automatically reverses direction of rotation after a certain interval, during which an internal vortex has been created. Under the influence of a positive temperature gradient and starting at a temperature of about +20°C, in the initial stages of this process (the starting temperature should not exceed +27°C), the energetic and other potential of the base water is first eliminated, before the water is regenerated to a much higher quality as the transformation, or biosynthesis, proceeds.

The egg-shaped vessel itself, which contains about 10–11 litres, is made of copper or copper alloys, silver-plated where required, (i.e. bio-metals, which have catalytic and diamagnetic or biomagnetic properties). The outer surface of the casing should be well-insulated and encircled by cooling pipes, although a quantity of ice can be used as a substitute or the device placed in a refrigerator. This external insulation is also necessary to prevent any leakage of the bio-electrical and biomagnetic energies that the operation produces.

Before filling the egg, the base water, if not distilled water, should first be boiled to remove any bacteria. Boiling also eliminates any other residual immaterial 'memories', which may be directly harmful. The starting product is then analysed for any deficiencies in its chemical composition so that whatever is added is in the right proportion, the yardstick for this being the chemical and gaseous composition of high-grade mountain spring water. Under no circumstances should the base water contain any chlorine which would produce complications in its final reconstitution as high-grade spring water.

Once this has been done, the egg is filled to the brim with water in order to exclude all atmospheric oxygen and air. The inlet valve is then closed and about 4 litres of water drained off as carbon-dioxide is simultaneously introduced. When the drive motor is switched on (about 300rpm), through vortical action and constant cooling the carbon-dioxide is absorbed into the water and is transformed into carbonic acid, creating a vacuum in the

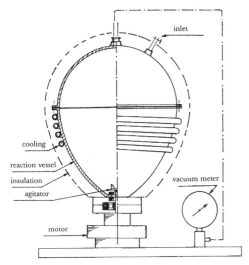

A schematic diagram of the apparatus for biosynthesis. The ingredients for biosynthesis are added together within the airtight egg shaped vessel made of synthetic material. The contents are then set into a hyperbolic centripetal spiral motion by the specially-shaped agitator. A cooling coil provides the appropriate temperature control. The vessel is enclosed within an insulating shell of hydrocarbon material to restrict the loss of 'implosion energy' created, instead concentrating it within the vessel so that biosynthesis can take place. The vacuum meter monitors the 'biological vacuum' formed if biosynthesis succeeds.

Apparatus for biological synthesis of spring water, constructed by Swedish biotechnicians.

Fig. 21.1

process. This should not be allowed to form too rapidly as it disadvantageously affects the end product. The development of the vacuum can be monitored with a suitable meter, absolute atmospheres of between 0.8 and 0.96 being sufficient. As a structural form, the egg is well able to resist this without collapse, the main problem here being an air-tight seal, which must be maintained at all times.

Apart from the liquefaction of the carbon-dioxide, the effect of this vacuum is to cause the intimate assimilation of the other ingredients, minerals and metallic trace-elements. Once the water has reached the anomaly point of +4°C the process of cold oxidation begins. Through the centripetal formation of the vortices, the carbones and hydrogen become highly active and hungry for the now passive oxygen and other elements, which become thoroughly bound and produce a stable emulsion.

The whole operation takes about ¾ of an hour and is preferably carried out before 9.00am, after which it should be left to stand in an external temperature of +3°C – +4°C for 24 hours, away from all light and heat, in order to become completely mature. If a thunderstorm is imminent, then production should be postponed until it has passed for, due to the associated rise in the number of positive ions in the atmosphere, the process, which involves the generation of negative ions, will not be a success.

Initially the amount of carbon-dioxide used can only be determined by experiment, i.e. by tasting the finished product. If carbon-dioxide is noticeable, then too much has been added, whereas if the water is too hard, its calcium content is excessive. If the water is both refreshing and invigorating then the proportions of carbon-dioxide and magnesium are correct. Here the problem confronting all of us is to know what refreshing and invigorating water actually tastes like, because in the main we are used to adulterated water, which while wet does neither. However, if the water lacks a refreshing taste or is indifferently invigorating, both of which are qualitative factors, then in the first case more magnesium should be added and in the second more carbon-dioxide.

When drunk fresh from the egg, the effect of this water is to break down all the body's excess acidity, which allows any over-acidified cells to breathe and take up oxygen, promoting a rapid return to health. When drunk the temperature of the water should not exceed +7°C and should be drunk in small amounts only. Above +9°C the quality of the water begins to deteriorate and precautions must be taken to ensure it does not reach this temperature. However, there is a time limit on its drinking, because 24 hours after maturation its diamagnetic energies disappear, which affects it healing qualities. According to Viktor Schauberger this water can barely be differentiated from high-grade mountain spring-water and, if sipped slowly by an impotent man, he will regain his potency.

For the proportions of trace-elements and other compounds in the mixture, the following is a guide for about 10 litres of water:

processes. At the same time, it will raise water to any desired height, for which almost no power of any kind is needed.

My machine is a body which consists of internal and peripheral nozzles, which replace the valves of present machines or supplement them...

My machines only require the impulse and manifest the reaction as an expulse, which not merely presses, but simultaneously sucks. This then results in the creation of resistance-less motion, due to the reciprocity which today's resistance makes use of as a "means of propulsion". [Here Viktor's use of the word 'resistance' may also allude to the unbending attitude of established science – CC]

The body is merely an antenna, whereas the transmitter is responsible for the phenomenon we call "motion". Motion is a function of temperaments, which within and about themselves are possessed of plus and minus in diverse shapes and

TABLE OF INGREDIENTS FOR 10 LITRES OF WATER[5]			
Potassium (K)	= 0.0034 mg/kg	Chlorine (Cl)	= 0.0257 mg/kg
Sodium (Na)	= 0.0776 mg/kg	Sulphate	= 0.1301 mg/kg
Calcium (Ca)	= 0.0215 mg/kg	Bicarbonate	= 0.0638 mg/kg
Magnesium (Mg)	= 0.00039 mg/kg	Nitrite	= 0.0001 mg/kg
Iron (Fe)	= 0.00042 mg/kg	Fluorine (F)	= 0.0028 mg/kg
Manganese (Mn)	= 0.0001 mg/kg	Thiosulphate	= 0.00055 mg/kg
Lithium (Li)	= 0.00022 mg/kg	Malic acid	= 0.0754 mg/kg
Strontium (Sr)	= 0.00047 mg/kg	Metaboric acid	= 0.00497 mg/kg
Aluminium (Al)	= 0.0002 mg/kg	Free CO_2	= 0.0054 mg/kg

In spite of having previously described the pernicious effects of chlorine in its pure form, in this context, however, chlorine is a necessary ingredient. Through the natural bio-electromagnetic ionising processes occurring during the maturation of the water it bonds with other elements, producing hydrochloric acid, for example, which acts as a catalyst and provides the optimum pH for pepsin, the major enzyme in the digestive juices.

21.3 The Repulsine

In a letter to Werner Zimmerman of 21st May 1936[6], Viktor describes the Repulsine (fig. 21.1) as follows:

This machine (30cm wide, 50cm high) vaporises, purifies and distills water by means of cold

sizes. Hence by altering the inner-atomic structure, we can displace the centre of gravity and thereby achieve that which we regard as pure, resistance-free motion; a motion, however, we have for so long not understood, because we ourselves are the resistance, which under the most difficult conditions, has to move itself in order to evolve.

The way this device functions is virtually the same as the Repulsator but, instead of being a sealed vessel in which the quantity of water is fixed, the operation of this apparatus is more or less continuous. The diagram, however, instead of the single-bladed impeller, shows two nested, half egg-shaped, waviform bowls made of silver-plated copper, mounted one above the other on the driveshaft, which otherwise do not touch one another. In the outer bowl, inlets are incorporated at the base to permit the entry into the serpentine cavity between the bowls of the raw water and ingredients entering at the top and flowing down the outside of the outer bowl. In this waviform cavity the distance between the two bowls gradually reduces towards the top.

In the process of flowing through, the water is subjected first to centrifugal force as

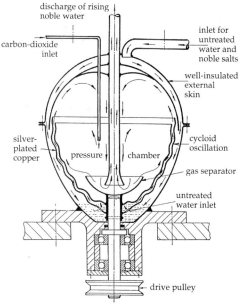

Fig. 21.2   **The Repulsine**

it is impelled from the central axis upwards and outwards, and then to a pulsating centripetal force which imprints it with certain vibrational energies as it cycloidally spirals its way up through the narrowing waviform cavity towards the open upper chamber. As we have seen, water cools when moved centripetally in vortices so, by the time this water reaches the upper, domed chamber it has already cooled considerably.

In this cooler state and having been moved centripetally, the water's existing content of carbones becomes increasingly stimulated. With the introduction of carbon-dioxide the overall carbone content is increased markedly. In combination with the downward cooling vortical flow around the central rising pipe which creates a partial

vacuum as the infused carbon dioxide is converted into carbonic acid, the increasingly hungry carbones begin to bind the dissolved oxygen as the water cycles cycloidally around the inside of the inner bowl. In this process the water becomes increasingly dense and at the same time, imbued with levitational energies arising through centripetence and the negatively charged carbones' unsatisfied demand for positively charged oxygen.

Since the area of greatest density is at the centre of the downward vortex immediately adjacent to the central riser pipe, whatever water reaches a temperature of $+4°C$ impacts on the smaller rotating dish of the gas separator and passes up the pipe. On the other hand any as yet undissolved gases and other elements, whose specific density is less and volume greater than the $+4°C$ water, are centrifugally impelled towards the exterior by the gas separator to rejoin the internal cycle until they too have been thoroughly cooled and absorbed.

Once the water has entered the riser pipe, which is of a design similar to the double-spiral pipe shown in figs.14.2 & 14.4, it then has the same composition and levitational energies as mountain spring water and will rise to any desired height. As such, this device is not a pump, as there is no pumping action, and it can therefore be driven with a fairly modest electric motor, which is merely required to rotate the nested, waviform bowls and gas separator alternately one way and then other as in the device discussed earlier.

21.4 *The Implosion Motor*

In this machine the water receives more or less the same treatment as previously described, namely the vessel is first filled to exclude air and then drained to a certain level with the compensating infusion of carbon-dioxide. This device, while at the same improving the quality of its drive-water, is principally aimed at the generation of power in the form of electricity, although mechanical power can also be ducted off it by attaching a pulley to the central shaft. The design shown in fig. 21.3 is the result of what I have managed to piece together from the various data in my possession and is intended to show the principle rather than an actual working machine.

The development of this machine provided Viktor with many headaches, because the whorl-pipes, the major components of the device, were both extremely difficult to design proportionally and equally difficult to fabricate. Viktor Schauberger based his initial design for these whorl-pipes on the shape of a Kudu antelope horn, the proportions of whose spiral shape and reducing diameter approximate the Golden Section (Phi). Its configuration is also that of the cycloid-spiral space-curve, which is the radial->axial path followed by the 'original' motion, or form-creating movement.

As a further refinement, whereas the overall cross-sectional profile of the whorl-pipe is egg-shaped (as shown at the top right hand corner of the diagram), in its finished form a $\frac{1}{4}$ egg-shaped indentation is incorporated, which runs for the full length of the whorl-pipe and which, viewed as a cross-section along the length of the pipe, either rotates in the same direction as the spiral twist of the pipe (left hand pipe on the diagram), or in the opposite direction (right-hand pipe on the diagram). Remembering the free-flowing function of the spiral-helical pipe (No. 2) in the Stuttgart investigation (chapter 14), the shape of the whorl-pipe directs the water away from the pipe walls, thereby reducing the friction and the associated resistance to a minimum or even a negative value. The effect of this centrifugal-centripetal dynamic is twofold: firstly, it imparts a double spiral motion to the water as it passes through, thereby cooling and condensing, it to its minimal volume; secondly, in association with certain catalysts (Viktor never revealed their true identity, but they may be gold and silver laminates, viz. patented spring-water device, chapter 15, or silicates, see below), it apparently triggers the inversion of the polarities of the contained substances. This may be the conversion from magnetic into bio-electric and electric into bio-magnetic (diamagnetic) for instance, or positive charges into negative charges and *vice versa*. In this process resistance-producing elements are converted into motion-enhancing ones through which dynagens in the form of levitational and diamagnetic energies are generated.

A number of these whorl-pipes are then attached to a central hub, whose lower portion is formed as a hollow cone, the bottom of which is well below water level. As this inverted propeller or centripulser is caused to rotate by the electric motor on the shaft to which the hub is attached, the water is subjected to centrifugal force as it is centrifuged down the whorl-pipes towards the exterior while simultaneously experiencing a double-spiral centripetal contraction as it passes through. This causes extreme compaction and, when it eventually exits from the 1mm diameter jet-nozzles at the tip of the whorl-pipe, it does so with tremendous force due to its high velocity and density.

At 1200 revolutions per minute and depending on the actual radius of the centripulser as a whole, the original texts record the actual exit velocity at about 1,290 metres per second, developing a thrust of 17.9 horsepower per jet, of which there are four per whorl-pipe. 1,290m/s is about four times the speed of sound and depending on the aperture of the jet-nozzles, this jet of water or air can be as solid and as hard as steel wire. The following eye-witness report by a certain Gretl Schneider who accompanied Arnold Hohl, a Swiss during one of his frequent visits to Viktor Schauberger in 1936–37, gives a graphic description of this phenomenon[7]:

Mr. Viktor Schauberger has demonstrated the machine to me. The previous huge construction is no more. It has been reduced to half its former size and in operation develops enormous power. I poured a pot of water into the bottom of it. The machine produced an almost inaudible sound and then a 'pfft' in the same instant and the water pierced right through a 4cm thick concrete slab and a 4mm thick super-hardened steel plate with such force that the water-particles, invisible to the eye due to their high velocity, penetrated right through all clothing and were experienced as lightning

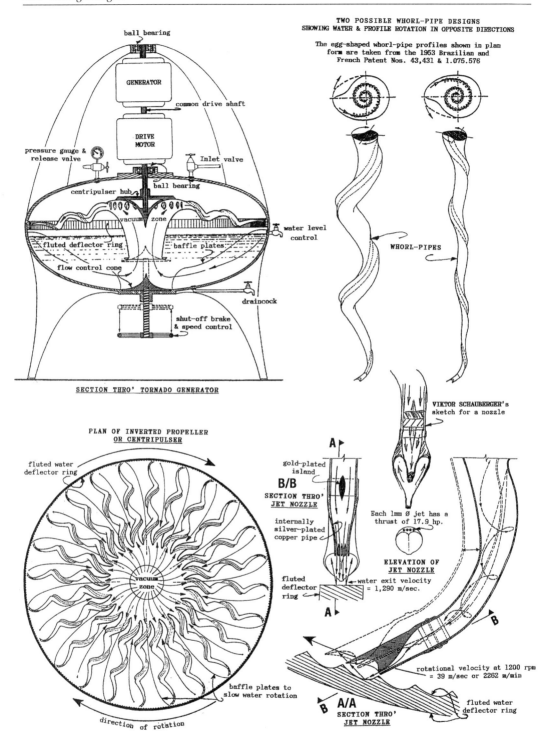

TWO POSSIBLE WHORL-PIPE DESIGNS
SHOWING WATER & PROFILE ROTATION IN OPPOSITE DIRECTIONS

The egg-shaped whorl-pipe profiles shown in plan
form are taken from the 1953 Brazilian and
French Patent Nos. 43,431 & 1.075.576

WHORL-PIPES

VIKTOR SCHAUBERGER's
sketch for a nozzle

Each 1mm Ø jet has a
thrust of 17.9 hp.

ELEVATION OF
JET NOZZLE

ball bearing

GENERATOR

common drive shaft

DRIVE MOTOR

pressure gauge &
release valve

Inlet valve

centripulser hub

ball bearing

vacuum zone

fluted deflector ring

baffle plates

water level
control

flow control cone

draincock

shut-off brake
& speed control

SECTION THRO' TORNADO GENERATOR

PLAN OF INVERTED PROPELLER
OR CENTRIPULSER

fluted water
deflector ring

vacuum
zone

direction of rotation

baffle plates to
slow water rotation

gold-plated
island

B/B

SECTION THRO'
JET NOZZLE

internally
silver-plated
copper pipe

fluted
deflector
ring

A

water exit velocity
= 1,290 m/sec.

A/A

SECTION THRO'
JET NOZZLE

rotational velocity at 1200 rpm
= 39 m/sec or 2262 m/min

fluted water
deflector ring

Fig. 21.3 **Tornado home-power generator**
Schematic design based on patent and other data.

needle-pricks on the skin. Water-glass was also passed through and solidified in 5cm long hairs on the outside of the casing, like bristles.

While Gretl Schneider may well have thought that all she had poured into the machine was common water, it was more probably water highly charged with silicates (compounds of silica and oxides – see chapters 11 & 13), since what was emitted was water-glass (Na_2SiO_3), a white substance formed of a solution of sodium silicate and water. With properties, some catalytic, that Viktor considered vital to healthy full-bodied water by way of emanations and particulate matter, it was through the constant corrasion of quartz and silicia-bearing rocks that water was enriched with fresh elements and charged with pure energy (effect of triboluminescence – see chapters 8 & 13). Moreover, the natural oscillating concentrative vortical flow of healthy water in streams also produced his 'emulsions' from the fine dispersions of minerals and trace-elements, no doubt also comprising silicates, which in the manner described below endowed the water with those upstream-moving levitational energies that enabled trout or salmon to surmount high waterfalls. In their passage through this machine, the natural movement of such emulsions and the processes associated with them were therefore faithfully copied. This intermixing, cohering function of vortical motion is also applicable to the creation of emulsions out of the gases and trace-gases of the atmosphere.

Using this machine in his research Viktor experimented with a number of different silicate suspensions as 'fuels' to drive it. Due to the rapid oscillation to which they were subjected in their whirling passage through the centripulser, both water and fine silica particles were homogenised through cooling vortical densation into a silicia gel or colloidal solution, i.e. emulsions. In operation the outer casing of the device also noticeably cooled. Other references allude to the fact that vibrated quartz particles in a dispersed consistency or colloidal suspension apparently exhibit levitational properties[8], which are further affirmed by experiments carried out in the mid-1920s. Here the exposure of a quartz crystal to certain powerful radio frequencies (electromagnetic vibrations) produced astonishing results. From its initial 15cm³ volume, the crystal increased in size by 800% and then, in company with the experimental apparatus weighing 25kg to which it was attached, levitated to a height of about 2 metres[9].

With no names mentioned in the above eye-witness report, here again we are confronted with the problem of precisely which machine was involved, but it seems most likely to be the one described above. Returning to our consideration of the whorl-pipes themselves, the tips of the whorl-pipes on which the nozzle-units are mounted are angled in the same direction as the centripulser's rotation, here shown clockwise on plan. The original whorl-pipes themselves, which on the diagram radiate rather like spokes, may have been more curved and wrapped around the central hub in the direction of rotation as in fig. 1.3b.

The design of the nozzle arrangement depicted here was suggested by Viktor's own sketch, which shows a cup-shaped cavity like a scoop immediately behind the jets. The intent of this is to catch the full retro-pulsive or recoil blast of the near-solid exiting water as it ricochets off the vertically fluted or scalloped band of metal running around the inner periphery of the housing. Once sufficient revolutions have been attained, the effect of this recoil is to make the centripulser self-rotate, thereby relieving the driving motor of some if not all of its load. While as shown here that the four jets are aligned perpendicular to the plane of rotation and impact simultaneously at one point on the scalloped peripheral ring, a more continuous retro-pulsive thrust would be achieved if they were placed one behind the other horizontally. In this way each jet would then recoil off the scalloped ring at a marginally different time and angle.

As the electricity generator is mounted on the same shaft, some of the electricity it produces is returned to supplement the drive motor if necessary, the remainder being free energy for whatever purpose, which could be used, for instance, to drive either of the devices discussed previously. If this machine functions as Viktor maintains, then the generator ought to produce ten times more power than the motor needs, in other words, there should be a nine-fold surplus of electric current.

In order to prevent the expressed water from continuing to circulate at high speed around the periphery of the containing vessel, vertical curved baffle-plates are fixed to the bottom and sides of the housing, which also direct the water back towards the central intake opening at the bottom of the centripulser hub, where it is immediately sucked upwards again with tremendous force to the waiting mouths of the whorl-pipes.

According to Viktor Schauberger, a starter motor is not strictly necessary and the initial impulse can be given by hand-cranking or with foot-pedals. Indeed the problem as with most of his machines is not how to start it, but how to stop it without damage, due to its high velocity rotation and the extraordinary repulsive force developed at the end of each nozzle. For this, it has been suggested that the best way is to cut off the water supply, which in fig. 21.3 is done by raising the coolie-hat shaped cone normally resident on

the floor of the outer housing during operation. This is attached to a threaded shaft and is screwed up to close off the lower intake opening on the centripulser hub. Another important aspect, not to be forgotten, is that the whole machine should be very firmly anchored to the floor to prevent it rising into the air as a result of the powerful levitational forces generated in the process.

21.4 The Trout Motor and the Biotechnical Submarine

A further or parallel development of the Implosion Motor is the Trout Motor. It forms the nose cone at the bow of the Biotechnical Submarine, shown respectively in figs. 21.4 & 21.5, which combines both centripulser and the waviform configuration of the nested bowls in the Repulsine (fig. 21.2). This centripulser, however, does not incorporate whorl-pipes as such, but the vortical process is apparently induced through the attachment of

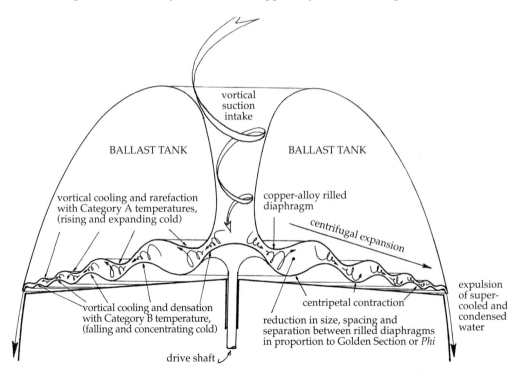

Fig. 21.4   **Detail of centripulser suction drive**

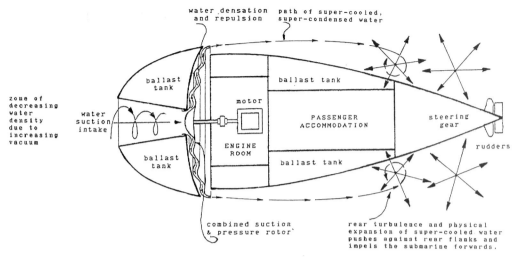

Fig. 21.5 **The biotechnical submarine**
(design principle)

butterfly-wing shaped, curved foils to the internal surfaces of the two converging waviform diaphragms at certain intervals (not shown on the diagram), the effect of which causes the driving medium, either air or water, to flow through as a series of vortices. The action and function of these rilled diaphragms is similar to those of the gills of a stationary trout, whence this motor gets its name.

Two factors are active here. Firstly, in chapter 4 it was stated that according to Viktor, the extreme limits of any pair of dialectic magnitudes (fig. 4.6) could only reach a boundary condition of 96% in the physical world. Secondly, in chapter 7 two different systems of temperature, Types *A* and *B*, were both identified as rising and expanding, and falling and concentrating forms of heat and cold.

Using the media of air or water, with his machines Viktor was able, through the rapid alternation of centripetal densation and diffusion, to interrupt the normal reversion of falling and concentrating cold to heat, by converting the cold to a rising and expanding form. When this reached its extreme limit of 96% it was then reconverted to the falling and concentrating form. This produces an extremely rapid cooling with which Viktor was able to cool water from +20°C to +4°C within seconds.

In this process the absorptive capacity of the carbones becomes so extreme under the powerful concentrative effect of centripetence, which creates a strongly negatively ionised atmosphere, that the oxygen they have already absorbed, which becomes passive with cooling, is thoroughly bound and becomes equally reduced to spacelessness. In other words both carbones and oxygen, together with any other elements or gases, are converted into a state of high-frequency, inter-dimensional, potential energy, which only requires slight heating to provide a massive expansion.

Going back to the two different forms of cold mentioned above, in fig. 21.4 we shall examine how their sequential alternation is achieved. As the waviform centripulser rotates, the water (or air if that medium was chosen) which is present between the two converging rilled diaphragms, is propelled towards the exterior through the action of centrifugal force. As it vacates this space, it is replaced by more water entering through the vortical suction intake, which creates a partial, and sometimes intense, vacuum in front of the submarine into which it is drawn. The intensity of this vacuum is dependent on the rotational velocity of the centripulser unit.

As can be seen on the diagrams, the waviform surfaces of the two diaphragms are not wholly parallel; that is to say, the respective crests and troughs of the two diaphragms are offset in their vertical relation, those of the lower diaphragm being closer to the central axis than those of the upper. The effect of this is to create alternating widening and constricting spaces. The intervals between the peaks of these rilled diaphragms, as well as the space between them, decreases in the proportion of the Golden Section.

As the water enters the first constriction at the bottom of the suction intake, it is impelled into further radial > axial, centripetal, vortical motion by the curved butterfly foils situated just in front of the constriction (not shown for reasons of diagrammatic clarity) and cools under the influence of centripetally-induced falling and concentrating cold. Having slipped frictionlessly through the constriction, it then enters the enlarging space and, with the temporary transfer to axial > radial vortical movement, it cools further under the influence of rising and expanding cold.

To get some idea of what is here involved, if you hold the palm of your hand in front of your open mouth and gradually purse your lips as you exhale, the temperature of the exhaled air increasingly cools. Through the successive alternation of these two forms of cold, the water is cooled not only very rapidly but, by the time it exits from the peripheral ports it is extremely dense, i.e. spacially reduced, and its content of carbones highly aggressive. In the same way that de-oxygenated water is expelled from the gills of the stationary trout and passes down its flanks, here too the super-cooled, carbone-rich water is thrust towards the stern of the submarine.

In this form of propulsion, however, we are not principally concerned with mechanical effects of reverse thrust, which may contribute to a certain extent, but rather with the sequential effects of physical dematerialisation at the bow, followed by physical expansion at the stern. As shown on fig. 21.5 this transformed water flows towards the rear of the elongated, egg-shaped body of the submarine hull where it reacts with the outside water of different specific density, temperature and physical composition. This causes it to expand rapidly, not only because of the higher external temperatures, but also because it reabsorbs those elements which were precipitated during the near instantaneous cooling (the precipitation of salts and minerals occurs with cooling under the absence of light and air – chapter 9, section 9.3).

This rapid physical expansion, however, occurs between the body of water lying astern and the submarine itself. In pressing outwards against both of these resistances, it encounters the submarine's tapering hull and closes in against it, causing the submarine, like the stationary trout, to move forwards like a bar of slippery soap squeezed between the fingers. This forward motion is further intensified through the vacuum created at the bow by the rapid intake of water by the centripulser.

21.6 The Klimator

This device, apparently the size of a boy's hat, is a generator capable of producing temperatures belonging to Type A artificially. Viktor described it as a miniature copy of the Earth which, through its 'original' form of motion could produce both rising and expanding cold and falling and concentrating heat, the former being lethal to all pathogenic bacteria.

With very high revolutions, the copper-alloyed centripulser causes ordinary air to move above the speed of sound, which centripulses the air to the point of molecular collapse and gives rise to a hitherto unknown form of atomic energy. This can be intensified as desired by varying the rate of rotation, with the result that natural forms of either heat or cold can be generated. With this device, instead of the usual hot head and cold feet symptomatic of conventional heating systems, the space is radiantly heated from above downwards in the same way that the Sun heats the Earth's atmosphere. As a result, the whole space is evenly suffused with heat.

On the other hand, at a different setting, the space is filled with an even dispersion of rising and expanding cold, producing the fresh air experienced in mountainous regions. This variation in temperature conditions is achieved by the incorporation of a small electric heating resistance or element. When a high current is passed through it, the rotational velocity of the centripulser is reduced and warm temperature conditions prevail. On the other hand, when

Fig. 21.6 **Prototype A** *(top)*,
Prototype B *(bottom)*

the heat of this is reduced, the rate of rotation is correspondingly increased, producing the mountain quality air mentioned above.

21.7 *The Flying Saucer*

As far as can be determined, the so-called 'Flying Saucer' functioned using slight modifications of the Trout Motor, but like the Klimator, rotated at much higher velocities, as the driving medium was air. The two prototypes shown in fig. 21.6 are different models of the same device (prototypes A upper and B lower). Whereas the Klimator is the size of a boy's hat, the size of the flying saucer is about 65cm in diameter. This may also be what has been referred to as a 'vacuum machine', which seems quite possible in the light of the condensing planetary movement of the media in the Trout Motor, since the centripulser can

use either air or water as the driving medium. There is also reason to believe that with this device experiments were also made using silica gel as a propellant.

The first of these devices was manufactured at Viktor's own expense by the Kertl company in Vienna in 1940 and was subsequently further developed at Schloss Schönbrunn. The purpose of these prototypes was two-fold:

1) the further investigation of free energy production, and
2) the validation of Viktor's theories on levitational flight.

Whereas the first case required the upper aerodynamic portion to be permanently fixed to the base, the 2nd case required its attachment to a quick-release coupling to permit its ascent once auto-rotation and the generation of levitational force had been achieved. To initiate the energetic process, a small high-speed electric motor was used, capable of producing between 10,000 and 20,000rpm. Despite its compact size, this machine generated such a powerful levitational force that when it was first switched on (without Viktor Schauberger's permission and in his absence!), it sheared the six $\frac{1}{4}$" diameter high-tensile steel anchor bolts and shot upwards to smash against the roof of the hangar. According to Viktor Schauberger's calculations, based on the data from previous tests, a 20cm diameter device with a rotational velocity of 20,000rpm would have generated levitational forces of such magnitude that it could have lifted a weight of 228 tonnes. Indeed, reports indicate that similar devices were built on a larger scale, as shown by an excerpt from an article about Viktor Schauberger written by A. Khammas in *Implosion* magazine, which states:

There are many rumours about what Schauberger was actually doing during this period, most of which suggest that he was in charge of developing 'flying discs' under contract to the army. It later become known that 'the 'flying disc' launched in Prague on the 19th of February 1945, which rose to an altitude of 15,000 metres in three minutes and attained a forward speed of 2,200 kph, was a development of the prototype he built at Mauthausen concentration camp. Schauberger wrote, 'I only first heard of this event after the war through one of the technicians who had worked with me'. In a letter to a friend, dated the 2nd August 1956, Schauberger commented, 'The machine was supposed to have been destroyed just before the end of the war on Keitel's orders.[10]

Here, and just before going to print, I was extraordinarily fortunate in having been presented with more detailed photographs of the flying saucer from America by Richard C. Feierabend, a former commander in the United States Navy[11]. These show the lower portion of what on the evidence would appear to be prototype A and will greatly facilitate the explanation of its function. Before doing so, however, we should familiarise ourselves with its construction by dismantling it layer by layer in conjunction with the cross-section (fig. 21.7) and the relevant illustrations (figs. 21.8–21.12).

In fig. 21.8 the flying saucer is shown mounted on a heavy cast metal base that

incorporates the gearbox from which two shafts protrude, one horizontally and the other downwards. The high-speed electric motor was most probably connected to the latter in order to spin the whole upper portion up to the critical rotational velocities of between 10,000 and 20,000 rpm, above which autorotation begins. Through reduction gearing the horizontal shaft seems likely to have been used for drawing off mechanical power. As far as the direction of rotation is concerned, since most electric motors (viewed from the shaftless end) rotate clockwise, then as the motor is mounted below with driveshaft uppermost, the centripulser would be imparted an anticlockwise spin when seen from above.

The outer cowling A made of 1.2mm thick copper sheet and with a central aperture can be seen in fig. 21.9, just below which there is an annular cast iron or aluminium ring about 5 cm deep and 1.5 cm thick projecting about 2cm beyond the cowling itself. This forms part of the base and is for ease of handling and protection of the whole apparatus when not in use. Through the aperture, part of the

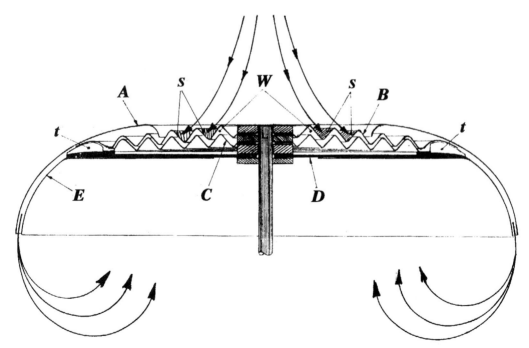

Fig. 21.7   **Cross-section through Flying Saucer**

immediately underlying concentrically rippled plate or diaphragm, also of copper, can be seen, which is depicted *in toto* in fig. 21.10. On this uppermost rilled plate *B* a series of slots *s* are incised at an angle on the inner sloping faces of the 2nd and 3rd rings, the slots on the inner 2nd ring being tapered towards the base, longer in length, more closely spaced and spanning from valley to crest. Through these the indrawn air is part sucked and part centrifuged into the space between plate *B* and plate *C*, the latter plate shown in fig. 21.11. When placed together as a unit, the combination of both plates and intervening waviform space *w* is what I refer to elsewhere as a 'centripulser', since in the form of multiple whorl-pipes or waviform cavity both essentially fulfil the same function. In comparison with the cross-section in fig. 21.4, where the centripulser element was composed from written descriptions, here the annular ripples of both plates *B* and *C* in fig. 21.7 are much more angular and their crests and valleys aligned vertically.

In comparing plates *B* & *C*, while both have 5 regularly spaced rings of equal size, the crest of the outermost being more rounded, plate *B* terminates with a 6th much wider peripheral cowl. Plate *C*, with only 5 rings, is nested inside an outer array of gill-like curvilinear turbine blades *t*, which are integral to plate *D* (fig. 21.12). While plates *B* and *C* are waviform, plate *D* is flat and either made of stainless steel, aluminium or silver-plated copper, as are the gill-like turbine blades. The slots between the blades curve first one way and then the other, the blade itself having a pronounced aerofoil shape. Attached to the underside of plate *D* is a further component, a dependent copper peripheral cowl *E* visible in fig. 21.11, which in association with upper cowling *A* directs the centripulser's emissions downwards and below the device. It also creates a concavity on the underside of the craft by which it is impelled upwards through the rapid expansion of the previously dematerialised or highly cooled and condensed air.

When assembled, plates *B*, *C* & *D* are fixed together at the hub with 6 bolts and separated with spacers. Cowling *E* is attached to plate *D*.

Fig. 21.8

Fig. 21.9

Cowling *A* and the outer rim of plate *B* on the other hand are fixed to the turbine blade array with 12 countersunk screws, plate *C* being fastened to plate *D* with 6 screws. Here, in view of the electromagnetic and atomic reactions generated during operation, it seems likely that the various components were partially or wholly insulated from one another, the above spacers perhaps being made of rubber or other insulating material. The size of the holes in cowling *A* would appear to confirm this, since they would allow for the insertion of both fixing screw and insulating sheath.

One item, noticeable by its absence, is the conical hub shown on both prototypes in fig. 21.6, which may be the vital component the Russians took from Viktor's apartment in

Vienna (chapter 1). If so, it would have been attached by a bolt screwed into the top of the central shaft shown in fig. 12.9. It seems more likely that the model examined here is indeed prototype *A*, because there appear to be no fixing points on the second ring on plate *B* corresponding to those on the hub of prototype B (fig. 21.6). The fact that the hub of this device totally covers the 3rd ring further confirms this, because the rapid intake of air would be too constricted. In contrast, the higher hub of prototype A has a number of slots in the sides and top, which would permit the free entry of air to the slots in rings 2 & 3. What actually happens inside the hub can only be speculated. Its half-egg shape, however, could suggest an inner, but inverted arrangement of the nested rilled bowls of the Repulsine described earlier (fig. 21.2), or some other form of centripetence inducing mechanism. So much for the construction.

Before we address the internal dynamics in more detail, it is first necessary to interpret Viktor's above reference to the *"compression of dematerialisation"*, for which we must turn to basic physics. In particular, the characteristics of the three most commonly known nuclear particles, the electron, proton and neutron, which respectively have the following external charges and relative atomic masses: Electron –, 0.000549 kg; Proton +,1.007277 kg; Neutron *zero*, 1.008665 kg. Since the neutron carries no external charge, it has hitherto been assumed that any internal positive and negative charges have cancelled each other out, i.e. there is no measurable external electric charge. According to current theory, because the neutron has zero charge it is able to penetrate the open structure of the atom and this way, through bombardment with a single neutron, a given element can be transformed into one with the next higher atomic number. Moreover, this 'uncharged' neutron is able to generate a magnetic field, although the origin of its 'magnetic-ness' apparently still remains an enigma.

Here let us take a leaf out of Viktor Schauberger's book and turn our thinking through 180°, for if the neutron, which has been observed to pulsate rhythmically and

has magnetic properties, is actually viewed as a magnetic or biomagnetic magnitude, then the whole picture changes and suddenly many things become clearer. Instead of a discrete subatomic particle, it can then be seen as a transpiercing, constantly moving force, the vibrant life-force of the atom, through which the atoms themselves evolve from hydrogen to uranium. It becomes the key energy-form that binds the nuclear particles together and which, in whole-numbered pulsations representing the entity – neutron, resonates with the electric fields of both proton and electron alike to form stable atomic structures.

In *Through the Curtain* by Dr Shafica Karagulla[12], wherein the magnetic nature of the neutron is affirmed, it is also described as a 'sounder binder', i.e., a higher form of vibratory energy but not a particle. Following from the above, it is this binding ability that transforms the base material of the hydrogen atom (1 proton+ and 1 electron-) into higher atoms. Without the formation of the latter and their subsequent combination into molecules, no life, no physical structures of any kind would be possible. Magnetism or biomagnetism is therefore synonymous with vitalising, animating neutronic energy and in energetic realms the neutron has thus a similar function to water in the physical world.

Furthermore, if the neutron's cohering activity is braked, such as happens with paraffin wax for example, then radioactive decay results, which is analogous to the decline in the health and stability of a human if its regular 'pulsations' of good drinking water cease. It is also to be remembered here that it is biomagnetism as an expression of levitation which is responsible for the 'uprightness and right-side-upness' of all organic life. When the uplift of life-force decreases, the ponderous effect of gravity increases. Curiously enough, the combined masses of both electron and proton amount to 1.007826 kg, which is 0.000839 kg less than the 1.008665 kg mass of the neutron. This seem to furnish further confirmation of the necessity for the slight predominance of magnetism over electricism if life is to continue and upwardly evolve as discussed in chapter

Fig. 21.10

Fig. 21.11

4. Through their 180° reinterpretation and re-examination many other factors in physics may also corroborate this other view of the neutron.

With the above in mind we shall now postulate a process that could enable the saucer to fly. Leaving aside the unknown role of the half-eggshaped hub, in principle what may happen is this: Due to the centripulser's high rate of rotation, air is drawn into the serpentine cavity between plates *B* and *C* via slotted rings 2 & 3 on plate *B*, where it is subjected initially to powerful centrifugal forces that cause the air molecules to accelerate axially–>radially away from the centre. In addition to being centrifuged, the air is made to oscillate rapidly up and down at the same time forming tight radial–>axial vortices at each bend in the waviform cavity, which increasingly cools and condenses it. This oscillating air also induces the sympathetic

vibration of the two enclosing waviform plates, as happens with loud-speakers, which further enhances the rapid emulsification of the aeriform substances.

Exposed to higher and higher velocities and forces in this centripulsing process, the air molecules are subjected to express cooling and more and more extreme densation through the simultaneous interaction of centrifugal and centripetal force. As we have seen above, the transformation of air into water produces an 816-fold reduction in volume and at lower revolutions the centripulser may well expel a certain amount of water as a result. The vacuity created by such a reduction in volume, however, produces an increasingly powerful suction into which more air is drawn. This happens so rapidly that an area of atmospheric rarefaction or partial vacuum is created immediately above the saucer. As the process continues and with high-speed revolutions in the order of 20,000 rpm, both vacuum and densation become intense. Indeed the centripulsion and the intensity of densation become so extreme and the resultant close-packing of the molecules so tight that the molecular and nuclear binding energies or valencies are affected in a way that triggers the antigravity effect. Apart from molecular compression, a point is reached where a large number of electrons and protons with opposite charges and directions of spin are forced into collision and annihilate one another. As lower rather than higher orders of energy and the basic building blocks of atoms, they are upwardly extruded as it were out of the physical and into virtual states.

In other words, they have been compressed back into their 4th dimensional origins, creating what Viktor referred to as a 'void' in the physical matrix, which in turn increases the inward suction of air to fill it. This is no inert, empty vacuity, however, but a living vacuum of huge potential, for all it now contains is pure neutronic energy, which in the light of the above should be the most primordial of life-cohering essences and therefore originate from higher, more sublimely dynamic realms such as the 5th. Freed of its function as the magnetic 'cement' of the

Fig. 21.12

now dematerialised particles, it interacts and energises the atomic nuclei of its physical diamagnetic counterpart, the copper components of the flying saucer, endowing them with antigravitational properties that contribute towards the craft's ascent.

The other contributor to levitation is the expulsion of the densely compressed emulsion of molecules and atoms that have not been 'virtualised'. Passing through the aerofoil slits of the turbine blades t, which diffuse and separate them prior to their exit between outer cowl A and inner cowl E, they subsequently expand with tremendous rapidity in the zone beneath the saucer, creating a strong pressure that thrusts it further into the area of rarefaction created above. In addition a glowing bluish-white discharge akin to ionisation is produced. In this instance, however, since no thermal effects are apparent apart from extreme cooling, we are here more probably concerned with triboluminescent bio-magnetic phenomena (chapters 8 & 13). Due to the mutual pressures exerted through exposure to such high compressive stress, the protons and electrons of the various elements in the dense aeriform emulsion quickly return to their former rest-orbits upon their release, and in so doing emit a cold bio-magnetic glow. The final point concerns the question of autorotation. This remains

problematic, because the key factor of the direction of rotation, while mooted above to have been anticlockwise, may actually have been the opposite. On strictly aerodynamic principles, the rapid passage of the air-emulsion through the aerofoil-shaped turbine blades (fig. 21.12) and its subsequent expulsion ought to create a 'lift' in a clockwise direction. This direction may indeed be correct, for in view of the vast magnitude of the forces in question, the extreme suction, extreme densation, extreme expansion, and in a certain sense the intense vacuum created over-unity supply of aeriform propellant, the whole apparatus may well disobey established laws and autorotate.

On the other hand, the levitative effect may have been produced by other means. Having inspected the device personally at Feierabend's home literally two days before this book went to print, the upper 'saucer' section appears to be securely attached to the lower heavy metal casting containing the driveshaft and gearbox. There is no indication of any quick-release mechanism by which the upper portion could detach itself from the lower, thus allowing the 'disc' to rise autonomously. From this it would seem that while it was able to autorotate, this particular device was destined for energy production as mentioned earlier. However, due to the extreme power of the levitation energies generated, it did so by accident, rather than by design. Recalling Professor Ehrenhaft's findings with regard to the light-induced movement of fine particles and the magnetising effect of light on matter in Chapter 1 where it was established that the forces involved in the spiral motion of the particles were 70 times stronger than gravity, then it may possibly be due to this effect that levitation of the device occurred. It has been reported that this machine emitted a halo of bluish-white light around the lower perimeter of the outer cowling A (fig. 21.9) when in operation, which has been described earlier as bio-magnetic light rather than ionisation. During the emulsion of the elements of the indrawn air, a higher form of triboluminescence may have been produced between the two rilled diaphragms due to the mutual 'abrasion' of the particles under extreme centripetal compaction, which would have infused and iridesced the whole of the interstitial space. As blue-white light it would have had a far higher frequency and intrinsic energy than red for example, and causing the particles of the air to spiral at extremely high velocities in the way described in Prof. Ehrenhaft's research. In the process they could well have been endowed with the same powerful antigravitational force, which, 70 times stronger than gravity, would have been of sufficient power to shear the anchor bolts cast into the concrete floor and lift the whole apparatus to the ceiling. These important questions, however, indeed all the processes described above, the effects and energies they produce and the extent to which they interact can only finally be resolved through experiment.

With the use of the various apparatuses described very briefly above, not only can virtually free energy be generated, but the whole system of transport can be revolutionised, rendering the present use of environmentally polluting fuels and the machines they drive obsolete. Moreover, water of a supreme quality can be produced very cheaply, which will not only vastly improve the health of humanity as a whole, but also the fertility and quality of produce grown with its use.

As a final note while the production of sufficient energy is one of the major problems confronting the world today, despite the obvious advantages offered by these machines, it must still be remembered and emphasised that the whole basis of life on this planet depends on the increase in the amount of vegetation and forest cover. In order to bring about the change for the better that we all so fervently desire, it is therefore necessary to institute both energy and reafforestation programmes simultaneously, the latter being given financial priority, for it is the one in most urgent need of attention.

Notes

1. For full texts see the *Eco-technology* series – Viktor Schauberger's writings in 3 vols: *The Water Wizard*, *The Fertile Earth* and *Schauberger's Revolution*, trans. & ed. by Callum Coats: Gateway, Bath, UK, 1997 (Nat.Book Network, Lanham, MD, USA & Banyan Tree Book Distr, Stirling, So. Australia).

2. *Mensch und Technik*, Year 24, Vol.2, 1993, (Spec.ed, para.7.7.8): devoted to recently discovered information on Viktor Schauberger contained in the Swiss, Arnold Hohls' notebook.

3. "New Approach to Cold Fusion" (Low-Temperature Nuclear Fusion), by I.L. Gerlovin, R.Kh. Baranova, and P.S. Baranov, *Zhurnal Obshchei Khimii*, Vol.62, No.1, pp.230–232, Jan.1992, published in English by Plenum, Article No. 0022-1279/92/6201-0193.

4. FFT stands for 'Fundamental Field Theory'.

5. "The Production of Noble Water" ("Die Herstellung von Edelwasser") by Aloys Kokaly: *Implosion* No.36, p.32.

6. *Mensch und Technik* (spec.ed.): pp. 42–43.

7. "Viktor Schauberger's Repulsator – Excerpts from an interview" *Mensch und Technik* vol.2, 1986, pp. 65–77.

8. p. 78, ibid. Synopsis of a report on the work of Kowski and Frost originally published with pictures in the September 1927 issue of "Science and Invention".

9. *Mensch und Technik* (spec. ed.): Para 7.7.9.

10. "Implosion" No. 83, p. 19, from an article by A. Khammas entitled "The Emergence of Biotechnology" ("Aufbruch der Biotechnik").

11. These photographs are of an apparatus, purportedly Viktor Schauberger's owing to its history and shape, although there are no identifying marks. In October 1994 it was given by Karl Gerchsheimer to Richard C. Feierabend, a former commander in the United States Navy, who very kindly made the photos available to me in time for publication.

12. *Through the Curtain* by Dr Shafika Karagulla (dec'd), in a chapter on p. 194 the neutron is described as having magnetic properties and the source of what is commonly termed magnetism. De Vorss & Co., Marina del Rey, CA, 1983.

22
LAST THOUGHTS

Having now moved gently through Viktor Schauberger's broad conceptual spectrum and its practical implementation, which has by no means been treated exhaustively, we have perhaps become aware of the scope that this completely new environmental and ecological paradigm offers the future. We have seen how the outpouring of energy in all its various dimensions and provenances is the primary cause, not only of ourselves, but of all we see around us, representing as it does the agency through which the originating idea is manifested by the Will-to-create.

As an expression of this higher desire, Life is procreated and projected into physical manifestation through the synthesis of dualities. The reciprocal interaction between pairs of opposing energetic magnitudes, the differences and diversity thus arising, produces the eternal pulsation and the ceaseless cycles that are life's hallmarks. This unstable state of evolutionary equipoise, founded often on extremely subtle differences in temperature, represents a particular level of energy. It can easily be upset if, through lack of understanding, effect is mistaken for cause, or worse, all these vital differences are expunged in the pursuit or imposition of uniformity.

Life is the manifestation of the harmonious interaction of individualities, each with its own qualities and particular capacities, which are impossible to compute. No two naturally created things can ever be truly identical because, in their creation they are the products arising from the influences existing at a given time in a given space, a space that grants each its special identity and characteristics and which cannot give birth to any other entity because it is already occupied by the evolving entity in question. Therefore, a little to the right, a little to the left, a little up or a little down, the prevailing conditions are marginally different and, in consequence give rise to a marginally different form which, while very similar is nevertheless not exactly identical.

Recalling Goethe's poem in chapter 3, as individualities we are all inextricably interwoven into the vital matrix of life as the physical manifestation of vortical concentrations, or whirling, vibrating cores of the universal energy that dynamises this whole Universe. We therefore cannot separate ourselves from it or from one another and, could we but see all these energies with our naked eyes, we might truly appreciate how interconnected we all are with everything else. While science purports to be the greatest exponent of objectivity, it too must eventually admit that the parameters it defines are subjective in their origin.

What, after all, is measurement? Where do we start measuring and at what scale? This depends on what is to be measured; whether it is the distance between stars in light-years or the separation between atoms in angstroms. It is a purely subjective decision which yardstick is applied to which. Due to the fine attenuation of its energies, the extreme radius of action of the electron is today still not known with any degree of accuracy, nor where its energetic effect ultimately ceases, some holding the view that it extends even to the furthest extremities of the Cosmos.

Should this be the case, where do we, as individuals, end and where do others begin? Where is the clear unequivocal division between you and me or between me and any other creature or organism on this planet? While at the level of the atom, the separation between one thing and another becomes problematic, at the level of electrons and the even smaller quarks this defies definition. We must, therefore, admit to ourselves that we too are part of every other. Each of us is Atlas, bearing the world upon his or her shoulders.

At any given moment the world is as it is because we, as individuals are in it. For when each individual, possessed of his or her own personal vibrations and emanations, electro-magnetic and otherwise, passes away, the balance of the whole alters very slightly to restore a new state of equilibrium. Each of us has an inescapable responsibility for the well-being of the whole, for through the power of our thoughts, behaviour and physical actions it is we who largely determine the outcomes.

In all honesty, therefore, we can no longer declare that the ubiquitous impersonal 'they' should do something about it, for the buck stops with each one of us. Would we strive for a better future, we must ensure that our activities are harmonious and in accord with Nature's omnipotent laws, for it is through their contradiction and arrogant disregard that we have brought about our own undoing.

This process of devaluation and devolution we have instigated has been accelerating on its downward path in step with the accelera-tion of mechanistic materialism. With our more celestial connections thus conveniently buried and competitiveness rising under the desire for the acquisition of material wealth, we wished to become creators and masters of the world controlling supply and demand. So we, like the Prodigal Son, began to take this world apart piece by piece to see how it had been put together. Analysis of everything down to the smallest detail, while valuable as the dialectic counterpart of synthesis, became

the overriding goal, each scientific discipline splitting into further and further branches. The synthesis and ultimate unity of all phenomena have therefore been lost under the plethora of minutiae.

All the various branches of science are becoming increasingly splintered into smaller and smaller fragments and as each fragment analyses further, then another split follows and overall comprehension diminishes com-mensurately. More and more resonant sys-tems of atoms are smashed in particle accelerators to try to perceive, for just one split second, the essential nature of the forces and energies that cohere them. What emerges in the patterns of destruction produced in cloud-chambers are spiralling energies whirl-ing to left and right, endowed with either positive or negative charges, which either separate, forming tighter and tighter vortices, or impact together and vanish completely. Ultimately all that has been seen is a particu-lar form of movement, but no clue is revealed as to what the quintessential nature of move-ment is and whence it originates.

Denying even the possibility of the exis-tence of a higher direction of affairs, we have turned our back on the central source of light, the hub of the cosmic wagonwheel, as it were. As we stand on the spokes of this wheel, looking out into the darkness, and move further and further into the looming obscurity, our shadows lengthen and increas-ingly abstract and complicated theories are proposed in order to explain this false reality. Moreover, as we move out, the gap between one spoke and the next widens, communica-tion between them becoming increasingly difficult as their common root lies so far away. There is no cohesion. Incoherence mul-tiplies. Our analytical approach to life has therefore blinded us to the true realities and underlying interdependencies.

Religion has also constricted the minds of humanity, the word religion itself being derived from the Latin root 'religere', which means 'to bind back' or 'to tie down'. Personalised concepts of a God or gods above us have dimmed the majesty of the ECI – Eternally Creative Intelligence – and have set us apart and outside as separate entities, instead of being contributing divinities within the body of the Divine. Through religion and its dogmas, a high fence has been erected between us and our rightful spiritual potential but, more importantly, between us and our full intercommunion with the ECI as represented by Nature. This has subjugated us initially to the dictates of an all-powerful Church, later to be followed by an all-powerful science.

Our station as the Chosen of God and being made in His or Her image has caused us to regard the Nature that nurtures us solely as our private preserve and as an object for exploitation. But what of the rest of Creation? Are not all other creatures also made according to the images of the ECI? For we certainly are not responsible for them. Despite all our scientific advances, even in genetics, we cannot actually create Life. We still cannot create that unknowable, unnameable spark that animates and quickens, however much we may poke and prod at what we have created.

These other creatures, too, are on the upward path of their evolution and since the procreation of new life-forms and fundamentally new species is beyond our power, we do not have the right to deny them their right to exist. Indeed the sixth of the Ten Commandments given to Moses states unequivocally "Thou shalt not kill!". This command is not qualified in any way and, if we assume that it is the true record of what was then stated, it should therefore be taken to mean precisely what it says. Its meaning is further amplified by verse 29 in Genesis:

And God said, Behold I have given you every herb bearing seed, which is upon the face of all the earth, and every tree, in which is the fruit of a tree yielding seed; to you it shall be for meat.

Through our sheer arrogance and supposedly 'special' position, however, we have perverted these directives to suit our own purposes and to absolve us from all responsibility for the death of lesser beings which, in our blindness, we do not see support our very existence. These, too, are infused with the spirit of the ECI and are part of the same intelligence that has given rise to our own

genesis. We should, therefore, adopt the Tibetan concept of 'Ahimsa', of harmlessness to all sentient beings, for such is the integrated inter-dependency of all life that whenever we harm the environment or even the smallest of creatures, we inevitably harm ourselves, and with their death we too are diminished.

While this may smack of rank idealism, we are nevertheless forced to admit that our present ideals and value systems have brought us no utopia. While there have been tremendous improvements in many areas of human endeavour and compassionate understanding, despite the constant promises of recovery, the human world is still in total disarray both economically and socially, and full of conflict. Intolerance is rife with man against woman, sect against sect, nation against nation, while the rich are comfortably buffered against increasing poverty and privation with full bellies just as bulbous as the bloated stomachs of the starving.

More and more restrictions are placed on our freedoms of word and deed, ostensibly desirable and for the good of all, while their reverse side insidiously claps yet another shackle on our independence. Falsity is heaped on falsity and one deception after another is foisted on us by those who seek to regulate events for their own benefit, while controlling every aspect of our lives by immersing us in irredeemable debt. Where is there any real humanity in all of this? Is this what we truly believe life is all about and is this how we would have it continue?

We are not alone in our travails, however, for this state of human strife, discord and spiritual instability is also mirrored in an increasingly diseased and sickening Nature who, in her present high state of fever shivers between record heat and record cold. Mother-Earth is now seeking, with all the forces at her command, to re-establish her own equilibrium and health, thrashing about with increasingly violent storms, sweating in catastrophic floods, parching with devastating droughts, writhing in all-consuming conflagrations and shivering in rending earthquakes. Beset from all sides by these awesome and terrifying events, we have the effrontery to call them 'natural disasters', blaming Nature for what we ourselves are responsible. For in the light of all that has been written previously, there can be little doubt that we are the true instigators of these cataclysmic episodes. These are not 'Acts of God', but misdeeds directly attributable to the senseless activities of humankind.

We therefore urgently need to propose a new set of higher ideals and work towards their realisation. Of necessity they must be at variance with those to which we presently subscribe and may cause much discomfort to those people who would resist or cannot accept change.

Before we set about proposing these new standards of behaviour and conduct, certain factors should perhaps be entertained, which may perhaps throw light on the origins of the present *status quo*. In Viktor's view, the physical conditions of the human world and Nature are the direct, legitimate and inevitable outcome of humanity's spiritual concepts and ideological convictions. They comprise the *vis generatrix*, as it were, which today has resulted in the over-predominance of centrifugence, explosion and over-heating, phenomena that are about to destroy our civilisation. Historically such a disaster overtook humanity before in the cataclysmic destruction of Atlantis, which Viktor held to be the result of the artificial over-stimulation of the levitative forces of implosion. Applying Viktor's logic to the analogous and now looming situation confronting humankind, it could be inferred that Atlantean society and technology were founded on concepts antithetical to those to which we presently adhere. From fig. 4.6 (p.63) we remember that levitation and implosion are associated with centripetence, carbones and the cooperative nurturing aspect of the female. By extension, Atlantean society may well have been matriarchal in which women would have held the principal positions of authority – queens, high-priestesses and oracles being much in evidence in recorded history. Under such a societal organisation in which feminine aspected energies and aspirations were supreme, it is conceivable that men were in a subordinate state, and very much in the same suppressed condition that women generally are today. With Atlantis destroyed, in the ensuing chaos the subjugated males seized the opportunity to reverse their intolerable situation, taking initiative and power back from women.

With the increasing suppression of women in historical times, the centrifugal nature of maleness and the divisiveness associated with it gradually became more and more out of balance. Mother-Earth was raped and shorn of all her treasures. Wars broke out as squabbles over land and wealth multiplied. Rivalry between men and other men increased as nation rose against nation. With few restraints to stem this rising disintegrative surge, women were further debased as competitive ideology gained ground, which has not only led to acceptance of competition as one of the principle strategies governing life and behaviour, but also to the view that the workings of Mother-Nature are equally competitive. Here it is to be remembered that these doctrines, both in religion and science, were mainly laid down by men.

In the process, we have again arrived at a world condition analogous to that which may have destroyed Atlantis so many thousands of years ago. The difference here being that, this time, we are about to destroy the planet as a result of the vast over-dominance of our centrifugal technology and its bedfellow, our competitive ideology. Of late the inevitable reaction has again become manifest as women fight for their rightful place as equals in a society composed almost evenly of men and women.

Unless enormous and sensitive care is taken, there is a great danger that everything will go overboard towards the opposite extreme and once again get wildly out of balance. Both womankind and mankind should therefore carefully, objectively and unemotionally review the present situation from a much higher perspective before taking any irreversible steps. As we have seen in the discussion of the male fertilising function of oxygen in its interaction with the fructigenic female carbones, when oxygen, which is associated with and becomes highly active through centrifugence, gets the upper hand, it becomes aggressive and destroys. On the other hand, with cooling it becomes passive and is bound by the female carbones, through which all life and evolution harmoniously unfold.

Perhaps, therefore, in the light of this natural evolutionarily productive and reproductive phenomenon, the role of men should not be to lead arrogantly on all occasions on the false assumption that this is a man's world which, as we have seen has brought such disaster upon us, but should be to lend their greater physical strength, generally more technical know-how and other complementary abilities, to a new society in which governance should be mainly, but not entirely, directed by women. Apart from their many other attributes, on this Mother-Earth women are the sustainers of the future, of which strife, discord and division are the greatest enemies.

For evolution to proceed harmoniously there has to be the right balance between antitheses; that is to say, the activity of all the various magnitudes in the right hand column of the table in fig. 4.6 (p.63) have to predominate slightly. However, it should be equally remembered that no single aspect can exist without its counterpart. There can be no existence for electricism without magnetism, no gravity without levity, no Mother-Earth without Father-Sun, no woman without man. Indeed, it may well be, too, that the ECI cannot exist unless we also exist as part of It. The ECI is the inseminator of the idea and we and all other life are the products of Its fecund manifestation.

A growing number of individuals, such as Prof. David Bohm (*Wholeness and the Implicate Order*[1]), the astronomer Sir Fred Hoyle (*The Intelligent Universe*[2]) and many others, have presented entirely new concepts of the cosmos, its functions and how it came into being, thereby contributing towards the growing impetus for the generation of a new paradigm. Organisations such as Greenpeace, Friends of the Earth and many more are on the increase, composed of thinking people who see the urgent need for change and who oppose, often with extraordinary personal courage and self-sacrifice, the conservative, self-interested forces and oppressive powers that strive to maintain the status quo.

Change is most certainly in the wind, but there will be no immediate change for the better until fundamentally new programs based on long term targets are put in hand and a new natural economic philosophy is espoused, remembering always that lasting economic prosperity of any kind is founded exclusively on an abundance and maintenance of healthy greenery and wholesome water.

If we would rebuild the forest, we cannot expect to reap any rewards in good quality timber for 200 to 300 years, for it takes that long for many trees to mature and produce high-quality seeds. In earlier centuries, people were far more aware of the continuity of life and the necessity to make provision for posterity. They planted avenues of oaks, knowing full well that they would never see them in their full maturity. More than ever before, this responsible attitude towards the environment needs to be resuscitated.

Our role should, therefore, be that of guardians of the future, of helpers, restorers and nurturers of all life, all the more so at this late hour if we are not to inaugurate our own oblivion. Too many species, each with its special characteristics and activities as instruments in Nature's orchestral masterpiece, largely still a mystery to us, have been sacrificed as our innate spirituality and sensitivity have been debased in the pursuit of economic and material wellbeing. In order to acquit ourselves properly in the future and to restore to ourselves the former dignity, worthy of administrators of the ECI's creative plan, we may once have possessed, it is high time that we took serious stock of what we have done and why we have done it, for which an all-encompassing integrated overview is absolutely essential.

Encompassing as it does a brief interpretation and synthesis of Viktor Schauberger's theories, if nothing more, this book may have given us a small glimpse of the obverse side of what we presently perceive as reality. It is becoming more and more clearly evident that we need to change our ways and practices drastically if we are to survive as a race. If it is to remain at the cutting edge of human endeavour, science too, as a leading influence on human thought and activity, will have to raise its sights and thinking one octave higher. In the process it will, perhaps, begin to appreciate its lack of omniscience and approach matters with a far greater humility than it has to date.

From all our analytical studies, it must have become increasingly apparent that knowledge is unlimited and, therefore, however much we may think we have learnt, it is still relatively insignificant when measured against the infinite, or the knowledge and wisdom immanent in realms and dimensions beyond our ken. As a vital first step, the development of a new technology, an eco-technology, harmonious and conforming to Nature's laws, is imperative and will demand a radical and fundamental change in our way of thinking and our approach to the interpretation of the established doctrines and facts of physics, chemistry, agriculture, forestry and water management. As a pointer as to how such a new technology should come about, let me quote Viktor Schauberger once more:

'How else should it be done then?', was always the immediate question. The answer is simple: **Exactly in the opposite way that it is done today!**[3]

What is needed, therefore, is a *volte face*, a complete about-turn. We need to turn our minds and bodies through 180° and once more face the central light of truth. Then all shadows vanish instantaneously, all obscurity disappears and in the bright illumination, we shall be able to perceive with great clarity all the various threads of life, the widespread spokes of the cosmic wagonwheel, returning and interconnecting with one another in the gleaming hub from which they all spring.

Suddenly all is simple, all complicated theories which have attempted to explain the inscrutable blackness fall away, banished into the gloom from whence they came. All at once there is light and, if we raise our eyes, we may even become aware of the sublime source from which all life, movement and being on this lonesome, but beautiful planet have sprung – that eternal, ethereal brilliance, radiant within the outer light.

Notes

1. *Wholeness and the Implicate Order*, by David Bohm: Ark Publishers.

2. *The Intelligent Universe*, by Sir Fred Hoyle: Michael Joseph, London, 1983.
3. *Our Senseless Toil*, Pt.I, p.10.

GLOSSARY

Abrasion: A process in which one material is caused to rub against another. Where one material is harder than the other, the softer will be reduced in size or smoothed by the removal of minute fragments. (See *corrasion*)

Bioelectricism: A higher, more ethereal form of electricity involved in electrical interactions in living systems and tissues. It is responsible for the healthy decomposition (not putrefaction) of formerly living matter and the subsequent transmutation of this into development-ripe raw material in consort with its counterpart – *biomagnetism*.

Biomagnetism: A higher, more ethereal form of magnetism and the counterpart of bioelectricism. It is the form of magnetism responsible for uplift (both physical and spiritual), levitation and the generation of life-enhancing energies.

Biometal: An alloy of two or more different metals with opposite charges and valencies, such as silver, which has a positive charge, and copper with a negative charge. According to Viktor Schauberger the former possesses male attributes and the latter, female.

Caisson: A floating metal canister, generally cylindrical in form. The one described in this book is closed at the top and open at the bottom, and is used to open and close the sluices of the reservoir. Open at both ends, it is more commonly used in bridge-building, to exclude water from the areas of the foundations, enabling their construction.

Cambium Layer: Generally the outer annular tissues of a tree trunk immediately underneath the bark. These are of varying thickness according to species. It is where the major growth processes take place as a result of the flow and interaction between the fluids contained in the xylem and phloem. Each year at its internal interface with the heartwood, the annual ring proper is formed.

Carbones: Principally those basic elements and raw materials of carbonous nature, although the term also includes all the elements of the chemist and physicist with the exclusion of oxygen and hydrogen. They are what Viktor Schauberger called "Mother-Substances", as they form the matrix from which all life is created.

Centrifugence: The function of so-called centrifugal force, which acts from the inside outwards. This is conventionally thought to eject any material exposed to it radially from the centre outwards, whereas in actual fact the material is expelled tangentially.

Centripetence: The function of centripetal force. This is a force that acts from the outside inwards. Its most frequently observed manifestation takes the form of vortices.

Centripulser: A device having a number of *whorl-pipes* attached to a central hollow hub, whereby the medium (water or air) is moved in such a way that the forces of *centrifugence* and *centripetence* operate on a common axis. As the water is centrifuged from the centre of the hub outwards through the whorl-pipes, it is also caused to inwind centripetally due to the spiral configuration of the latter.

Corrasion: A process of mutual *abrasion*.

Cycloid-Spiral-Space-Curve Motion: This can be a simple helical or spiral motion about the longitudinal axis, which on occasion pulsatingly expands from and contracts towards this axis. It can also embody a double spiral movement, in which the moving medium spirals about itself, while simultaneously following a spiral path. It is a form of motion analogous to the rotation of the Earth about the Sun, where the Earth gyrates about its own axis while moving along its orbital path. It is the form of motion Viktor Schauberger referred to as the "original" or "form-originating" motion responsible for the evolutionary dynamics of the Earth and Cosmos.

Densation: The process of becoming physically denser or more condensed.

Dielectric Value: This refers to the capacity of a given substance to resist the transfer of an electric charge. The base value for a dielectric is that of a vacuum = 1. Water has one of the highest dielectric values, namely 81, which means that it is 81 times more resistant to the transfer of a charge than is a vacuum.

Dynagens: The entities or *ethericities* belonging to the 4th and 5th dimensions which enhance the creation of *dynamic energy* on lower planes of existence.

Dynamic Energy: This is energy that has more to do with the energising of all life-processes, subtle and otherwise, than purely physical phenomena for which the term *kinetic energy*, i.e. energy in motion, is normally used. (See *potential energy*)

Ecliptic: The circular path of the Sun across the heavens as viewed from the Earth and the angle it subtends relative to the plane of the equator. This varies according to season or the position of the Earth on its orbit around the Sun, reaching a maximum of about 23.4° north of the Equator on the 21 June (northern summer solstice) and 23.4° south of the Equator on the 21 December (northern winter solstice).

Electricism: The term Viktor Schauberger coined to describe the general characteristics and functions of the energies operating within the domain of what is commonly called electricity.

Emanation: Any form of gaseous, vaporous, ethereal, spiritual, or electromagnetic emission of radiation, rays or energies.

Etherialisation: The process of raising or exalting energies or matter to higher, more subtle states of being.

Ethericities: This refers to those supra-normal, energetic, bio-electic, bio-magnetic, catalytic, high-frequency, vibratory, super-potent energies of quasi-material, quasi-etheric nature belonging to the 4th and 5th dimensions of being.

Exosphere: The highest defined stratum of the atmosphere containing rarefied helium and hydrogen gases, which eventually merges with interstellar space. Its lower limit lies about 645km above the surface of the Earth.

Ferro-magnetism: The most commonly understood form of magnetism as in horseshoe and other forms of permanent magnets, in which the magnetic dipole moments of the atoms of such elements as iron and cobalt become aligned and operate in unison, creating a strong magnetic field.

Fibonacci Series: The name given to a mathematical progression of whole numbers discovered by the Italian mathematician Leonardo of Pisa, otherwise known as Fibonacci (an abbreviation of *filius Bonacci* or son of Bonacci) and published in his book *Liber Abacci* in 1202. This series begins with the numbers 1 (first term) and 2 (second term), which are then added to produce a third term – 3. The second term (in this case the 2) then becomes the first and is added to the former third term (now the second) to produce a further third term. The series results in the number sequence 1, 2, 3, 5, 8, 13, 21, 34, 55, 89, etc. and through the division of each subsequent first term by the second produces an increasingly accurate value for the so-called *Golden Section* and its reciprocal.

Foramen: A naturally-occurring orifice, aperture or short passage in living tissues, such as leaves, bones, etc.

Fructigens: The *ethericities* (subtle energies) responsible for increasing the fecundity or capacity for fructification and fertilisation of and by living things.

Golden Section: One of the so-called 'Divine Proportions' and is derived from the Fibonacci Series. Also known as Phi (the Greek letter ϕ), its components are related in the proportion of 1:1.618033988, or the reciprocal ratio of1:0.618033988. This is the only number wherein the decimal portions of the reciprocals and the square of the number itself have the same value, i.e $(1.618033988)^2 = 2.618033988$ and $1/1.618033988 = 0.618033988$.

Half-Hydrological Cycle: A truncated version of the full hydrological cycle in which no rainwater infiltrates the ground, but either drains away over the ground surface or re-evaporates into the atmosphere with unnatural rapidity, leading to excessive agglomerations and the uneven distribution of water vapour.

Harmonically-Structured Energy: The type of energy responsible for and comprised in the formation and structure of physical matter due to the harmonic and therefore mutually attractive resonances and forces that occur between the various atoms concerned.

Hydrological Cycle: The full, balanced and regulated natural cycle of water from deep within the Earth to the upper regions of the atmosphere and back, in which rainwater is able to percolate into the ground and the amount of atmospheric water is more evenly distributed and maintained at a more or less constant level. (See *half-hydrological cycle*)

Immature Water: Groundwater that has not yet accumulated and absorbed minerals, salts and trace-elements, which it requires in order to become mature.

Impeller: A mechanism for moving water or other liquid mechanically.

Centrifugal impeller: the intake of water is along the axis of rotation in front of and perpendicular to the radially-ribbed impeller disc and is expelled tangentially under pressure at right-angles to the direction of inflow due to the action of centrifugal force. It has a disintegrative effect on water.

Centripetal impeller: The water is introduced tangentially and exits axially in a longitudinal vortex down the central axis of rotation, which creates suction, cools and coheres the structure of the water.

Indifference: Generally speaking, an unstable state of equilibrium where the organism or system in question is possessed of its highest potential, vitality, health and energy and is therefore able to operate at the optimal temperature and/or energy level appropriate to its proper function. Viktor Schauberger also defined this condition as "temperatureless". For human beings this state of indifference obtains at a temperature of +37° Celsius, and for water relates to its condition of least volume, highest density and energy content at a temperature of +4° Celsius, its so-called anomaly point.

Inertia: The tendency or capacity of a given object or system to resist movement, acceleration or any change of status.

Juvenile Water: Akin to *immature water*, the term juvenile generally refers to rainwater, which lacks minerals, salts and trace-elements.

Kinetic Energy: Energy in motion or doing work. (See *potential energy* and *dynamic energy*)

Laminar Flow: A condition in which the various strata of water within a given water-body flow without turbulence.

Law of Anti-conservation of Energy: The law postulated by Viktor Schauberger, where the amount of available energy, *potential*, *dynamic* or *kinetic* is not constant, which, by means of the appropriate device or dynamic process, can

be increased at will to virtually any order of magnitude. It is the rational counterpart of the *Law of Conservation of Energy*.

Law of Ceaseless Cycles: The primordial, immutable law of Nature that governs and is responsible for all cyclical phenomena such as the changing seasons, the alternation between night and day, the ebb and flood of tides, the diurnal fluctuations in the flow of sap in trees, the alternating pulsations between electric and magnetic fields, the movement of galaxies, and so on.

Law of Communication: The law relating to liquids, which states that if any two or more bodies of a given liquid, water for instance, communicate directly with one another via some form of opening, then the surfaces of the respective liquids are brought to a common, uniform level, provided always that they have the same specific density or weight.

Law of Conservation of Energy: The law stating that the amount of energy throughout the Universe is finite; that there can neither be more nor less energy, which therefore always remains constant and thus can never be lost. Energy merely changes from one form to another, such as the transfer from a *potential* state to a *kinetic* state and vice versa.

Law of Gravity: The law governing the attraction of bodies towards the centre of a heavenly body or the mutual attraction between two or more such bodies. (See *Law of Levity*)

Law of Levity: The law postulated by Viktor Schauberger that governs and is responsible for all upward movement of energy, uplift, upward growth, the upright stature of human beings, animals and other organisms, and is the counterpart to the Law of Gravity. As the force of gravity decreases the force of levity increases.

Law of Thermodynamics, Second: The law related to temperature derived from the *Law of Conservation of Energy*, stating inter alia that with no additional input of energy from some external source, the energy in all closed systems (the whole universe included) will eventually be transformed into heat and ultimately reduced to a condition of uniform temperature known as the 'Heat Death'.

Laya Point: From the Sanskrit, meaning the point where all differentiation, material or otherwise, has ceased. It is an immaterial focus or state of spiritual or energetic potential in a neutral condition and whatever emerges from it becomes active life.

Lignification: The process by which the cells in the cambium layer of trees become rigid and are transformed into wood proper through the accretion of lignin in the cell-walls.

Loschmidt Number: First calculated by Joseph Loschmidt (1821–1895), the Loschmidt Constant or Loschmidt Number (N_L) determines the number of particles per unit volume of an ideal gas at standard temperature and pressure and has a value of 2.68719×10^{25} per cubic metre, equal to the number of particles, atoms or molecules, contained in 1 mole of carbon 12.

Nascent Spring Water: *Immature water* within the central stratum of the groundwater, having a temperature of about +4° Celsius.

Natural Capital: The basic elements and raw materials, organic and otherwise, from which Nature creates all life and develops new species, the latter representing the interest accruing from the natural capital.

Naturalesque: Refers to artificially contrived processes or mechanical devices that conform to or emulate Nature's laws, or operate in a naturally correct way.

Obliquity of the Earth's Axis: The angle subtended between the Earth's axis of rotation and the *ecliptic*.

Over-Unity: A phenomenon contrary to the Conservation of Energy Law and to the Second Law of Thermodynamics, in which the amount of energy input is less than the energy output. An over-unity generator, therefore, is a device that produces more energy than it requires to operate. This is otherwise known as 'free energy'.

Permittivity: Measured in farads, this relates to the extent to which a given substance can resist or transfer an electric charge.

Phloem: The vascular tissues within the cambium layer of plants that conduct sugars, proteins, absorbed atmospheric gases and predominantly negatively ionised substances down the stem of trunk from the leaves.

Potential Energy: Stored energy or energy that as yet is unmanifested as *dynamic* or *kinetic energy*.

Qualigens: The *ethericities* responsible for the enhancement of quality and increase in quality matter.

Ring-Shakes: Circular cleavages between the annual rings of trees that run parallel to the grain.

Seepage Spring: A spring that is formed when percolating groundwater encounters an impervious stratum and drains away over the stratum surface under the influence of *gravity* towards the point of egress. The temperature of such springs generally conforms to the ambient ground temperature.

Stomata: Pores in the surface of leaves that control the emission and absorption of gases, water vapour, etc.

Temperament: In Viktor Schauberger's terminology, this refers to the behaviour, character, gender and intrinsic properties, sometimes temperature-induced, of various immaterial and other energies, such as *electricism, biomagnetism, gravity* and *levity* as well as the media of earth, air and water.

Temperature Gradients: In terms of Viktor Schauberger's concepts, temperature gradients are principally related to the direction of movement of temperature within and between the respective temperatures of the ground, water and atmosphere, which can either take a positive or negative form. A positive temperature gradient occurs when the direction of temperature movement is towards the anomaly point of water, i.e. towards +4° Celsius. A negative temperature gradient occurs when the direction of temperature movement is either upwards or downwards from +4° Celsius.

Triboluminescence: An internal glow or luminescence produced when two or more crystalline rocks of similar composition are rubbed hard together or struck against one another and is attributed to the energy given off by the electrons contained the rocks as they return from a pressure-induced, excited state to their rest orbits. As a phenomenon it can occur both in air and under water.

Turbidity: A measure of the opaqueness, cloudiness or muddiness of water due its content of suspended matter.

Whorl-Pipes: Pipes, principally made of copper or its alloys, having a spiral configuration akin to that of a Kudu antelope, through which the transported medium is caused to move centripetally and vortically in a double spiral motion.

Xylem: The vascular tissue within the *cambium layer* of plants that conducts water and dissolved minerals, salts, trace-elements and predominantly positively ionised substances from the roots towards the leaves.

BIBLIOGRAPHY

1. Works of Viktor Schauberger

"The Biological Vacuum – The Optimal Driving Force For Machines": *Implosion*.

"The Development of Steppeland in Germany" ("Die Versteppung Deutschlands".

"The Dying Forest" ("Der sterbende Wald"), Pt.I: *Tau*, 1936.

Eco-technology – Viktor Schauberger's writings in 3 vols: *The Water Wizard, The Fertile Earth* and *Schauberger's Revolution*, collected, translated and edited by Callum Coats: Gateway, Bath. (Nat. Book Network, Lanham, MD, U.S.A.) 1997.

"Electrolysis", *Der Wiener Tag*, 1932.

"The First Biotechnical Practice" ("Die erste biotechnische Praxis"). *Implosion*.

"The Forest and its Significance" ("Der Wald und seine Bedeutung"): *Tau*, 1936.

"Let the Upheaval Begin!" ("Den Umbruch beginnen!") *Implosion*.

Letter to Dr. Ehrenberger, Min. for Agric. & Forestry, Vienna. *Tau*, 1936.

"The Mechanical Generation of Life-Force" ("Maschinelle Erzeugung der Lebenskraft"): *Implosion*.

"Natural Farm Husbandry" ("Naturnahe Landwirtschaft") *Implosion*.

"Nature's Secrets Unveiled" ("Entschleierte Naturgeheimnisse"): *Implosion*.

Our Senseless Toil – The Source of the World Crisis ("Unsere Sinnlose Arbeit – die Quelle der Weltkrise"), 1933–1934: Krystall Verlag, Vienna.

"The Ox and the Chamois": *Tau*, 1936.

"Return to Culture" ("Zurück zur Kultur").

"Temperature and the Movement of Water" ("Temperatur und Wasserbewegung"): *Die Wasserwirtschaft*, 1930.

"The Winding Way to Wisdom" ("Der gewundene Erkenntnisweg"): *Implosion*.

2. Works cited, by other authors

Alberts, B, et al: *The Molecular Biology of the Cell*: Garland, New York.

Alberts, B. et al: "Chlorophyll Structure" in *The Molecular Biology of the Cell*: Garland, New York, U.S.A., 1983.

Alexandersson, Olof: *Living Water – Viktor Schauberger & the Secrets of Natural Energy*: Gateway, Bath, 1982 (Nat. Book Network, Lanham, MD, USA).

Asimov, Isaac: *Guide to Science: 1 – The Physical Sciences* Penguin Books, Harmondsworth, UK.

Attinger, Dr. Ernst O.: "Hydrodynamics of Blood Flow": Univ. Virginia Med. Cntr, Charlottesville, VA, U.S.A.

Auguros, Robert & Stanciu, George: *The New Biology*: New Science Library, Shambala, 1987.

Bird, C. & Tompkins, P.: *The Secret Life of Plants*, Harper, New York, 1989.

Bird, C. & Tompkins, P.: *Secrets of the Soil*, Harper, New York, 1989.

Blavatsky, H.P.: *The Secret Doctrine*, Theosophical Pub.Ho., Adyar, India.

Bohm, David: Wholeness and the Implicate Order: Ark Publishers.

Brandstätter, Leopold: "What happens next?" ("Wie geht esweiter?"): *Implosion*.

Brandstätter, Leopold: *Implosion statt Explosion*, Linz, Austria.

Cater, Joseph H.: *The Awesome Life-Force*: Cadake Industries, Winter Haven, FL, U.S.A., 1984.

Campe, Joanna, (ed): Remineralise the Earth: 152 South St, Northampton, MD, U.S.A.

Churchward, James: *The Lost Continent of Mu*: Spearman, London, 1959.

Coats, S. David: *Old MacDonald's Factory Farm*: Continuum, New York.

Davis, K.S. et al: *Water – The Mirror of Science*,: Heinemann Educ., London, 1964.

Diamond, Dr John: *Your Body Doesn't Lie*, (Behavioural Kinesiology): Harper & Row, New York, 1979.

Do-ring: *The Urga Manuscript*, Transl. Maj. Gregory Pearson; Colin Smythe, Gerrards Cross, U.K.

Electricity & Magnetism, Cambridge Univ. Press, 1908.

Etidorpha: Health Research, Box 70, Mokelumne Hill, CA 95245, U.S.A.

Fuller, John G.: *The Ghost of 29 Megacycles*: Signet ed. 1986, New American Lib., New York.

Gerlovin, Baranova & Baranov: "New Approach to Cold Fusion" (Low-Temperature Nuclear Fusion), *Zurnal Obshchei Khimii*, Plenum, 1992.

Hamaker, John & Weaver, Don: *The Survival of Civilisation*, self-published.

Hohls, Arnold (notebooks of, on Viktor Schauberger): *Mensch und Technik*, 1993.

Hoyle, Sir Fred: *The Intelligent Universe*: Michael Joseph, London, 1983.

Jansen, P.Ph. et al: *Principles of River Engineering*: Longman, Harlow.

Jenny, Hans: *Kymatik/Cymatics*: Basilims, Basel, Switzerland (now defunct).

Khamas, A.: "The Emergence of Biotechnology" ("Aufbruch der Biotechnik"): *Implosion*.

Kokaly, Aloys: "Home Power Generator – an Illusion?" ("Das Heimkraftwerk – eine Illusion?"): *Implosion*.

Kokaly, Aloys: "The Legacy of Viktor Schauberger" ("Die Erbe Viktor Schaubergers"): *Implosion*.

Kokaly, Aloys: "The Production of Noble Water" ("Die Herstellung von Edelwasser"): *Implosion*.

Kutschera, I., & Lichtenegger, E. *Wurzelatlas; mitteleuropaischer Grunlandpflanzen*, Vol. 1, "Monocotyledoneae" 1982, and Vol. 2, "Pteridophyta und Dicotyledoneae", 1992: Gustav Fischer, Stuttgart, Germany.

Lackenbucher, Raimund: "The Death of Viktor Schauberger" ("Der Tod des Viktor Schauberger"): *Implosion*.

Linder, II.: *Das Bild der Modernen Physik* "The Formation of Electromagnetic Waves": Urania, Leipzig, Germany.

Lovelock, James: *The Ages of Gaia*: W.W. Norton, New York.

Lorek, Kurt: "The Spiral Plough" ("Der Spiralpflug"), *Implosion*.

Ott, Dr John N.: *Health and Light*: Devin-Adair, Greenwich, CT, U.S.A., 1973.

Our Common Future: World Comm. on Environment: Oxford Univ. Press, Oxford, 1987.

Pettigrew, J. Bell: *Design In Nature*: Longmans, London, 1908.

Phaidon Concise Encyclopedia of Science and Technology, © 1978 Andromeda Oxford, UK.

Pöpel, Prof. Franz. "Report Concerning the Preliminary Investigation of Helical Pipes with Various Shapes of Pipe-Wall" ("Bericht über die Voruntersuchungen mit Wendelrohren mit verschiedener Wandform"): Stuttgart Univ. of Technology, Germany, 1952.

Reich, Wilhelm: "Harmony as a Question of Existence" ("Harmonie als Existenzfrage") *Implosion*.

Sheldrake, Rupert: *The New Science of Life*: Blond & Briggs, London, 1981.

Snoek, Helmut: *Das Buch von Steinmehl*: Orac-Pietsch, Germany.

Spalding, Baird T.: *Life and Teaching of the Masters of the Far East*: De Vorss, Marina Del Rey, CA, U.S.A.

Tame, David, *The Secret Power of Music*: Inner Traditions, Rochester, VT, U.S.A.

Trees and the New Earth, p.117.

Van Allen, James A.: *Interplanetary Particles and Fields*, © 1975 by Scientific American, Inc.

Vilee, Claude A. et al: *Biology*: Saunders, Philadelphia PA, U.S.A.

Wissenschaftliche Grundlagen der Homöopathie, "Scientific Foundations of Homeopathy": Barthel Berlin, Germany.

"Global warming rings true", *New Scientist*, Sept. 1991.

"The Water Cycle", in *The Biosphere*, Scientific American, 1970: W.H. Freeman, New York, U.S.A.

3. Recommended Further Reading:

Alder, Vera Stanley, *The Fifth Dimension*: Weiser, York Beach, ME, U.S.A., 1940.

Baker, R. St. Barbe, *I Planted Trees*: Lutterworth, London, 1944.

Sahara Challenge: Lutterworth, London, 1954.

Bird, C.: *The Divining Hand – the 500 year-old Mystery of Dowsing*: Dutton, New York 1979; Schiffer, Atglen, PA, USA, 1993.

Bird, C., *The Persecution & Trial of Gaston Naessens*, Kramer, Tiburon, CA, U.S.A.

Blavatsky, H.P., *Isis Unveiled, vols I & II*: Theosophical, Wheaton, IL, U.S.A., 1877.

Capra, Fritjof, *The Tao of Physics*: Wildwood, London, 1975.

The Turning Point – Science, Society & Rising Culture: Simon & Schuster, New York, U.S.A., 1982.

Cathie Bruce L., *Bridge to Infinity – Harmonic 371244*: Quark, Auckland, NZ, 1983.

Harmonic 695 – The UFO and Antigravity: Reid, Wellington, NZ, 1971.

The Pulse of the Universe – Harmonic 288: Reid, Wellington, NZ, 1977.

Cook, Theodore, Andrea, *The Curves of Life*: Dover, New York, U.S.A., 1979.

Constable, Trevor James, *The Cosmic Pulse of Life*: Merlin, CA, U.S.A., 1976.

Douglas Hume, E., *Béchamp or Pasteur?*: Daniel, Saffron Walden, 1947.

Dudley, Nigel, *The Death of Trees*: Pluto, London, 1985.

Gardner, E.L., *The Web of the Universe*: Theosophical, London, 1936.

Gribbin, John, *Hothouse Earth-Greenhouse Effect & Earth*: Black Swan, 1990.

Huntley, H.E., *Divine Proportion – Study of Mathematical Beauty*: Dover, New York, 1970.

Milner, Denis, *The Loom of Creation*: Daniel, Saffron Walden.

Exploration in Consciousness: Daniel, Saffon Walden.

Murchie, Guy, *Music of the Spheres, vols. I & II*: Houghton Mifflin, Boston, U.S.A., 1961.

Playfair, G.L. & Hill, Scott, *The Cycles of Heaven*: Souvenir, London, 1978.

Rudhyar, Dane, *The Magic of Tone & the Art of Music*: Shambhala, Boston, U.S.A., 1982.

Schell, Jonathan, *The Fate of the Earth*: Pan, London, 1982.

Schwenk, Theodor, *Sensitive Chaos*: Steiner: London, 1965.

Steiner, Rudolf, *The Nature of Substance*: Steiner, London, 1966.

Stevens, Peter S., *Patterns in Nature*: Penguin, 1974.

Young, Arthur M., *The Geometry of Meaning*: Delacorte, New York, U.S.A., 1976.

The Reflexive Universe – Evolution of Consciousness: Delacorte, New York, U.S.A., 1976.

Zukav, Gary, *Dancing Wu Li Masters – Overview of New Physics*: Morrow, New York, U.S.A., 1975.

ABOUT THE AUTHOR

Callum Coats was born in London on 19th July 1939, but by the age of thirteen he had already seen a great deal of the world. His parents were internationally involved in the Theosophical Society which resulted in long periods in India and other non-European countries. He was at school at Gordonstoun in Scotland, renowned for its enlightened educational ideas, with a final year at its sister Salem School in Germany, and he speaks French and German fluently. In 1967 received a master's degree in architecture from the Architectural Association in London, practising first in London and then in Queensland, Australia where he now lives.

Callum first heard about the ideas of Viktor Schauberger at the age of 17, but it was not until February 1977 that his mother introduced him to Viktor's physicist and mathematician son Walter Schauberger. Astonished that no material on these ecologically important ideas was available in English, he decided to abandon architecture and devote himself to their study.

Callum spent three years working full-time with Walter at his Pythagoras-Kepler System Institute in Lauffen, Austria, and studying Viktor's archives. He helped revise the translation of *Living Water*, the introductory work on Viktor Schauberger by Olof Alexandersson (Pub.1981). In the intervening fifteen years, Callum has devoted all his resources and time to writing *Living Energies* and to translating, collating and editing Viktor Schauberger's books, articles and letters into the major archive of his work: *Eco-Technology: Viktor Schauberger's writings on Subtle Energies in Nature*, and its associated volumes.

Callum Coats has always had an abiding interest in Nature and natural phenomena. He is an accomplished speaker, and any enquiries about Schauberger's ideas, and about lectures, should be addressed to him care of the publishers.

INDEX